Before We Are Born

Basic Embryology and Birth Defects

Second Edition

Keith L. Moore, M.Sc., Ph.D., F.I.A.C., F.R.S.M.

Professor and Chairman, Department of Anatomy
University of Toronto Faculty of Medicine
Toronto, Ontario, Canada

Illustrated Primarily by

Glen Reid, B.Sc., A.A.M.

Medical Illustrator, Faculty of Medicine
University of Manitoba
Winnipeg, Manitoba, Canada

W. B. Saunders Company

Philadelphia   London   Toronto   Mexico City   Rio de Janeiro   Sydney   Tokyo

W. B. Saunders Company: West Washington Square
                           Philadelphia, PA 19105

                           1 St. Anne's Road
                           Eastbourne, East Sussex BN21 3UN, England

                           1 Goldthorne Avenue
                           Toronto, Ontario M8Z 5T9, Canada

                           Apartado 26370—Cedro 512
                           Mexico 4, D.F., Mexico

                           Rua Coronel Cabrita, 8
                           Sao Cristovao Caixa Postal 21176
                           Rio de Janeiro, Brazil

                           9 Waltham Street
                           Artarmon, N.S.W. 2064, Australia

                           Ichibancho, Central Bldg., 22-1 Ichibancho
                           Chiyoda-Ku, Tokyo 102, Japan

Library of Congress Cataloging in Publication Data

Moore, Keith L.
  Before we are born.

  1. Embryology, Human. 2. Fetus—Abnormalities.
I. Title. [DNLM: 1. Abnormalities. 2. Embryology.
QS 604 M822b]
QM601.M757 1983   612'.64   82-24009
ISBN 0-7216-1024-2

Listed here is the latest translated edition of this book together with
the language of the translation and the publisher.

Japanese—Ishiyaku Publishers Inc.
          Tokyo, Japan

Greek—C. Litsas Medical Books & Publications
          Athens, Greece

Portuguese—Disco CBS Industria E Comercia Ltda.
          Rio de Janeiro, Brazil

Spanish—Nueva Editorial Interamericana SA de CV
          Mexico 4 D.F., Mexico

Reprinted with revisions, February, 1977

The illustration on the front cover is a photograph of an embryo of about 51 days.

Before We Are Born: Basic Embryology and Birth Defects   ISBN 0-7216-1024-2

Last digit is the print number: 9   8   7   6   5   4   3

To our second grandchild
KRISTIN ELIZABETH SEMCHUK
daughter of Karen and Bob

Our first grandchild, Melissa Moore,
is featured in the author's other text,
The Developing Human.

PREFACE

This book is designed to arouse the beginning student's interest in embryology and its clinical application. The illustrations, many in color, are designed to help the student visualize developmental processes and time sequences.

In preparing this edition, each chapter has been carefully reviewed and revised to ensure that the material is up to date and suitable for the students to whom it is directed. Students desiring more details about any of the subjects should refer to the author's textbook *The Developng Human: Clinically Oriented Embryology,* 3rd edition, 1982.

The wide acceptance of this book would indicate that it meets the requirements of many students in acquiring a basic understanding of human development and of the common congenital malformations. Since the first edition was published, there has been an increased interest in embryology and in the vulnerability of the developing embryo to radiation, drugs, and chemicals. In this edition the common and medically important congenital malformations of organs are discussed immediately after the normal development. This provides a better understanding of normal and abnormal development. The summaries of the chapters have been improved so that students can easily review the important points covered in the chapters.

Besides new illustrations and additions to the text, a number of figures have been redrawn or modified in the light of teaching experience. A few have been omitted. Color has also been added to several more drawings to facilitate understanding. For this work I owe thanks to Dorothy Irwin; Glen Reid prepared most of the illustrations in the first edition of this book.

The *Nomina Embryologica*, approved by the Tenth International Congress of Anatomists in Tokyo, 1975, has been followed and, in accordance with international agreement, the terminology departs from strict Latin in most cases by anglicizing the terms. There is also some use of eponyms (e.g., Meckel's diverticulum and Down syndrome) because students will need to recognize these terms when they are used in specialty texts and by clinical teachers.

While working on this edition, I have had the benefit of receiving helpful criticism from students from many parts of North America, and suggestions from a number of embryologists who have kindly written to me or sent reprints of their publications. To all these people I express my most sincere thanks.

Mrs. Jill Weinheimer and my wife, Marion, have carefully and cheerfully typed changes and new additions to the text. Dorothy Irwin modified many of the drawings and prepared all the new illustrations. Robert Kangilaski,

Medical Editor, W. B. Saunders Company, and Walter Bailey, President and General Manager of the W. B. Saunders Company of Canada, have given me much help with this edition. To all the above, I express my sincere thanks.

KEITH L. MOORE

CONTENTS

1

INTRODUCTION

Human development begins when an ovum from a female is fertilized by a sperm from a male. Development is a process of change that transforms the fertilized ovum or *zygote* into a multicellular human being.

Most developmental changes occur during the embryonic and the fetal periods, but important changes also occur during the other periods of development: infancy, childhood, adolescence, and adulthood.

STAGES OF DEVELOPMENT

Development can be divided into *prenatal* and *postnatal* periods, but it is important to understand that *development is a continuous process*. Birth is a dramatic event during development, but important developmental changes occur after birth (e.g., in the teeth and the female breasts).

The developmental stages occurring before we are born are illustrated in the *Timetables of Human Prenatal Development* (Figs. 1–1 and 1–2). The following list explains the terms used in these timetables and other commonly used ones.

Zygote. This cell is the *beginning* of a human being. It results from the fertilization of an ovum by a sperm. The expression "fertilized ovum" refers to the zygote.

Cleavage. Division or cleavage of the zygote by mitosis[1] forms daughter cells called *blastomeres*. The blastomeres become smaller and smaller at each succeeding cell division (see Fig. 3–3).

Morula. When 12 to 16 blastomeres have formed, the ball of cells is called a morula because it resembles the berry-like fruit known as a mulberry (L. *morus*, mulberry).

Blastocyst. After the morula passes from the uterine tube into the uterus, a cavity forms in it, known as the *blastocyst cavity* (see Fig. 3–3E). This converts the morula into a blastocyst.

Embryo. The cells of the blastocyst which give rise to the embryo appear as an *inner cell mass* (see Fig. 3–3E). The term embryo is not usually used until the *embryonic disc* forms (day 8). The *embryonic period* extends until the end of the eighth week, by which time the beginnings of all major structures are present. By the end of this period characteristics are present that mark the embryo as definitely human.

Fetus. After the embryonic period, the developing human is called a fetus. During the *fetal period* (ninth week to birth), many systems develop further. Although developmental changes are not so dramatic as those occurring during the embryonic period, they are very important. The rate of body growth is remarkable, especially during the third and fourth months, and weight gain is phenomenal during the terminal months.

Conceptus. This term is used when referring to the embryo and its membranes, i.e., the *products of conception*.

Abortion (L. *abortio*, miscarriage). This term refers to the birth of an embryo or of a fetus before it is viable (mature enough to survive outside the uterus). All terminations of pregnancy that occur before 20 weeks are called *abortions*. About 15 per cent of all recognized pregnancies end in *spontaneous abortions* (ones that occur naturally), usually during the first 12 weeks. Legal *induced abortions* are brought on purposefully, usually by *suction curettage* (evacuation of the embryo and its membranes from the uterus). *Therapeutic abortions* are induced owing to the mother's poor health, or to prevent the birth of a severely malformed child.

Abortus. This term describes any product or all products of an abortion. An embryo or a *nonviable fetus* and its membranes weighing less than 500 gm is called an *abortus* (see Fig. 8–3).

Primordium (L. *primus*, first + *ordior*, to begin). This term refers to the first trace or

---

[1] A method of division of a cell by means of which two daughter cells receive identical complements of chromosomes. For details of this process, see a histology or a biology textbook.

Text continued on page 6

TIMETABLE OF HUMAN PRENATAL DEVELOPMENT

1 to 6 weeks

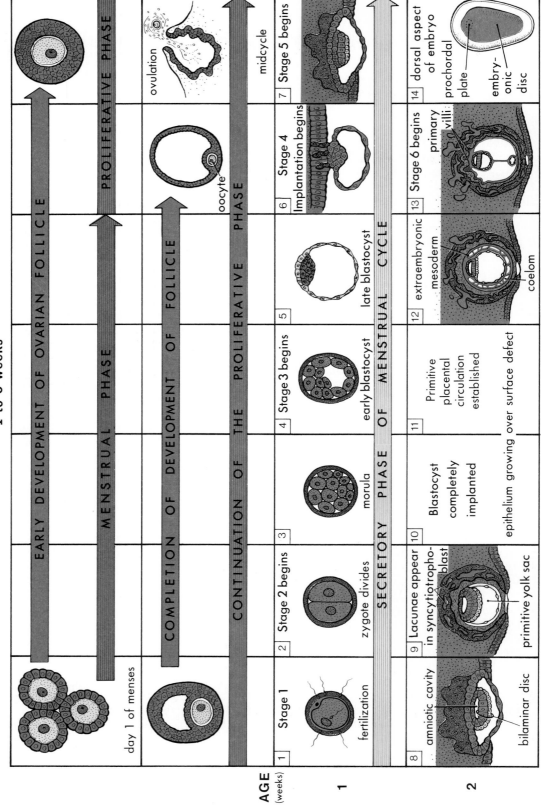

EARLY DEVELOPMENT OF OVARIAN FOLLICLE

MENSTRUAL PHASE

PROLIFERATIVE PHASE

COMPLETION OF DEVELOPMENT OF FOLLICLE

CONTINUATION OF THE PROLIFERATIVE PHASE

SECRETORY PHASE OF MENSTRUAL CYCLE

day 1 of menses

ovulation

midcycle

| 1 | Stage 1 | | 2 | Stage 2 begins | | 3 | Stage 3 begins | | 4 | | | 5 | | | 6 | Implantation begins | | 7 | Stage 5 begins |

fertilization

zygote divides

morula

early blastocyst

late blastocyst

oocyte

Stage 4

| 8 | amniotic cavity | | 9 | Lacunae appear in syncytiotropho-blast | | 10 | Blastocyst completely implanted | | 11 | Primitive placental circulation established | | 12 | extraembryonic mesoderm | | 13 | Stage 6 begins primary villi | | 14 | dorsal aspect of embryo |

bilaminar disc

primitive yolk sac

epithelium growing over surface defect

coelom

prochordal plate

embry-onic disc

AGE (weeks)

1

2

2

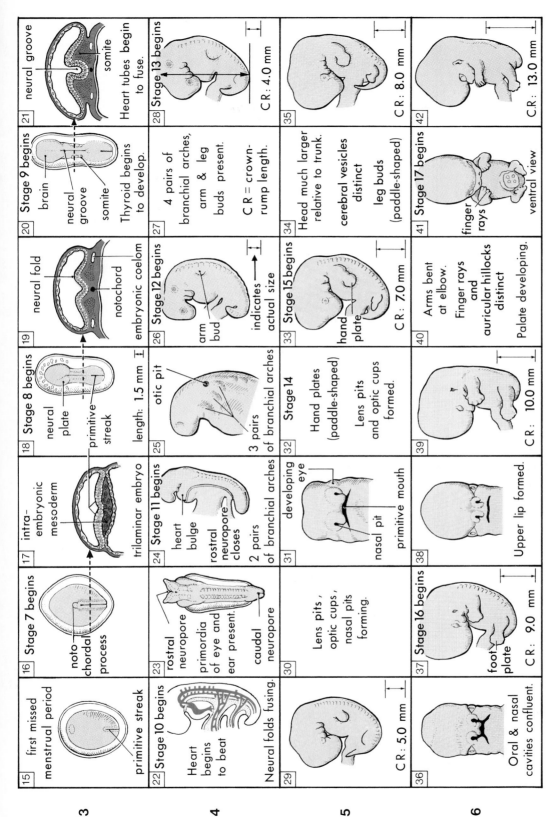

Figure 1–1 Development of an ovarian follicle containing an oocyte, ovulation, and the phases of the menstrual cycle are illustrated. *Development begins at fertilization,* about 14 days after the onset of the last menstruation. Cleavage of the zygote in the uterine tube, implantation of the blastocyst, and early development of the embryo are also shown. The main features of developmental stages in human embryos are illustrated. For a full discussion of embryonic development, see Chapter 6.

The following text appears within the figure panels:

15	16	17	18	19	20	21

15 first missed menstrual period — primitive streak

16 Stage 7 begins — notochordal process — primitive streak

17 intra-embryonic mesoderm — trilaminar embryo

18 Stage 8 begins — neural plate — primitive streak — length: 1.5 mm

19 neural fold — notochord — embryonic coelom

20 Stage 9 begins — brain — neural groove — somite — Thyroid begins to develop.

21 neural groove — somite — Heart tubes begin to fuse.

22 Stage 10 begins — Heart begins to beat — Neural folds fusing.

23 rostral neuropore — primordia of eye and ear present — caudal neuropore

24 Stage 11 begins — heart bulge — rostral neuropore closes — 2 pairs of branchial arches

25 otic pit — 3 pairs of branchial arches

26 Stage 12 begins — arm bud — indicates actual size

27 4 pairs of branchial arches, arm & leg buds present. — C R = crown-rump length.

28 Stage 13 begins — C R : 4.0 mm

29 C R : 5.0 mm

30 Lens pits, optic cups, nasal pits forming.

31 developing eye — nasal pit — primitive mouth

32 Stage 14 — Hand plates (paddle-shaped) — Lens pits and optic cups formed.

33 Stage 15 begins — hand plate — C R : 7.0 mm

34 Head much larger relative to trunk. — cerebral vesicles distinct — leg buds (paddle-shaped)

35 C R : 8.0 mm

36 Oral & nasal cavities confluent.

37 Stage 16 begins — foot plate — C R : 9.0 mm

38 Upper lip formed.

39 C R : 10.0 mm

40 Arms bent at elbow. — Finger rays and auricular hillocks distinct — Palate developing.

41 Stage 17 begins — finger rays — ventral view

42 C R : 13.0 mm

3

TIMETABLE OF HUMAN PRENATAL DEVELOPMENT
7 to 38 weeks

AGE (weeks)

7

- **43** — CR: 16.0 mm.
- **44** — Stage 18 begins / Eyelids beginning
- **45** — Tip of nose distinct / Toe rays appear / Ossification may begin / CR: 17.0 mm
- **46** — Loss of villi / Smooth chorion forms.
- **47** — genital tubercle / urogenital membrane / anal membrane ♀ or ♂
- **48** — Stage 19 begins / Trunk elongating and straightening
- **49** — CR: 18 mm

8

- **50** — Upper limbs longer & bent at elbows / Fingers distinct
- **51** — Anal membrane perforated / Urogenital membrane degenerating. / Testes and ovaries distinguishable.
- **52** — Stage 21 begins
- **53** — Stage 21 / External genitalia still in sexless state but have begun to differentiate.
- **54** — Stage 22 begins / genital tubercle / urethral groove / anus ♀ or ♂
- **55** — Beginnings of all essential external and internal structures are present.
- **56** — Stage 23 / CR: 30 mm

9

- **57** — beginning of fetal period
- **58** — (image)
- **59** — Genitalia show some ♀ characteristics but still easily confused with ♂.
- **60** — phallus / urogenital fold / labioscrotal fold / perineum ♀
- **61** — Genitalia show fusion of urethral folds. / Urethral groove extends into phallus.
- **62** — phallus / urogenital fold / labioscrotal fold / perineum ♂
- **63** — CR: 50 mm

10

- **64** — Face has human profile. Note growth of chin compared to day 44.
- **65** — (image)
- **66** — Face has human appearance.
- **67** — clitoris / labium minus / urogenital groove / labium majus ♀
- **68** — Genitalia have ♀ or ♂ characteristics but still not fully formed.
- **69** — glans penis / urethral groove / scrotum ♂
- **70** — CR: 61 mm

The Fetal Period

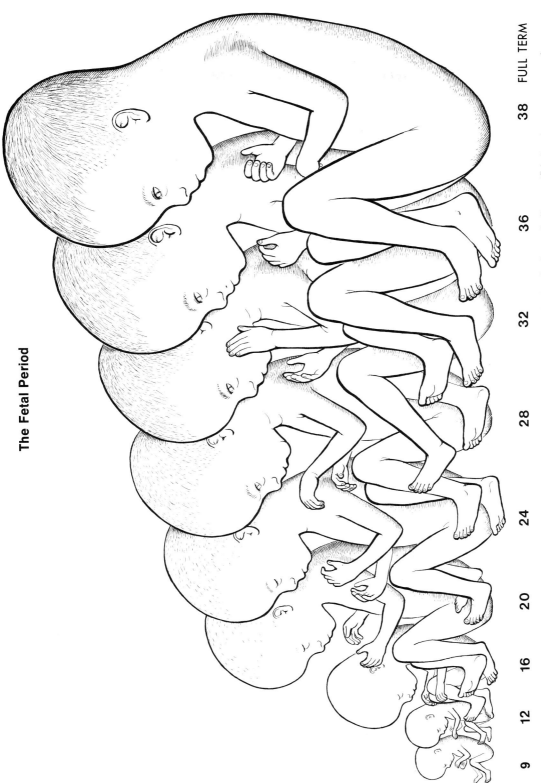

9 12 16 20 24 28 32 36 38 FULL TERM

Figure 1–2 The embryonic period ends at the end of the eighth week; by this time, the beginnings of all essential structures are present. The fetal period, extending from the ninth week until birth, is characterized by growth and elaboration of structures. Sex is clearly distinguishable by 12 weeks. The above 9- to 38-week fetuses are about half actual size. For more information, see Chapter 7.

indication of an organ or structure, i.e., its earliest stage of development. The term *anlage* has a similar meaning.

Miscarriage. This word is used colloquially to refer to any interruption of pregnancy that occurs before a fetus is viable (i.e., a spontaneous abortion). In medical description, it is most accurate to use the term *spontaneous abortion* for the birth of an embryo or a fetus prior to about 20 weeks; thereafter the event is called a *premature birth.*

Trimester. Obstetricians commonly divide the nine calendar months, or period of gestation (stages of intrauterine development), into three 3-month periods called *trimesters.*

THE IMPORTANCE OF EMBRYOLOGY

The study of prenatal stages of development, especially those occurring during the embryonic period, helps us to understand the normal relationships of adult body structures and the causes of congenital malformations. The embryo is extremely vulnerable during the first three months to large amounts of radiation, viruses, and certain drugs (see Chapter 9). The physician's knowledge of normal development and the causes of congenital malformations aid in giving the embryo the best possible chance of developing normally. Much of the modern practice of obstetrics involves what might be called ''applied developmental biology.''

The significance of embryology is readily apparent to pediatricians because many of their patients have disorders resulting from maldevelopment, e.g., spina bifida and congenital heart disease. Progress in surgery, especially in the pediatric age group, has made knowledge of human development more clinically significant. The understanding of most congenital malformations (e.g., cleft palate and cardiac defects) depends upon an understanding of normal development and the deviations that have occurred.

HISTORICAL HIGHLIGHTS

If I have seen further, it is by standing on the shoulders of giants.

SIR ISAAC NEWTON
English mathematician, 1643–1727

This statement emphasizes that each new study of a problem rests on a base of knowledge established by earlier investigators.

Every age gives explanations according to its knowledge and experience, and so we should be grateful for their ideas and neither sneer at them nor consider them as final. Man has always been interested in knowing how he originated, how he was born, and why some people develop abnormally.

The Greeks made important contributions to the science of embryology. The first recorded embryological studies are in the book of Hippocrates, the famous Greek physician of the fifth century B.C. In the fourth century B.C., Aristotle wrote the first known account of embryology, in which he described development of the chick and other embryos. Galen (second century A.D.) wrote a book entitled *On the Formation of the Foetus* in which he described the development and nutrition of fetuses.

Growth of science was slow during the Middle Ages, and few high points of embryological investigation are known to us.

It is cited in the *Koran,* The Holy Book of the Muslims, that human beings are produced from a *mixture of secretions* from the male and the female. Several references are made to the creation of a human being from a *droplet,* and it is also suggested that the resulting organism settles in the woman like a seed, six days after its beginning. (The human blastocyst begins to implant about six days after fertilization.) Reference is also made to the

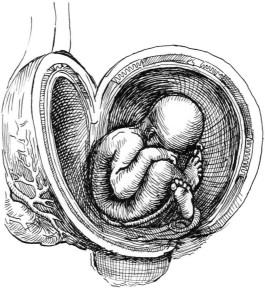

Figure 1–3 Reproduction of Leonardo da Vinci's drawing (15th century) showing a fetus in an opened uterus.

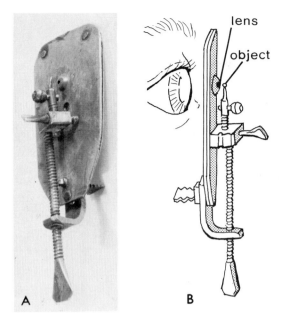

Figure 1–4 *A,* Photograph of a *1673 Leeuwenhoek microscope. B,* Drawing of a lateral view illustrating its use. The object was held in front of the lens on the point of the short rod, and the screw arrangement was used to adjust the object under the lens.

leech-like appearance of the early embryo. (The embryo of 22 to 24 days resembles a leech, or bloodsucker, in appearance.) The embryo is also said to resemble "a chewed substance" like gum or wood. (The somites shown in Figure 6–5B somewhat resemble the teethmarks in a chewed substance.)

The Koran also states that the embryo develops within "three veils of darkness." This probably refers to (1) the maternal abdominal wall, (2) the uterine wall, and (3) the amnio-chorionic membrane.

In the fifteenth century, Leonardo da Vinci made accurate drawings of dissections of the pregnant uterus and associated fetal membranes (Fig. 1–3).

In 1651 Harvey studied chick embryos with simple lenses and made observations on the circulation of blood. Early microscopes were simple (Fig. 1–4), but they opened a new field of observation. In 1672 de Graaf observed little chambers (undoubtedly what we now call blastocysts) in the rabbit's uterus and concluded that they came from organs he called ovaries.

Malpighi, in 1765, studying what he believed to be unfertilized hen's eggs, observed early embryos. As a result, he thought the egg contained a miniature chick. In 1677 Hamm and Leeuwenhoek, using an improved microscope, first observed human sperms, but they did not understand the sperm's role in fertilization: they thought it contained a miniature human being (Fig. 1–5).

In 1775, Spallanzani showed that both the ovum and the sperm were necessary for initiation of a new individual. From his experiments, he concluded that the sperm was the fertilizing agent.

Great advances were made in embryology when the *cell theory* was established in 1839 by Schleiden and Schwann. The concept that the body was composed of cells and cell products soon led to the realization that the embryo developed from a single cell, the zygote.

The *principles of heredity* were developed in 1865 by an Austrian monk named *Gregor Mendel,* but medical scientists and biologists did not understand the significance of these principles in the study of mammalian development for many years.

Flemming observed chromosomes in 1878 and suggested their probable role in fertili-

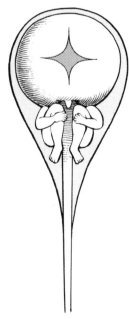

Figure 1–5 Copy of a seventeenth century drawing by Hartsoeker of a sperm. The miniature human being within it was thought to enlarge after it entered an ovum.

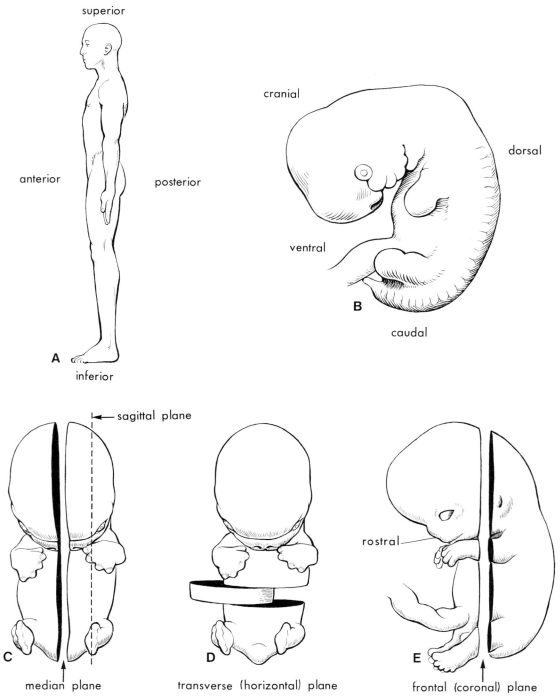

superior

cranial

dorsal

anterior posterior

ventral

B

caudal

A

inferior

← sagittal plane

rostral

C **D** **E**

median plane transverse (horizontal) plane frontal (coronal) plane

Figure 1–6 Drawings illustrating descriptive terms of position, direction, and planes of the body. *A*, Lateral view of a human adult in the anatomical position. *B*, Lateral view of a five-week embryo. *C* and *D*, Ventral views of six-week embryos. *E*, Lateral view of a seven-week embryo.

zation. In 1883 von Beneden observed that mature germ cells have a reduced number of chromosomes. The first significant observations on human chromosomes were made by von Winiwarter in 1912. In 1923 Painter concluded that there were 48 chromosomes. This number was universally accepted until 1956, when Tjio and Levan reported finding only 46 chromosomes. This number is now universally accepted.

DESCRIPTIVE TERMS

In descriptive anatomy and embryology, several terms of position and direction are used, and various planes of the body are referred to in sections. All descriptions of the adult are based on the assumption that the body is erect, with the upper limbs by the sides and the palms directed forward (Fig. 1–6A). This is called the *anatomical position*.

The terms *anterior* or *ventral* and *posterior* or *dorsal* are used to describe the front or back of the body or limbs, and the relations of structures within the body to one another. In embryos, dorsal and ventral are always used (Fig. 1–6B), and the embryo is generally assumed to be lying on its ventral surface with its dorsal surface upward.

Superior or *cranial* and *inferior* or *caudal* are used to indicate the relative levels of different structures. In embryos, cranial and caudal are used to denote relationships to the head and tail ends, respectively. The term *rostral* is used to indicate the relationships of structures to the nose (Fig. 1–6E). Distances from the source of attachment of a structure are designated as *proximal* or *distal*; e.g., in the lower limb the knee is proximal to the ankle and the ankle is distal to the knee.

The *median plane* is a vertical plane passing through the center of the body, dividing it into right and left halves (Fig. 1–6C). The terms *lateral* and *medial* refer to structures which are respectively farther from or nearer to the median plane of the body. A *sagittal plane* is any vertical plane passing through the body parallel to the median plane (Fig. 1–6C). A *transverse (horizontal) plane* refers to any plane that is at right angles to both the median and frontal planes (Fig. 1–6D). A *frontal (coronal) plane* is any vertical plane that intersects the median plane at a right angle; it divides the body into front (anterior or ventral) and back (posterior or dorsal) parts (Fig. 1–6E).

Various terms are used to describe sections of embryos made through the aforementioned planes. A *median section* is one cut through the median plane. Longitudinal sections parallel to the median plane, but not through it, are called sagittal sections. A vertical section through the frontal (coronal) plane is known as a *frontal (coronal) section*. Sections through the transverse plane are called *transverse (horizontal) sections*, or simply *cross sections. Oblique sections* are neither perpendicular nor horizontal, but are slanted or inclined.

SUGGESTED SUPPLEMENTARY READING

Ham, A. W., and Cormack, D. H.: *Histology*, 8th ed. Philadelphia, J. B. Lippincott Company, 1979, pp. 44–55.
Cell division, as occurs during cleavage, is discussed in detail. Although written primarily for medical students, it is easy to read.
Leeson, T. S., and Leeson, C. R.: *Histology*, 4th ed. Philadelphia, W. B. Saunders Company, 1981, pp. 67–73.
A shorter account of mitosis written for students in biomedicine and biology.
Needham, J.: *A Histology of Embryology*, 2nd ed. Cambridge, Cambridge University Press, 1959.
One of the few books which describes the fascinating history of embryonic studies.

2

REPRODUCTION

Members of all multicellular species have a more or less *limited life span.* Consequently, if they are to survive there must be a mechanism for the production of new individuals.

Human reproduction, like that of most animals, involves the fusion of sex cells or gametes—an ovum from the female and a sperm from the male. The reproductive system in both sexes is designed to insure the successful union of the sperm and the ovum, a process known as *fertilization.*

THE REPRODUCTIVE ORGANS

Each sex has *sex organs* which transmit the *sex cells* or gametes from the *sex glands* or gonads (Fig. 2–1). The sex organ in the male, called the *penis,* deposits the sperms in the female genital tract (see Fig. 2–9). In the female the *vagina* is a receptacle for the sperms and the *uterus* nourishes the embryo and retains it until birth.

THE FEMALE REPRODUCTIVE ORGANS

The *ova* (female sex cells) are produced by two oval-shaped *ovaries* located in the superior part of the pelvic cavity, one on each side of the uterus (Fig. 2–1A). When released from the ovary at *ovulation* (see Fig. 2–8), the ovum passes into one of two trumpet-shaped *uterine tubes* (Figs. 2–1A and 2–2A). These tubes open into the horns of the pear-shaped *uterus* (womb), which contains and nourishes the embryo or fetus until birth.

Structure of the Uterus (Fig. 2–2). The uterine wall consists of three layers: (1) a very thin outer layer or *perimetrium*; (2) a thick smooth-muscle layer or *myometrium*; and (3) a thin, inner lining layer, the mucosa or *endometrium.*

Three layers of the endometrium can be distinguished microscopically: (1) a thin, superficial *compact layer* of densely packed, swollen connective tissue around the necks of the glands; (2) a thick *spongy layer* of fluid-filled or edematous connective tissue containing the dilated, tortuous bodies of the glands; and (3) a thin *basal layer* containing the blind ends of the glands. The compact and spongy layers disintegrate and are shed at *menstruation* and after a birth, and so are commonly called the *functional layer.*

The *vagina* is a muscular tube that passes to the exterior from the inferior end of the uterus, called the *cervix.* The vagina is the female organ that receives the male organ or penis during *sexual intercourse* (see Fig. 2–9). It also serves as a temporary receptacle for the sperms before they begin their passage through the uterus and uterine tubes.

The External Sex Organs (Fig. 2–3). These are known collectively as the *vulva.* Two external folds of skin, the *labia majora* (large lips), enclose the opening of the vagina. Inside these folds are two smaller folds of mucous membrane called *labia minora* (small lips). The *clitoris* is at the junction of these folds; it is a small, erectile organ that is homologous to the penis. The vagina and urethra open into a cavity known as the *vestibule* (the cleft between the labia minora).

THE MALE REPRODUCTIVE ORGANS

The *sperms* (male sex cells) are produced in the *testes,* two oval-shaped glands which are suspended in the *scrotum,* a loose pouch of skin (Fig. 2–1B). Each testis consists of many highly coiled *seminiferous tubules* which produce the sperms. The sperms pass into a single, complexly coiled tube, the *epididymis,* where they are stored. From the inferior end of the epididymis, a long straight tube, the *ductus deferens* (vas deferens), passes from the scrotum through the inguinal canal into the abdominal cavity. It then descends into the pelvis where it fuses with the duct of the *seminal vesicle* to form the *ejaculatory duct* which enters the *urethra.* The urethra is a tube leading from the urinary

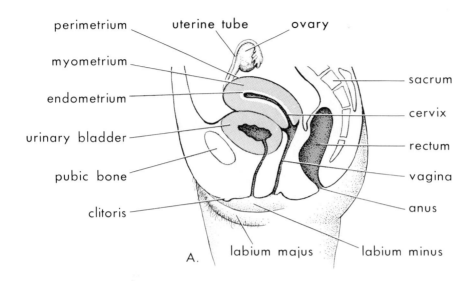

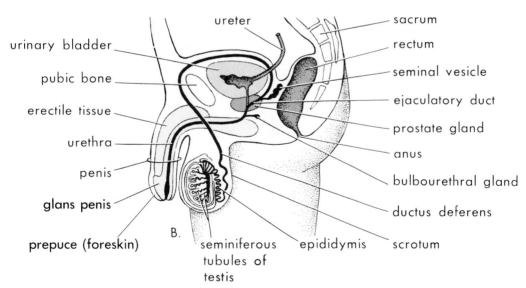

Figure 2–1 Schematic sagittal sections of the pelvic region showing the reproductive organs. *A*, Female. *B*, Male.

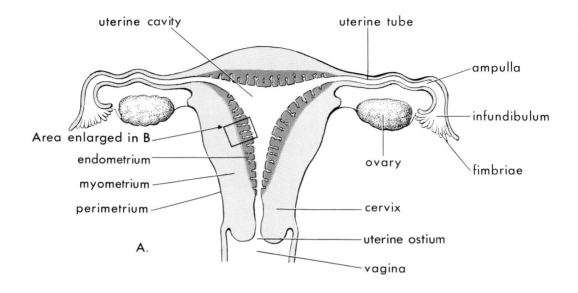

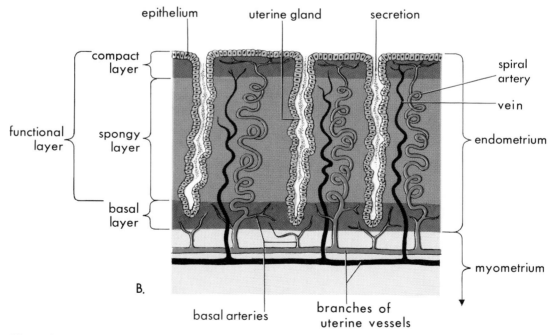

Figure 2–2 *A*, Diagrammatic frontal section of the uterus and uterine tubes. The ovaries and vagina are also indicated. *B*, Detail of the area outlined in *A*. The endometrium (mucosa) is subject to cyclic changes in response to ovarian secretory activity (see Fig. 2–7).

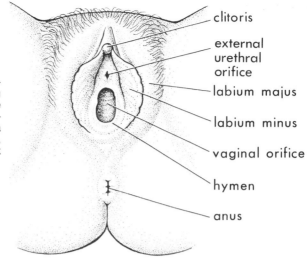

Figure 2–3 The external female genital organs, known collectively as the vulva. The opening at the inferior end of the alimentary canal, the anus, is also shown. In most women the labia majora are opposed and usually conceal the labia minora. The labia majora are fatty folds of skin, whereas the labia minora are thin folds of pink mucous membrane.

clitoris

external urethral orifice

labium majus

labium minus

vaginal orifice

hymen

anus

bladder to the outside of the body; its spongy part runs through the *penis*. Within the penis the urethra is flanked by three columns of spongy erectile tissue. During sexual excitement this tissue becomes filled with blood under increased pressure; this causes the penis to become erect and thus able to enter the vagina. Ejaculation of *semen* (sperms in seminal fluid produced by various glands, e.g., the seminal vesicles and prostate) occurs when the penis is further stimulated.

GAMETOGENESIS

Gametogenesis (gamete formation) is the process of formation and development of specialized generative cells or gametes (germ cells). This process, which involves the chromosomes and the cytoplasm of the gametes, prepares these cells for *fertilization* (union of the male and female gametes). During gametogenesis, the chromosome number is reduced by half, and the shape of the cells is altered.

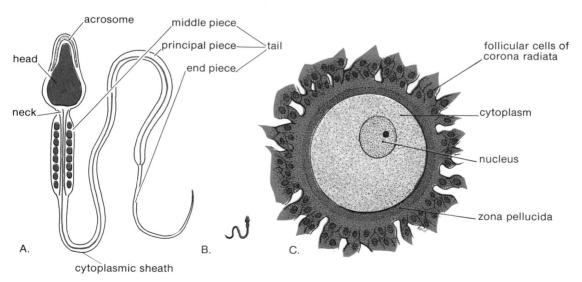

acrosome

middle piece

principal piece — tail

end piece

head

neck

follicular cells of corona radiata

cytoplasm

nucleus

zona pellucida

A.   B.   C.

cytoplasmic sheath

Figure 2–4 *A*, Drawing showing the main parts of a human sperm (×1250). The head, composed mostly of the nucleus, is covered by the acrosome. *B*, A sperm drawn to about the same scale as the ovum. *C*, Drawing of a human ovum (secondary oocyte) (×200), surrounded by the zona pellucida and corona radiata.

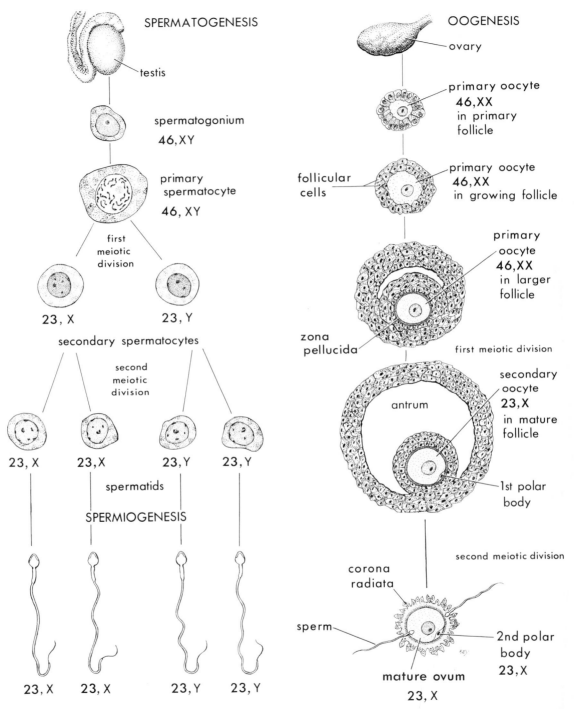

Figure 2–5 Drawings comparing spermatogenesis and oogenesis. Oogonia are not shown in this figure because all oogonia differentiate into primary oocytes before birth. The chromosome complement of the germ cells is shown at each stage. The number designates the total number of chromosomes, including the sex chromosome(s) shown after the comma. Note that (1) following the two meiotic divisions, the diploid number of chromosomes, 46, is reduced to the haploid number, 23; (2) *four sperms* form from one primary spermatocyte, whereas only *one* mature ovum results from maturation of a primary oocyte; and (3) the cytoplasm is conserved during oogenesis to form one large cell, the mature oocyte or ovum.

THE GERM CELLS OR GAMETES

The *sperm* and the *ovum* (the male and female germ cells or gametes) are highly specialized *sex cells* (Figs. 2–4 and 2–5). They contain half the usual number of chromosomes (i.e., 23 instead of 46). The number of chromosomes is reduced by the process of *meiosis* which occurs during the formation of gametes or *gametogenesis,* a process known as spermatogenesis in males and *oogenesis* in females (Fig. 2–5).

Meiosis consists of two cell divisions during which the chromosome number is reduced to half (23, the *haploid number*) that present in other cells in the body (46, the *diploid number*). During the final stages of maturation, the two chromosomes in each of the 23 pairs are separated from each other and distributed to different cells. Therefore each mature germ cell (sperm or ovum) contains one member of each pair of the chromosomes present in the immature germ cell (primary spermatocyte or primary oocyte). For more details and easy-to-follow illustrations of meiosis, see Thompson and Thompson (1980).

The significance of meiosis is that it provides for constancy of the chromosome number from generation to generation by producing *haploid sex cells.* Meiosis also allows the independent assortment of maternal and paternal chromosomes among the gametes. *Crossing over,* by relocating segments of the maternal and paternal chromosomes, serves to "shuffle" the genes and thereby produce a recombination of genetic material.

SPERMATOGENESIS

The term *spermatogenesis* refers to the entire sequence of events by which spermatogonia are transformed into spermatozoa, or sperms. This maturation process begins at puberty (about 14 years) and continues into old age.

The mature sperm is a free-swimming, actively motile cell consisting of a *head* and a *tail* (Fig. 2–4A). The head, forming most of the bulk of the sperm, consists of the nucleus. The anterior two thirds of the nucleus is covered by the *acrosome,* an organelle containing enzymes that are believed to facilitate sperm penetration of the corona radiata and zona pellucida during fertilization.

The tail of the sperm consists of three segments: the *middle piece,* the *principal piece,* and the *end piece.* The tail provides the motility of the sperm, which assists in its transport to the site of fertilization. The middle piece of the tail contains the energy-producing cytoplasmic and mitochondrial apparatus. The junction between the head and the tail is called the *neck* (Fig. 2–4A).

The early germ cells, or *spermatogonia,* which have been dormant in the seminiferous tubules of the testes since the fetal period, begin to increase in number at *puberty.* After several mitotic or ordinary cell divisions, the spermatogonia grow and undergo gradual changes which transform them into *primary spermatocytes* (Fig. 2–5), the largest germ cells in the seminiferous tubules. Each primary spermatocyte subsequently undergoes a reduction division,[1] called the *first meiotic division,* to form two haploid[2] *secondary spermatocytes* which are about half the size of primary spermatocytes. Subsequently, these secondary spermatocytes undergo a *second meiotic division* to form four haploid *spermatids* which are about half the size of secondary spermatocytes. During this division, there is no further reduction in the number of chromosomes; although part of meiosis, it is like a mitotic division. The spermatids are gradually transformed into *mature sperms* by an extensive process of differentiation known as *spermiogenesis.* Spermatogenesis, including spermiogenesis, requires about 64 days for completion and normally continues throughout the reproductive life of the male.

OOGENESIS

The term *oogenesis* refers to the entire sequence of events by which oogonia are transformed into ova. This maturation process begins before birth, but it is not completed until after *puberty* (12 to 15 years).

During early fetal life, primitive ova or *oogonia* proliferate by mitotic division. These oogonia enlarge to form *primary oocytes* before birth (Fig. 2–5). As the primary oocyte forms, ovarian stromal cells sur-

---

[1] This process of reduction by an atypical method of cell division is called *meiosis*; it consists of two specialized divisions called the first and second meiotic divisions (Fig. 2–5).

[2] In humans, body cells and early sex cells have 46 chromosomes (the diploid number). Mature sex cells have 23 chromosomes (the haploid number).

follicular
cells

nucleus of
primary oocyte

zona
pellucida

cumulus
oophorus

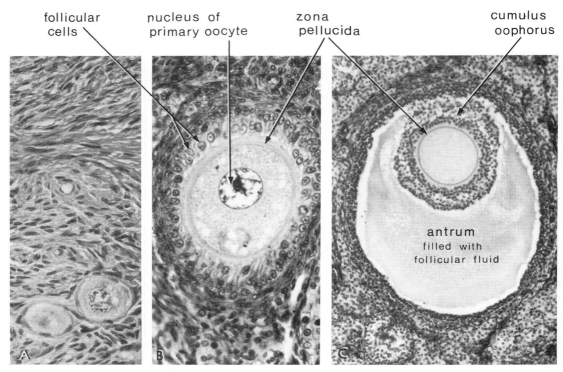

antrum
filled with
follicular fluid

Figure 2–6 Photomicrographs of sections from adult human ovaries. *A*, Ovarian cortex showing two primordial follicles (×250). *B*, Growing follicle containing a primary oocyte, surrounded by the zona pellucida and a stratified layer of follicular cells (×250). *C*, An almost mature follicle with a large antrum. The oocyte, embedded in the cumulus oophorus, does not show a nucleus because it has been sectioned tangentially (×100). (From Leeson, T. S., and Leeson, C. R.: *Histology,* 3rd ed. Philadelphia, W. B. Saunders Company, 1981.)

round it and form a single layer of flattened follicular cells. The primary oocyte enclosed by this layer of follicular cells is called a *primordial follicle* (Fig. 2–6*A*).

The primary oocytes remain dormant in the ovaries until puberty and then increase in size. A deeply staining membrane, the *zona pellucida,* forms around the oocyte (Figs. 2–4*C* and 2–6*B* and *C*). Shortly before ovulation the primary oocyte completes the *first meiotic division*. Unlike the corresponding stage of spermatogenesis, however, the division of cytoplasm is unequal. The *secondary oocyte* receives almost all the cytoplasm (Fig. 2–6*B*) and the *first polar body* or cell receives hardly any (Fig. 2–5); this small nonfunctional cell soon degenerates.

At ovulation the nucleus of the secondary oocyte begins the *second meiotic division,* but progresses only to metaphase, where division is arrested. If *fertilization occurs,* the second meiotic division is completed and most cytoplasm is again retained by one cell, the *mature ovum* (Fig. 2–5). The other cell,

called the *second polar body,* is very small and soon degenerates.

The ovum released at ovulation is surrounded by the *zona pellucida* and a layer of follicular cells called the *corona radiata* (Fig. 2–4*C*). Compared with ordinary cells, it is truly large and is barely visible to the unaided eye as a tiny speck. At least two million primary oocytes are usually present in the ovaries of a newborn female infant. Many of these regress during childhood so that by puberty only 30,000 to 40,000 remain. Of these, only about 400 mature and are expelled at ovulation during the reproductive period.

COMPARISON OF THE SPERM AND OVUM

The sperm and ovum are dissimilar in several ways because of their adaptation to specialized roles. The ovum is massive compared to the sperm (Fig. 2–4) and is immotile, whereas the microscopic sperm is highly motile. The ovum has an abundance of cytoplasm containing yolk granules which provide nutrition during the first week of development. The sperm bears little resemblance to an ovum or to any other cell because of its sparse cytoplasm and specialization for motility.

With respect to sex chromosome constitution, there are *two kinds of normal sperm* (Fig. 2–5): 22 autosomes plus an X chromosome (i.e., 23,X); and 22 autosomes plus a Y chromosome (i.e., 23,Y). However, there is only *one kind of normal ovum*: 22 autosomes plus an X chromosome (i.e., 23,X).

ABNORMAL GERM CELLS

The ideal maternal age for reproduction appears to be from 18 to 30 years of age (Smith et al., 1978). The likelihood of a chromosomal abnormality in the ovum and the embryo increases significantly after the age of 35. It is also undesirable for the father to be older than this because the likelihood of a fresh gene mutation (alteration) increases with paternal age. The older the father at the time of conception, the more likely he is to have accumulated mutations that the embryo might inherit (Thompson and Thompson, 1980). This relationship does not hold for all dominant mutations and is not an important consideration in older mothers.

Chromosomal Abnormalities. During meiosis, homologous chromosomes sometimes fail to separate and go to opposite poles of the cell. As a result of this error of cell division, known as *nondisjunction*, some germ cells have 24 chromosomes and others have only 22.

If a germ cell with 24 chromosomes fuses with a normal one during fertilization, a zygote with 47 chromosomes forms. This condition is called *trisomy* because of the presence of three representatives of a particular chromosome, instead of the usual two. If a germ cell with only 22 chromosomes fuses with a normal one, a zygote with 45 chromosomes forms. This condition is known as *monosomy* because only one representative of a particular chromosome is present, instead of the usual pair. For a description of the clinical conditions associated with numerical disorders of chromosomes, see Chapter 9.

Morphological Abnormalities. Up to 10 per cent of the sperms in an ejaculate may be grossly abnormal, but it is generally believed that they do not fertilize oocytes owing to their lack of normal motility. Most, if not all, morphologically abnormal sperms are unable to pass through the mucus in the cervical canal. X-rays, severe allergic reactions, and certain antispermatogenic agents have been reported to increase the percentage of abnormally shaped sperms in man. Such sperms are not believed to affect fertility unless their number exceeds 20 per cent.

REPRODUCTIVE CYCLES

Commencing at puberty and normally continuing throughout the reproductive years, *human females undergo monthly reproductive or sexual cycles* involving the hypothalamus, pituitary gland (hypophysis cerebri), ovaries, and uterus (Fig. 2–7). Changes also occur in the uterine tubes, vagina, and mammary glands. These cycles prepare the female reproductive system for pregnancy. Small blood vessels carry "releasing factors" from the hypothalamus to the anterior pituitary gland which regulates this gland's production of gonadotropins: *follicle-stimulating hormone* (FSH) and *luteinizing hormone* (LH).

THE OVARIAN CYCLE

The gonadotropins (FSH and LH) produce cyclic changes in the ovaries (development of follicles, ovulation, and corpus luteum formation) known as the *ovarian cycle* (Figs. 2–7 and 2–8). In each cycle, FSH promotes growth of 5 to 12 primary follicles; however, usually only one of them develops into a mature follicle and ruptures through the surface of the ovary, expelling its oocyte (Fig. 2–8). Hence, most follicles degenerate and never mature. As the oocyte and follicle degenerate, they are replaced by connective tissue, forming a *corpus atreticum*.

Follicular Development (Figs. 2–5 to 2–7). Development of a follicle is characterized by (1) growth and differentiation of the primary oocyte, (2) proliferation of follicular cells, and (3) development of a connective tissue capsule, the *theca folliculi*. The follicle soon becomes oval in shape and the ovum eccentric in position because the follicular cells proliferate more rapidly on one side. Subsequently, fluid-filled spaces appear around the follicular cells; these spaces soon

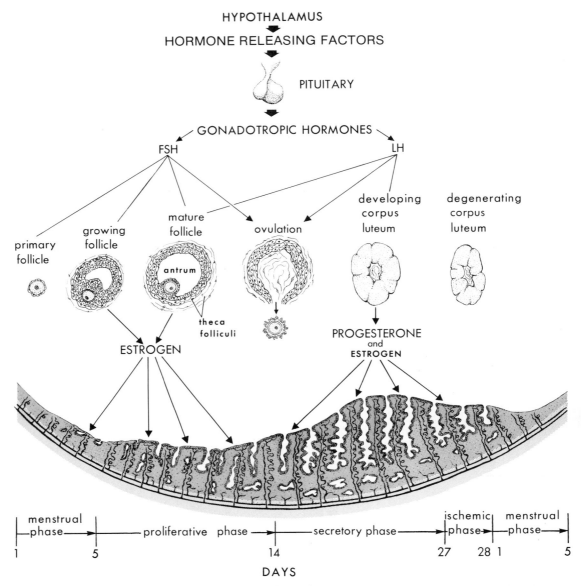

Figure 2–7 Schematic drawing illustrating the interrelations of the hypothalamus, hypophysis (pituitary gland), ovaries, and endometrium. One complete menstrual cycle and the beginning of another are shown. Changes in the ovaries, called the ovarian cycle, are promoted by the gonadotrophic hormones (FSH and LH). Hormones from the ovaries (estrogens and progesterone) then promote changes in the structure and function of the endometrium, called the uterine cycle. Thus, the cyclical activity of the ovary is intimately linked with changes in the uterus.

coalesce to form a large fluid-filled cavity, the *follicular antrum*. When the antrum forms, the ovarian follicle is called a *secondary or vesicular follicle*. The oocyte gets pushed to one side of the follicle, where it is surrounded by a mound of follicular cells, the *cumulus oophorus*, and projects into the antrum (Figs. 2–6C and 2–8A).

Development of follicles is initially induced by FSH, but final stages of maturation require LH as well. Growing follicles produce *estrogen*, a female sex hormone which regulates development and function of the reproductive organs.

Ovulation (Fig. 2–8).   Ovulation usually occurs about two weeks before the next ex-

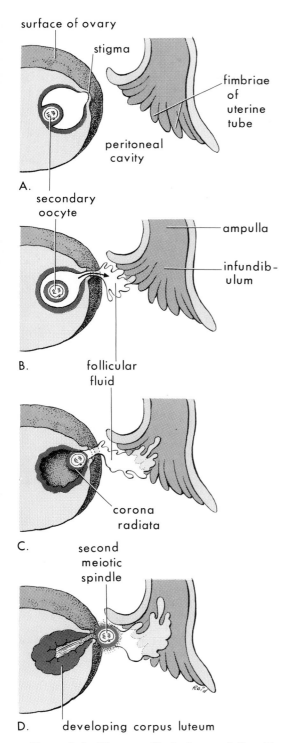

surface of ovary

stigma

fimbriae
of
uterine
tube

peritoneal
cavity

A.

secondary
oocyte

ampulla

infundib-
ulum

B.   follicular
fluid

corona
radiata

C.   second
meiotic
spindle

D.   developing corpus luteum

Figure 2–8 Diagrams illustrating ovulation. The stigma ruptures and the oocyte is expelled with the follicular fluid.

pected menstrual period, i.e., about 14 days after the first day of the menstrual period in the typical 28-day cycle (Fig. 2–7). Under FSH and LH influence, the follicle undergoes a sudden growth spurt, producing a swelling on the surface of the ovary. A small oval avascular spot, the *stigma*, soon appears on this swelling. During ovulation the ovarian surface ruptures at the stigma and the oocyte is expelled with the follicular fluid from the follicle and the ovary. The released ovum or oocyte is surrounded by the *zona pellucida* and one or more layers of radially arranged follicular cells which form the *corona radiata* (Fig. 2–4C).

Some women do not ovulate owing to an inadequate release of gonadotropins; as a result they are unable to become pregnant. In some of these patients *ovulation can be induced* by the administration of gonadotropins or by administration of an ovulatory agent (clomiphene citrate). This drug stimulates the release of pituitary gonadotropins (FSH and LH), which usually results in maturation of the ovarian follicle, ovulation, and development of the corpus luteum. The incidence of multiple pregnancy increases up to tenfold when ovulation is induced. Apparently, the fine control of FSH output is not present in these cases, and multiple ovulations occur, leading to multiple pregnancies.

The Corpus Luteum. At ovulation the walls of the follicle collapse (Fig. 2–8D) and, under LH influence, develop into a glandular structure known as the corpus luteum (Figs. 2–7 and 2–8D). It secretes *progesterone* and some estrogen. These hormones, particularly progesterone, cause the endometrial glands to secrete and prepare the endometrium for implantation of the blastocyst (Figs. 3–4 and 4–1). If the ovum is fertilized, the corpus luteum enlarges to form a *corpus luteum of pregnancy* and increases its hormone production. If the ovum is not fertilized, the corpus luteum begins to degenerate 10 to 12 days after ovulation (Fig. 2–7) and is called a *corpus luteum of menstruation*.

THE MENSTRUAL CYCLE

The cyclic changes occurring in the endometrium constitute the uterine cycle, commonly referred to as the menstrual cycle because menstruation is an obvious event. The common length of a cycle is 28 days, but this may vary markedly from individual to individual and between cycles of the same individual. In 90 per cent of healthy young women, the length of the endometrial cycles ranges between 23 and 35 days. Almost all these variations result from alterations in the duration of the proliferative phase.

Ovarian hormones cause cyclic changes in the structure of the reproductive tract, notably the endometrium. Although divided into four phases (Fig. 2–7), it must be stressed that *the menstrual cycle is a continuous process,* each phase gradually passing into the next one.

The Menstrual Phase. The first day of menstruation is counted as the beginning of the menstrual cycle. The functional layer of the uterine wall (Fig. 2–2B) is sloughed off and discarded during menstruation which typically occurs at 28-day intervals and lasts for three to five days.

The Proliferative Phase. Estrogen causes regeneration of the epithelium, lengthening of the glands, and multiplication of connective tissue cells. There is a twofold to threefold increase in the thickness of the endometrium during this phase of repair and proliferation. Early during this phase, a continuous surface epithelium covers the endometrium; the glands increase in number and in length, and the spiral arteries elongate but do not reach the surface during this phase.

The Secretory Phase. Progesterone induces the glands to become tortuous and to secrete profusely, and the connective tissue to become grossly edematous (a condition in which there are large amounts of fluid in the intercellular spaces).

When fertilization does not occur, the secretory endometrium enters into an *ischemic* (*premenstrual*) *phase* during the last day or two of the menstrual cycle (Fig. 2–7). The ischemic phase is usually considered to be the last part of the secretory phase. The ischemia (localized deficiency of blood) gives the endometrium a pale appearance and occurs as the spiral arteries constrict intermittently. This intermittent constriction of spiral arteries results from the decreasing secretion of hormones by the degenerating corpus luteum. In addition to vascular changes, the hormone withdrawal results in a stoppage of glandular secretion, a loss of interstitial fluid, and a marked shrinking of the endometrium.

Toward the end of the ischemic part of the secretory phase, the spiral arteries become constricted for longer periods. Eventually, blood begins to seep through the ruptured walls of the spiral arteries into the surrounding stroma. Small pools of blood soon form and break through the endometrial surface, resulting in bleeding into the uterine lumen and the beginning of another menstrual phase.

As small pieces of the endometrium become detached and pass into the uterine cavity, the torn ends of the arteries bleed into the uterine cavity, resulting in an average loss of 35 ml of blood. Eventually, over three to six days, the entire compact layer and most of the spongy layer are discarded in the menstrual flow. The remnants of the spongy layer and the basal layer remain to undergo regeneration during the subsequent proliferative phase of the endometrium. Consequently, *the cyclic activity of the ovary is intimately linked with cyclic changes in the endometrium* (Fig. 2–7).

If pregnancy does not occur, the reproductive or menstrual cycles normally continue until the end of a woman's reproductive life, usually between the ages of 47 and 52. If pregnancy occurs, the menstrual cycles stop and the endometrium passes into a pregnancy phase. With the termination of pregnancy, the ovarian and menstrual cycles resume after a variable period of time (usually 6 to 10 weeks if the woman is not breastfeeding her baby).

GERM CELL TRANSPORT AND VIABILITY

Ovum Transport. The ovum leaves the ovary with the escaping follicular fluid. The finger-like *fimbriae* of the uterine tube (Fig. 2–8A) move to and fro over the ovary and "sweep" the ovum into the tube. The ovum passes into the *ampulla* of the tube (Fig. 2–8B), largely as a result of the beating action of cilia on some tubal epithelial cells, but partly by muscular contractions of the tubal wall.

Sperm Transport. About 200 to 500 million of the sperms stored in the epididymis are deposited in the vagina during the process of ejaculation occurring during sexual intercourse (Fig. 2–9). The sperms pass by movements of their tails into the cervical canal, but passage of the sperms through the remainder of the uterus and the uterine tubes results mainly from contractions of the walls

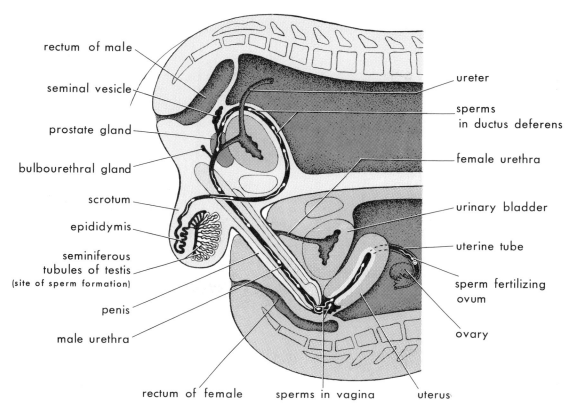

Figure 2–9 Schematic sagittal section of the male and female pelves showing the penis in the vagina. The sperms are produced in the seminiferous tubules of the testis and stored in the epididymis. During ejaculation the sperms pass along the ductus deferens and into the urethra where they mix with secretions from the seminal vesicles, prostate, and bulbourethral glands. This mixture, called semen, is deposited in the superior portion of the vagina, close to the external opening of the uterus. The sperms pass through the cavity of the uterus and into the uterine tubes, where fertilization occurs.

of these organs. It is not known how long it takes sperms to reach the fertilization site, but the time of transport is probably not more than an hour. Only a few hundred sperms reach the fertilization site in each uterine tube.

GERM CELL VIABILITY

Ova. Studies on early stages of development indicate that the ovum is usually fer-

tilized within 12 hours after expulsion of the secondary oocyte at ovulation, and observations have shown that in vitro the unfertilized human secondary oocyte dies within 12 to 24 hours.

Sperms. Most sperms probably do not survive for more than 24 hours in the female genital tract. However, there is suggestive evidence that some sperms may be able to fertilize an ovum for as long as three days after insemination.

SUMMARY

Human reproduction involves the fusion of an ovum from a female and a sperm from a male. The reproductive system in both sexes is designed to insure the union of these sex cells. The ovum produced by the ovary is

expelled from it at ovulation and passes into the uterine tube. The sperms are produced by the seminiferous tubules of the testes and stored in the epididymis. During the process of ejaculation, occurring during sexual intercourse, the sperms are deposited in the vagina. They soon pass through the cervical canal, the uterine cavity and along the uterine tube to the ampulla where fertilization occurs if an ovum is present.

SUGGESTED SUPPLEMENTARY READING

Moore, K. L.: *Clinically Oriented Anatomy*. Baltimore, William & Wilkins Company, 1980.
Chapter 3 contains several colored illustrations of the reproductive organs and several clinically oriented problems.
Page, E. W., Villee, C. A., and Villee, D. B.: *Human Reproduction. Essentials of Reproductive and Peri-natal Medicine,* 3rd ed. Philadelphia, W. B. Saunders Company, 1981.
Chapter 1 gives an overview of the reproductive processes, emphasizing the regulation of human reproduction. Chapter 2 would also be worth reading at this time.
Smith, D. W., Bierman, E. L., and Robinson, N. M.: *The Biologic Ages of Man: From Conception Through Old Age,* 2nd ed. Philadelphia, W. B. Saunders Company, 1978.
This small book provides an integrated portrayal of human development from conception (fertilization) through old age.
Thompson, J. S., and Thompson, M. W.: *Medical Genetics,* 3rd ed. Philadelphia, W. B. Saunders Company, 1980.
Details about human chromosomes, meiosis, and crossing over are clearly described and illustrated in Chapter 2. Medical applications of chromosome analysis are also discussed.

THE FIRST WEEK OF DEVELOPMENT

Development begins at fertilization when a sperm fuses with an ovum to form a *zygote* (Gr. *zygotos,* yoked together). The zygote is the first cell of a new human being. The zygote undergoes cell division and many complex changes occur before the developing human is able to live independently.

FERTILIZATION

Capacitation of Sperms.   Before a mature motile sperm can penetrate the corona radiata and zona pellucida surrounding a secondary oocyte, it must undergo capacitation, an *activation process* that takes about seven hours. It is generally accepted that this process consists of enzymatic changes that result in the *removal of a glycoprotein coat* and seminal plasma proteins from the plasma membrane over the acrosome. No morphological changes are known to occur during the capacitation process.

Usually, sperms are capacitated in the uterus or the uterine tubes by substances in the secretions of the female genital tract. Follicular fluid is also known to have capacitating properties.

The Acrosome Reaction.   An acrosome reaction may occur after capacitation of a sperm. This sequence of events, occurring during passage of the sperm through the corona radiata (Fig. 3–1*B*), consists of structural changes. The outer membrane of the acrosome fuses at many places with the overlying cell membrane of the sperm head, and the fused membranes then rupture, producing multiple perforations through which the enzymes in the acrosome escape. Progesterone seems to stimulate the acrosome reaction. It is present in large amounts in the follicular fluid released at ovulation (Fig. 2–8) and between the follicular cells of the corona radiata. Enzymes that are believed to facilitate

passage of the sperm through the corona radiata and the zona pellucida are released from the acrosome during the acrosome reaction. *Hyaluronidase* enables the sperm to penetrate the corona radiata. *Trypsin-like substances* and a *zona lysin* digest a pathway for the sperm through the zona pellucida.

Fertilization is the sequence of events that begins with contact between a sperm and a secondary oocyte, and ends with the fusion of the nuclei of the sperm and ovum and the intermingling of maternal and paternal chromosomes at the metaphase of the first mitotic division of the zygote (Fig. 3–2*D* and *E*).

Fertilization usually occurs in the intermediate dilated portion of the uterine tube called the *ampulla* (see Fig. 2–2*A*) and consists of the fusion of a sperm with an ovum (Figs. 3–1 and 3–2).

Fertilization may be summarized as follows:

1. The sperm passes through the corona radiata (Fig. 3–1).

2. The sperm penetrates the zona pellucida, digesting a path by the action of enzymes released from its acrosome.

3. The sperm head attaches to the surface of the ovum.

4. The ovum reacts to sperm contact in two ways: (a) the zona pellucida and the ovum's cell membrane change so that the entry of more sperms is prevented, and (b) the secondary oocyte completes the second meiotic division and expels the second polar body (Fig. 3–2*B*). The ovum is now mature and its nucleus is called the female pronucleus.

5. The sperm head enlarges to form the male pronucleus as the tail of the sperm degenerates (Fig. 3–2*C*).

6. The male and female pronuclei fuse in the center of the ovum where they come into contact, they lose their nuclear membranes, and their chromosomes intermingle (Fig. 3–2*D*).

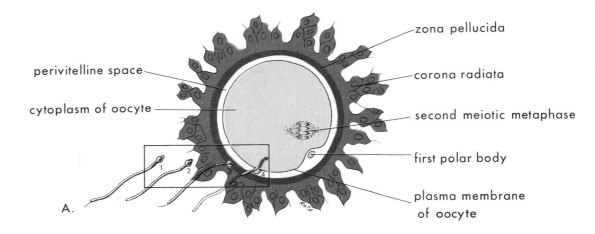

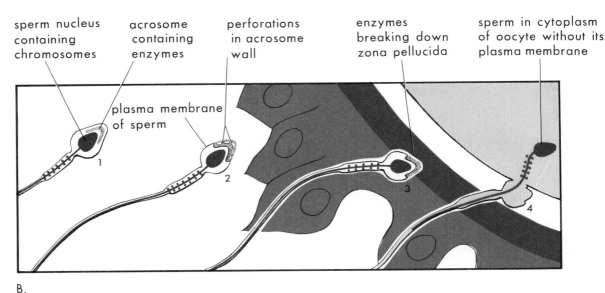

Figure 3–1 Diagrams illustrating early stages of fertilization. The acrosome reaction and the penetration of a sperm into an ovum are shown. The detail of the area outlined in *A* is given in *B*: (1) sperm during capacitation, (2) sperm undergoing the acrosome reaction, (3) sperm digesting a path for itself by the action of enzymes released from the acrosome, (4) sperm head fusing with ovum. Note that the sperm enters the oocyte but leaves its plasma membrane behind. (See Fig. 3–2 for the later stages of fertilization.)

RESULTS OF FERTILIZATION

1. Restoration of the Diploid Number. Fusion of the two haploid germ cells (each with 23 chromosomes) produces a zygote, which is a diploid cell with 46 chromosomes, the normal number for the human species. One member of each of the 23 pairs of chromosomes is derived from each parent.

2. Species Variation. Because half the chromosomes come from the mother and the other half from the father, the zygote con-

tains a new combination of chromosomes that differs from that of either of the parents. Within each chromosome are numerous hereditary factors called *genes,* each of which differs from others and controls the inheritance of one or more characteristics. Consequently, fertilization forms the basis of biparental inheritance and insures variation of the human species.

Meiosis allows independent assortment of maternal and paternal chromosomes among the germ cells. Crossing over of chromo-

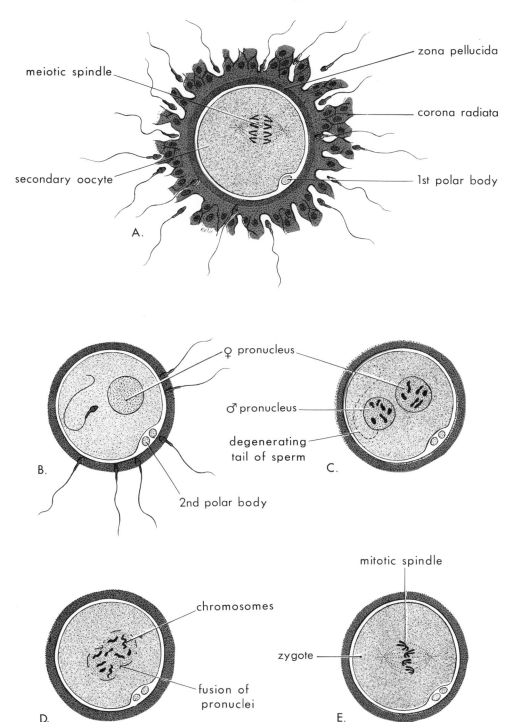

Figure 3–2   Diagrams illustrating fertilization. *A*, Secondary oocyte about to be fertilized. (Only four of the 23 chromosome pairs are shown.) *B*, The corona radiata has disappeared; a sperm has entered the ovum, and the second maturation division has occurred. *C*, The sperm head has enlarged to form the male pronucleus. *D*, The pronuclei are fusing. *E*, The chromosomes of the zygote are arranged on a mitotic spindle in preparation for the first cleavage division. The polar bodies are small nonfunctional cells that soon degenerate.

somes, by relocating segments of the maternal and paternal chromosomes, serves to "shuffle" the genes, thereby producing a recombination of genetic material. (For more details, see Moore, 1982.)

3. Sex Determination. The embryo's sex is determined at fertilization by the kind of sperm that fertilizes the ovum. Fertilization by an X-bearing sperm produces an XX zygote, which normally develops into a fe-

male, whereas fertilization by a Y-bearing sperm produces an XY zygote, which normally develops into a male. Hence, *it is the father rather than the mother whose gamete determines the sex of their offspring.*

4. Initiation of Cleavage. Fertilization of the ovum by a sperm also initiates early human development by stimulating the zygote to undergo mitotic cell division or cleavage into two blastomeres.

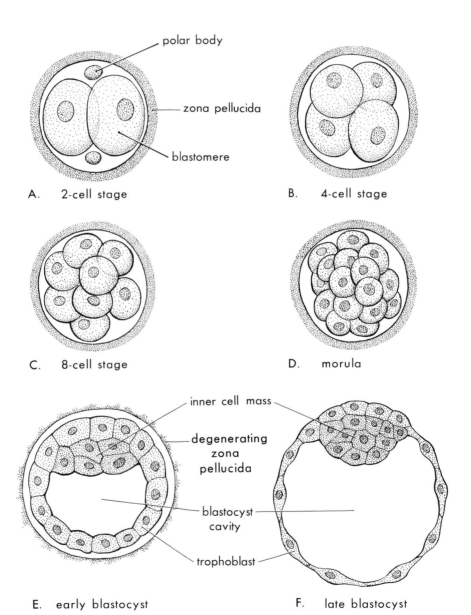

Figure 3–3   Drawings illustrating cleavage of the zygote and formation of the blastocyst. *E* and *F* are sections of blastocysts. Note that the zona pellucida has disappeared by the last blastocyst stage (about five days). The polar bodies shown in *A* are small, nonfunctional cells that soon degenerate.

CLEAVAGE

As the zygote passes down the uterine tube, it undergoes cell division. Mitotic division of the zygote into two daughter cells, called *blastomeres* (Fig. 3–3*A*), begins shortly after fertilization. Subsequent divisions follow rapidly upon one another, forming progressively smaller blastomeres (Fig. 3–3*B* to *D*). The term cleavage is used to describe the mitotic divisions of the zygote.

By the third day, a solid ball of 16 or so blastomeres has formed, which is called a *morula* (from Latin *morus*, meaning "mulberry." The morula is a mulberry-like cellular mass). It enters the uterus and fluid

passes into the morula from the uterine cavity and collects between its cells. As the fluid increases, it separates these cells into two parts: (1) an outer cell mass called the *trophoblast* (from Greek *trophe*, meaning "nutrition," and *blastos*, meaning "germ" or "bud"; the trophoblast later forms the major part of the placenta) and (2) a group of centrally located cells known as the *inner cell mass* (embryoblast). The inner cell mass subsequently differentiates into the *embryo*.

By the fourth day the fluid-filled spaces fuse to form a single large space known as the *blastocyst cavity*. This converts the morula into a *blastocyst* (Fig. 3–3*E*). The inner cell mass (future embryo) projects into the

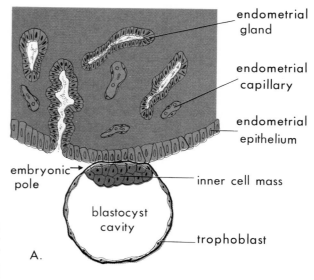

Figure 3–4 Drawings of sections illustrating early stages of implantation. *A*, Six days; the trophoblast is attached to the endometrial epithelium at the embryonic pole of the blastocyst. *B*, Seven days; the syncytiotrophoblast has formed from the trophoblast, has penetrated the endometrial epithelium, and has started to invade the endometrial stroma (connective tissue).

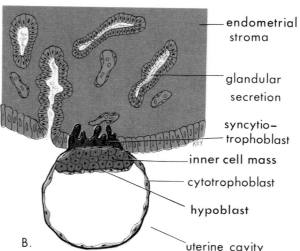

blastocyst cavity and the trophoblast forms the wall of the blastocyst (Fig. 3–3F). The blastocyst lies free in the uterine secretions for about two days. On about the fifth day the *zona pellucida* degenerates and disappears (Fig. 3–3E and F). The blastocyst attaches to the maternal uterine epithelium on about the sixth day (Fig. 3–4A). The trophoblastic cells soon begin to destroy the adjacent endometrial cells (Fig. 3–4B).

As invasion of the trophoblast proceeds, two cell layers form: (1) an inner *cytotrophoblast* (cellular trophoblast), and (2) an outer *syncytiotrophoblast* (syncytial trophoblast). The finger-like processes of the syncytiotrophoblast penetrate the endometrial epithelium and invade the endometrial stroma. By the end of the first week, the blastocyst is superficially implanted in the lining (endometrium) of the uterus (Fig. 3–4B).

As the blastocyst implants, early differentiation of the inner cell mass occurs. A layer of cells, called the *hypoblast* or primitive embryonic endoderm, appears on the free surface of the inner cell mass (Fig. 3–4B). The hypoblast later forms the roof of the primary yolk sac (see Fig. 4–1C).

In vitro fertilization of human ova and cleavage of the zygotes have been achieved by several investigators. Most studies have been carried out on infertile women with occluded uterine tubes, with the intention of establishing pregnancy by transferring a morula (cultured in vitro) into the uterus. This technique offers hope to some infertile women who wish to have children. Synchronizing the endometrium and the cleavage stage of the zygote appears to present the major problem with this technique, because in vitro development is 20 to 30 per cent retarded in development as compared with normal in vivo development.

Abnormal Zygotes and Spontaneous Abortion. About 15 per cent of all zygotes result in detectable spontaneous abortion, but this estimate is undoubtedly low because the loss of zygotes during the first week is thought to be high. The actual rate is unknown because the women do not know they are pregnant at this early stage. Clinicians frequently have a patient who states that her last menstrual period was delayed by one or two weeks and that then her menstrual flow was unusually profuse. Very likely, such a patient has had an early spontaneous abortion.

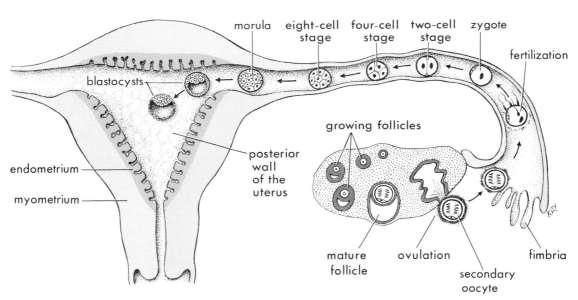

Figure 3–5 Diagrammatic summary of the ovarian cycle, fertilization, and development during the first week. *Development begins at fertilization.* The secondary oocyte is released from the ovary at ovulation and passes into the uterine tube where it is met and fertilized by a sperm. The zygote divides repeatedly as it passes down the uterine tube and becomes a morula. The morula enters the uterus, develops a cavity and becomes a blastocyst. The blastocyst then begins to invade the endometrial lining of the posterior wall of the uterus, as shown in Figure 3–4B.

Early abortion occurs for a variety of reasons, one being the presence of chromosomal abnormalities in the zygote.

This early loss of zygotes, once called *pregnancy wastage,* appears to represent a disposal of abnormal conceptuses that could not have developed normally, i.e., a natural prenatal screening of embryos.

SUMMARY

Fertilization usually occurs in the ampulla of the uterine tube. The process is complete when the haploid male and female pronuclei fuse to form a *zygote* (Fig. 3–5). This diploid cell is the beginning of a new human being. As it passes down the uterine tube, the zygote undergoes cell division or *cleavage* into a number of smaller cells called *blastomeres.* About three days after fertilization, a ball of 16 or so blastomeres, the *morula,* enters the uterus. A cavity soon forms in the morula, converting it into a *blastocyst* consisting of an *inner cell mass* and a *blastocyst cavity.* The zona pellucida disappears and the blastocyst contacts the lining of the uterus. The trophoblastic cells invade the uterine epithelium and underlying endometrial stroma. By the end of the first week, the blastocyst is superficially implanted in the endometrium of the uterus.

The *results of fertilization* are: (1) restoration of the diploid number of chromosomes; (2) variation of the species; (3) determination of sex; and (4) initiation of cleavage of the zygote.

SUGGESTED SUPPLEMENTARY READING

Edwards, R. G., and Fowler, R. E.: Human embryos in the laboratory. *Sci. Am.* 233:44, 1970.
A good description with clear illustrations of in vitro fertilization.
Moore, K. L.: *The Developing Human. Clinically Oriented Embryology*, 3rd ed. Philadelphia, W. B. Saunders Company, 1982.
This book was written for medical students and gives more details of early human development.
Smith, D. W., Bierman, E. L., and Robinson, N. M.: *The Biologic Ages of Man: From Conception Through Old Age,* 2nd ed. Philadelphia, W. B. Saunders Company, 1978.
Discusses early spontaneous abortions and their causes.

4

THE SECOND WEEK OF DEVELOPMENT

IMPLANTATION

Implantation or embedding of the blastocyst in the endometrium (mucosa) of the uterus is completed during the second week of development. Changes also occur in the inner cell mass which result in the formation of a two-layered thick plate called the *embryonic disc* that will differentiate into the embryo. The *amniotic cavity, yolk sac, connecting stalk,* and *chorion* also develop during the second week.

The mucosa of the uterus is in the *secretory phase* (see Fig. 2–7) at the time of implantation. The actively erosive *syncytiotrophoblast* continues to invade the endometrium containing connective tissue, capillaries, and glands, and the blastocyst slowly sinks within the endometrium. As more trophoblast contacts the endometrium, the trophoblast proliferates and differentiates into two layers (Fig. 4–1A). The *cytotrophoblast* is composed of cells whereas the *syncytiotrophoblast* consists of a thick multinucleated protoplasmic mass. The syncytiotrophoblast at the embryonic pole (adjacent to the embryo) soon forms a large, thick, multinucleated mass (Fig. 4–1B).

Isolated spaces, or *lacunae,* appear in the syncytiotrophoblast which soon become filled with blood from ruptured maternal capillaries and secretions from eroded endometrial glands (Fig. 4–1C). This nutritive fluid or *embryotroph* passes to the embryonic disc (early embryo) by diffusion.

Small spaces appear between the inner cell mass and the invading trophoblast. These spaces soon coalesce to form a slitlike *amniotic cavity* (Fig. 4–1A).

As the amniotic cavity forms, changes occur in the inner cell mass, resulting in the formation of a flattened, essentially circular *embryonic disc*. It consists of two layers: (1) the *epiblast,* consisting of high columnar cells related to the amniotic cavity, and (2) the *hypoblast,* consisting of small cuboidal cells related to the blastocyst cavity.

As the amniotic cavity enlarges, a thin epithelial roof, the *amnion,* forms from cytotrophoblastic cells. The epiblast forms the floor of the amniotic cavity and is continuous peripherally with the amnion (Fig. 4–1C). Concurrently, other cells from the trophoblast form a thin *exocoelomic membrane* which encloses a cavity known as the *primary* (primitive) *yolk sac* (Fig. 4–1C). The human yolk sac contains no yolk, but it is an essential structure that has an important role during later development of the embryo (see Chapter 8). Some trophoblastic cells give rise to a layer of loosely arranged tissue around the amnion and the primary yolk sac. This is called *extraembryonic mesoderm.*

The *10-day conceptus* (the embryo and its membranes) is completely embedded in the endometrium (Fig. 4–2). For a day or so a small defect may be recognized by a *closing plug* consisting of a blood clot and cellular debris (Figs. 4–2 and 4–3). By day 11 isolated spaces are visible within the extraembryonic mesoderm; these spaces rapidly fuse to form large isolated cavities of *extraembryonic coelom* (Figs. 4–2B and 4–3B). By day 12 the endometrial epithelium covers over the blastocyst, producing a minute elevation or wart-like bulge on the endometrial surface.

Meanwhile, adjacent syncytiotrophoblastic lacunae have fused to form intercommunicating *lacunar networks* (Fig. 4–2B), the primordia of the *intervillous spaces* of the placenta (see Chapter 8). The endometrial capillaries around the implanted embryo have also become dilated to form *sinusoids* and some have been eroded by the syncytiotrophoblast. Maternal blood now seeps into the lacunar networks and soon begins to flow slowly through the lacunar system, establishing a primitive *uteroplacental circulation.* When maternal blood flows into the *syncytiotrophoblastic lacunae,* its nutritive sub-

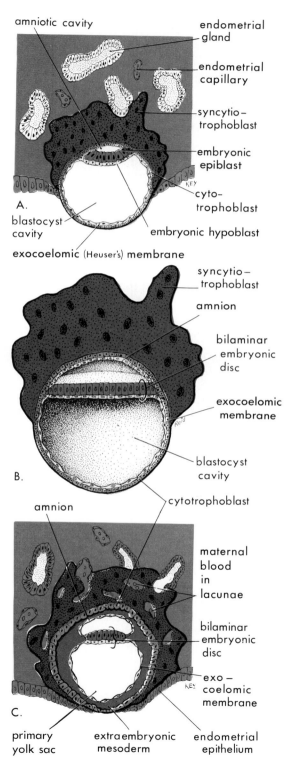

amniotic cavity

endometrial gland

endometrial capillary

syncytio-trophoblast

embryonic epiblast

cyto-trophoblast

blastocyst cavity

embryonic hypoblast

exocoelomic (Heuser's) membrane

A.

syncytio-trophoblast

amnion

bilaminar embryonic disc

exocoelomic membrane

blastocyst cavity

B.

cytotrophoblast

amnion

maternal blood in lacunae

bilaminar embryonic disc

exo-coelomic membrane

endometrial epithelium

C.

primary yolk sac

extraembryonic mesoderm

Figure 4–1 Drawings illustrating the implantation of a blastocyst into the endometrium. The actual size of the conceptus is about 0.1 mm. *A*, Drawing of a section through a blastocyst partially implanted in the endometrium (about 8 days). Note the slitlike amniotic cavity. *B*, An enlarged three-dimensional sketch of a slightly older blastocyst after removal from the endometrium. Note the extensive syncytiotrophoblast at the embryonic pole and the much larger amniotic cavity. *C*, Drawing of a section through a blastocyst of about 9 days implanted in the endometrium. (Based on Hertig and Rock, 1945.) Note the spaces or lacunae appearing in the syncytiotrophoblast: These lacunae soon begin to communicate with the endometrial blood vessels and glands.

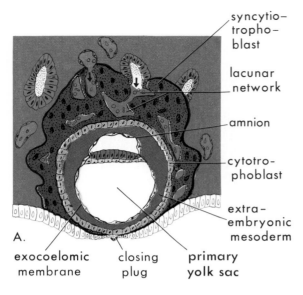

syncytio-
tropho-
blast

lacunar
network

amnion

cytotro-
phoblast

extra-
embryonic
mesoderm

A.

exocoelomic   closing   primary
membrane   plug   yolk sac

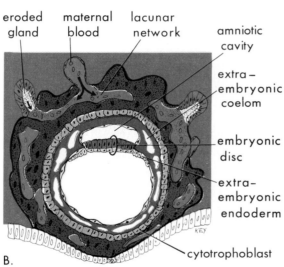

eroded   maternal   lacunar
gland   blood   network

amniotic
cavity

extra-
embryonic
coelom

embryonic
disc

extra-
embryonic
endoderm

cytotrophoblast

B.

Figure 4–2 Drawings of section through implanted blastocysts. *A*, 10 days; *B*, 12 days. (Based on Hertig and Rock, 1941.) This stage of development is characterized by the intercommunication of the lacunae filled with maternal blood. Note in *B* that large cavities have appeared in the extraembryonic mesoderm, forming the beginning of the extraembryonic coelom. Also note that extraembryonic endodermal cells have begun to form on the inside of the primary yolk sac.

stances become available to the embryonic tissues over the very large surface of the syncytiotrophoblast. As both arterial and venous branches of the maternal blood vessels come into communication with the syncytiotrophoblastic lacunae, blood circulation is established. Oxygenated blood passes into the lacunae from the *spiral arteries*, and deoxygenated blood is removed from them via the veins of the uterus (see Fig. 2–2*B*).

By the end of the second week, a defect is no longer present in the endometrial epithelium (Fig. 4–4*A*). *Primary chorionic villi* (finger-like projections of the chorion) have also

formed (Fig. 4–5). These will later differentiate into the chorionic villi of the placenta (see Chapter 8). The isolated coelomic spaces in the extraembryonic mesoderm have now fused to form a single large extraembryonic coelom. This fluid-filled cavity surrounds the amnion and yolk sac, except where the amnion is attached to the chorion by the *connecting (body) stalk* (Fig. 4–4*B*). As the extraembryonic coelom forms, the primitive yolk sac decreases in size, resulting in a smaller *secondary yolk sac*.

The extraembryonic coelom splits the extraembryonic mesoderm into two layers (Fig.

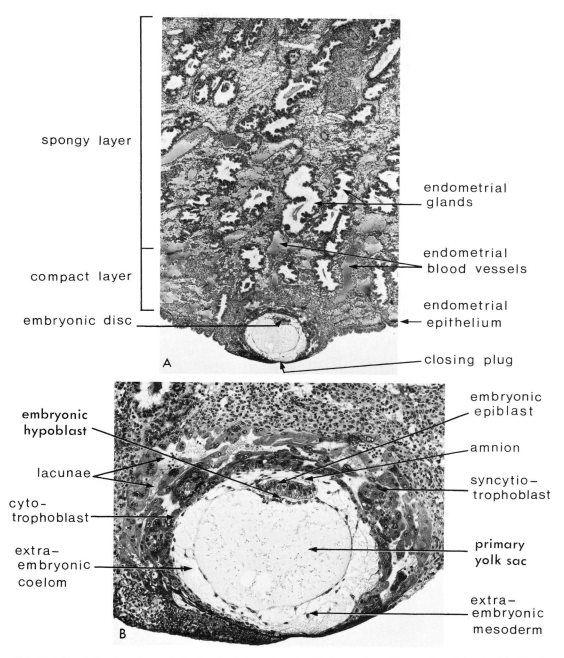

spongy layer

compact layer

embryonic disc

endometrial glands

endometrial blood vessels

endometrial epithelium

closing plug

A

embryonic hypoblast

lacunae

cyto-trophoblast

extra-embryonic coelom

B

embryonic epiblast

amnion

syncytio-trophoblast

primary yolk sac

extra-embryonic mesoderm

Figure 4–3 *A*, Section through the implantation site of a 12-day embryo. The embryo is embedded in the compact layer of the endometrium (×30). *B*, Higher magnification of the conceptus and surrounding endometrium (×100). (From Hertig, A. T., and Rock, J.: *Contr. Embryol. Carneg. Instn., Wash. 29*:127, 1941. Courtesy of the Carnegie Institution of Washington.)

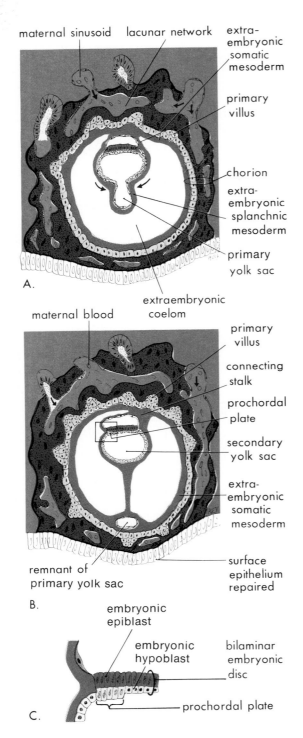

A.

B.

C.

Figure 4–4 Drawings of sections through implanted human embryos. (Based mainly on Hertig et al., 1956.) In these drawings note that (1) the defect in the surface epithelium of the endometrium has disappeared; (2) a small secondary yolk sac has formed inside the primary yolk sac as it is "pinched off"; (3) a large cavity, the extraembryonic coelom, now surrounds the yolk sac and the amnion, except where the amnion is attached to the chorion by the connecting stalk; and (4) the extraembryonic coelom splits the extraembryonic mesoderm into two layers: extraembryonic somatic mesoderm lining the trophoblast and covering the amnion, and extraembryonic splanchnic mesoderm around the yolk sac. The trophoblast and extraembryonic somatic mesoderm together form the chorion, which eventually gives rise to the fetal part of the placenta. *A*, 13 days, illustrating the decrease in relative size of the primary yolk sac and the early appearance of primary chorionic villi at the embryonic pole. *B*, 14 days, showing the newly formed secondary yolk sac and the location of the prochordal plate (future site of mouth) in its roof. *C*, Detail of the prochordal plate area outlined in *B*.

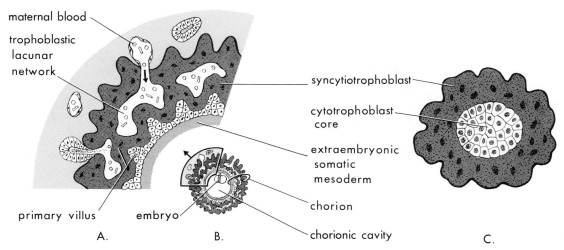

Figure 4–5 *A*, Detail of the section (outlined in *B*) of the wall of the chorionic sac. *B*, Sketch of a 14-day conceptus to illustrate the chorionic sac and the shaggy appearance created by the primary villi (×6). *C*, Drawing of a transverse section through a primary chorionic villus (×300).

4–4*A* and *B*): the *extraembryonic somatic mesoderm* lines the trophoblast and covers the amnion, and the *extraembryonic splanchnic mesoderm* covers the yolk sac. The extraembryonic somatic mesoderm and the trophoblast together constitute the *chorion* (Fig. 4–5*B*).

The chorion forms a sac within which the embryo and its attached amniotic and yolk sacs are suspended by the connecting stalk (Fig. 4–5*B*). The amniotic sac (with the embryonic epiblast forming its "floor") and the yolk sac (with the embryonic hypoblast forming its "roof") are analogous to two balloons

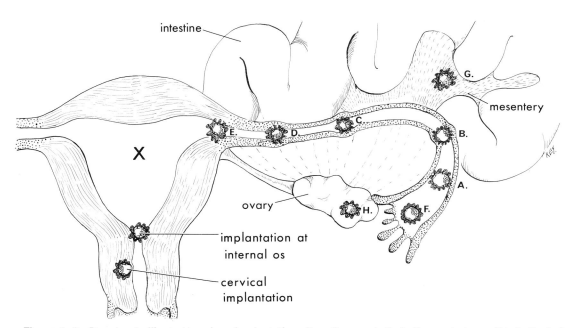

Figure 4–6 Drawing to illustrate various implantation sites; the usual site in the posterior wall is indicated by an X. The approximate order of frequency of ectopic (extrauterine) implantations is indicated alphabetically. *A* to *F*, Tubal pregnancies. *G*, Abdominal pregnancy. *H*, Ovarian pregnancy.

pressed together to form the bilaminar embryonic disc and suspended by a cord (the connecting stalk) from the inside of a larger balloon (the chorionic sac).

IMPLANTATION SITES

Intrauterine Sites (Fig. 4–6). The blastocyst usually implants in the midportion of the body of the uterus, slightly more frequently on the posterior wall than on the anterior wall. Implantation in the inferior segment of the uterus near the *internal ostium* (os; internal orifice of the cervix) results in *placenta previa*, a placenta that covers the internal ostium. This condition may cause severe bleeding during pregnancy.

Extrauterine Sites (Figs. 4–6 to 4–8). Implantation often occurs *outside the cavity of the uterus*. It includes tubal, cervical, and interstitial types. *More than 90 per cent of ectopic implantations occur in the uterine tube* (Fig. 4–7). About 60 per cent of tubal pregnancies are in the ampulla or infundibulum of the uterine tube (Figs. 4–7 and 4–8). The incidence of tubal pregnancy varies from 1 in 80 to 1 in 250 pregnancies, depending on the socioeconomic level of the population studied (Page et al., 1981).

There are several causes of *ectopic tubal pregnancy*, but it is usually related to factors that delay or prevent transport of the dividing zygote to the uterus, for example, alterations resulting from *pelvic inflammatory disease*. In some cases, the blockage results from a previous tubal infection that has damaged the mucosa, causing adhesions between its folds.

Ectopic tubal pregnancies usually result in rupture of the uterine tube and hemorrhage during the first eight weeks, followed by death of the embryo. Tubal rupture and subsequent hemorrhage constitute a threat to the mother's life and so are of major clinical importance. The affected tube and embryo are removed (Fig. 4–7).

Cervical pregnancy is very rare (Fig. 4–6). Some of these pregnancies are not recognized because the conceptus is expelled early in the gestation. In other cases, the placenta of the embryo becomes firmly attached to the fibrous and muscular parts of the cervix, often resulting in bleeding and subsequent surgical intervention, e.g., *hysterectomy* (excision of the uterus).

Blastocysts may implant in the ovary (Fig. 4–6*H*) or in the abdominal cavity (Fig. 4–6*G*), but *ovarian and abdominal pregnancies are extremely rare.* In exceptional cases, an

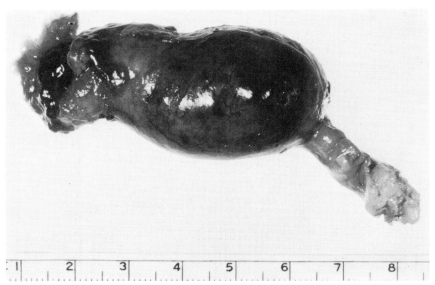

Figure 4–7 Photograph showing the gross appearance of an unruptured ectopic pregnancy located in the ampulla of the uterine tube. When the chorionic sac distends the tube, partial separation of the placenta and rupture of the tube often occur. Spurts of blood escape from the ruptured tube and its infundibulum (shown at the left). Tubal rupture and the associated hemorrhage constitute a threat to the mother's life. (From Page, E. W., Villee, C. A., and Villee, D. B.: *Human Reproduction. Essentials of Reproductive and Perinatal Medicine,* 3rd ed. Philadelphia, W. B. Saunders Company, 1981.)

uterine tube   chorionic sac

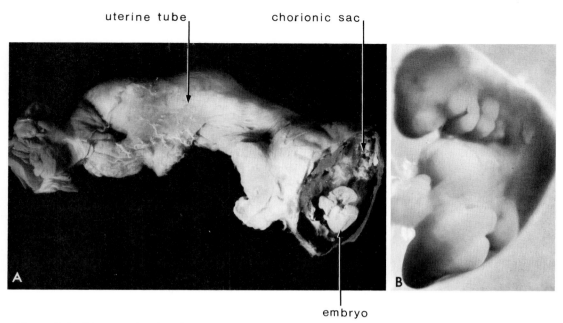

embryo

Figure 4–8   Photographs of a tubal pregnancy. *A*, The uterine tube has been sectioned to show the conceptus implanted in the mucous membrane (×3). *B*, Enlarged photograph of the normal-appearing four-week embryo (×13). Ectopic pregnancies occur most often in the ampulla of the uterine tube. This serious condition may be caused by a delay in the passage of the dividing zygote along the tube. Ectopic tubal pregnancy results in death of the embryo and usually sudden massive bleeding from the ruptured tube. (Photographed by Professor Jean Hay, Department of Anatomy, University of Manitoba.)

abdominal pregnancy may progress to full term, and the fetus may be delivered alive. Usually an abdominal pregnancy creates a serious condition because the placenta often attaches to vital structures and causes considerable bleeding.

Inhibition of Implantation. The administration of relatively large doses of estrogen ("morning-after" pills) for several days after sexual intercourse will prevent pregnancy by inhibiting implantation of the blastocyst that may develop. Normally, the endometrium progresses to the secretory phase of the menstrual cycle as the zygote forms, undergoes cleavage, and the blastocyst enters the uterus.

The large amount of estrogen, usually administered as the synthetic estrogen *diethylstilbestrol* (*DES*), disturbs the normal balance between estrogen and progesterone that is necessary for preparation of the endometrium for implantation of the blastocyst (see Fig. 2–7). When the secretory phase does not occur, implantation cannot take place, and the blastocyst soon dies.

This treatment results in the death of the blastocyst rather than in prevention of its formation; therefore, use of this method is largely restricted to special cases in which impregnation is not desired, e.g., after a rape or failure of a contraceptive method in a woman over 40. Another reason this method is not used routinely for birth control is that the treatment is associated with a relatively high frequency of nausea, vomiting, and other adverse effects. *Contraception is preferable to contraimplantation.*

Various types of *intrauterine devices* (IUDs) also prevent implantation of the blastocyst, presumably by inducing a foreign-body response in the endometrium that inhibits implantation.

EARLY ABORTIONS

Abortion is defined as the termination of pregnancy before 20 weeks' gestation, i.e., *before the period of viability*. Almost all abortions during the first three weeks occur spontaneously, that is, they are not induced. The frequency of early abortions is difficult to establish because they often occur before the

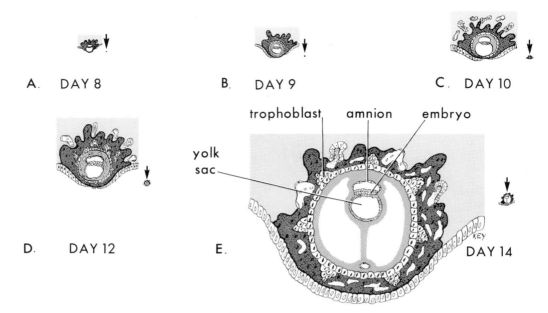

A. DAY 8   B. DAY 9   C. DAY 10

D. DAY 12   E.   DAY 14

Figure 4–9 Drawings of sections of human blastocysts during the second week, illustrating the rapid expansion of the trophoblast and the relatively minute size of the embryos (×25); the sketches indicated by the arrows show the actual size of the blastocysts.

woman is aware she is pregnant. An abortion just after the first missed period is very likely to be mistaken for a delayed menstruation.

A study of 34 embryos recovered from women of known fertility revealed that 10 of them were so abnormal that they probably would have aborted by the end of the second week. The incidence of chromosome abnormalities in early spontaneous abortions is high (about 61 per cent). Summarizing the data of several studies, it has been estimated that about 50 per cent of all known sponta-

neous abortions result from chromosomal abnormalities. The higher incidence of early abortions in older women probably results from the increasing frequency of nondisjunction during oogenesis (see Chapter 2).

It has been estimated that from one third to one half of all zygotes never survive to form blastocysts and implant. Failure to implant may result from a poorly developed endometrium, but probably in many cases there are chromosomal abnormalities in the zygote.

SUMMARY

Rapid proliferation of the trophoblast occurs during the second week (Fig. 4–9). Lacunae develop in the syncytiotrophoblast and fuse to form *lacunar networks*. The syncytiotrophoblast erodes maternal blood vessels and blood seeps into the networks, forming a primitive *uteroplacental circulation*.

Primary *chorionic villi* form on the external surface of the chorionic sac. Implantation is complete when the conceptus is wholly embedded within the endometrium and the surface epithelium grows over the embedded blastocyst.

Concurrently, *extraembryonic mesoderm* arises from the inner surface of the trophoblast and reduces the relative size of the blastocyst cavity, forming a primary *yolk sac*. As the *extraembryonic coelom* forms from spaces in the extraembryonic mesoderm, the primary yolk sac becomes smaller. The *amniotic cavity* appears as a slitlike space between the trophoblast and the inner cell mass.

The inner cell mass differentiates into a *bilaminar embryonic disc* consisting of a layer of embryonic *epiblast* and a layer of embryonic *hypoblast*. A localized thickening of the hypoblast, called the *prochordal plate*, indicates the site of the future mouth.

SUGGESTED SUPPLEMENTARY READING

Carr, D. H., and Gedeon, M.: Population cytogenetics of human abortuses; *in* Hook, E. B., and Porter, I. H. (Eds.): *Population Cytogenetics: Studies in Humans.* New York, Academic Press, 1977, pp. 1–9.
The very high incidence of chromosome abnormalities found in spontaneous early abortions is described in this article.

Hertig, A. T.: The overall problem in man; *in* Benirschke, K. (Ed.): *Comparative Aspects of Reproductive Failure.* New York, Springer-Verlag, 1967.
Dr. Hertig was one of the first persons to study early stages of human development.

Moore, K. L.: *The Developing Human. Clinically Oriented Embryology,* 3rd ed. Philadelphia, W. B. Saunders Company, 1982, pp. 40–51.
More details of the second week of human development are given. In addition, four clinically oriented problems are presented.

Page, E. W., Villee, C. A., and Villee, D. B.: *Human Reproduction. Essentials of Reproductive and Perinatal Medicine,* 3rd ed. Philadelphia, W. B. Saunders Company, 1981.
Chapter 10, ''Disorders of Embryonic Development,'' includes a comprehensive account of ectopic pregnancy.

5

THE THIRD WEEK OF DEVELOPMENT

The third week is a period of rapid development of the embryo from the embryonic disc. It follows the first missed menstrual period (see the *Timetable of Human Prenatal Development*, Fig. 1–1). Cessation of menstruation is usually the first sign that a woman may be pregnant.

Relatively simple and rapid tests are now available for detecting pregnancy. These tests depend on the presence of *human chorionic gonadotropin* (hCG), a hormone produced by the syncytiotrophoblast and excreted in the mother's urine (see Chapter 8).

Bleeding at the expected time of menstruation does not rule out pregnancy because there may be some bleeding from the implantation site in some cases. This *implantation bleeding* results from leakage of blood into the uterine cavity from disrupted blood vessels around the implantation site. When such bleeding is interpreted as menstruation, an error occurs in determining the expected delivery date of the baby.

The third week is important because *three germ layers develop* and *three important structures form* (the primitive streak, the notochord, and the neural tube).

GASTRULATION

The process by which the bilaminar embryonic disc is converted into a trilaminar embryonic disc is called gastrulation.

THE PRIMITIVE STREAK

Early in the third week, a thick linear band of embryonic epiblast, known as the *primitive streak,* appears caudally in the midline of the dorsal aspect of the embryonic disc (Figs. 5–1 and 5–2A). As the primitive streak elongates by addition of cells to its caudal end (Fig. 5–3), its cranial end thickens to form a *primitive knot.* The primitive streak gives rise

to mesenchymal cells which form loose embryonic connective tissue, often called *mesoblast.* The mesoblast spreads laterally and cranially to form a layer between the epiblast and the hypoblast known as the *intraembryonic mesoderm* (Fig. 5–2B). Some mesoblastic cells invade the hypoblast and displace the hypoblastic cells laterally. This newly formed layer is known as the *embryonic endoderm.* The cells that remain in the epiblast form the layer called the *embryonic ectoderm.* Hence, the epiblast is the source of embryonic ectoderm, embryonic mesoderm, and most, if not all, embryonic endoderm.

Formation of the intraembryonic mesoderm converts the bilaminar embryonic disc into a trilaminar, or three-layered, embryonic disc (Fig. 5–2E and F).

Cells migrate cranially from the primitive knot and form a midline cord known as the *notochordal process* (Figs. 5–2C and D and 5–3B). This cord grows between the ectoderm and endoderm until it reaches the *prochordal plate,* which indicates the future site of the mouth. The notochordal process can extend no further because the prochordal plate is firmly attached to the overlying ectoderm, forming the *oropharyngeal membrane* (Figs. 5–3C and 5–4C). Caudal to the primitive streak a circular area forms which is known as the *cloacal membrane.* The embryonic disc remains bilaminar here also because the ectoderm and endoderm are fused (Figs. 5–3C and 5–4E).

Growth Changes in the Embryonic Disc. Initially the embryonic disc is flat and essentially circular, but it soon becomes pear-shaped (Fig. 5–3A and B) and then elongated as the notochordal process grows (Fig. 5–3C and D). Expansion of the embryonic disc occurs mainly in the cranial region; the caudal end remains more or less unchanged. Much of the growth and elongation of the em-

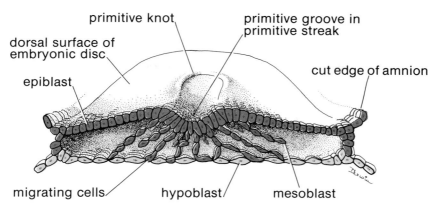

primitive knot

primitive groove in
primitive streak

dorsal surface of
embryonic disc

cut edge of amnion

epiblast

migrating cells   hypoblast   mesoblast

Figure 5–1   Drawing of the cranial half of the embryonic disc during the third week. The disc has been cut transversely to show the migration of mesenchymal cells from the primitive streak. This illustration also indicates that the definitive embryonic endoderm probably also arises from the epiblast. Presumably, the hypoblastic cells are displaced to extraembryonic regions.

bryonic disc results from the continuous migration of mesenchymal cells from the primitive streak.

Fate of the Primitive Streak.   The primitive streak continues to form mesenchyme until about the end of the fourth week; thereafter, mesenchyme production from this source slows down. The primitive streak quickly diminishes in relative size and becomes an insignificant structure in the sacrococcygeal region of the embryo (Fig. 5–3D). Normally it undergoes degenerative changes and disappears, but primitive streak remnants may persist and give rise to a tumor known as a *sacrococcygeal teratoma*.

THE NOTOCHORD

The notochord is a cellular rod that develops from the *notochordal process* (Fig. 5–4) and defines the *primitive axis of the embryo*. In a lower chordate, *Amphioxus,* the notochord forms the skeleton of the adult animal. This cellular rod forms a midline axis in the human embryo and the basis of the axial skeleton (vertebral column, ribs, sternum, and skull).

The notochord is the structure around which the vertebral column forms (see Chapter 16). It degenerates and disappears where it is surrounded by the vertebral bodies, but persists as the *nucleus pulposus* of each intervertebral disc.

The notochord also induces the overlying ectoderm to form the neural plate, the primordium of the central nervous system. By the end of the fourth week, the notochord is almost completely formed and extends from the oropharyngeal membrane cranially to the primitive knot caudally.

NEURULATION

The formation of the *neural plate* and the *neural folds* and their closure to form the *neural tube* are called neurulation (Figs. 5–3 to 5–6).

THE NEURAL TUBE

As the notochord develops, the embryonic ectoderm over it and the adjacent mesoderm thicken to form the *neural plate* (Figs. 5–3, 5–4, and 5–6A). This plate gives rise to the *central nervous system* (see Chapter 17).

The neural plate first appears close to the primitive knot, but as the notochordal process elongates, the neural plate broadens and eventually extends cranially as far as the *oropharyngeal membrane* (Fig. 5–3C). On about the eighteenth day, the neural plate invaginates along its central axis to form a *neural groove* with neural folds on each side (Figs. 5–3D, 5–5, and 5–6). By the end of the third week, the *neural folds* at the middle of the embryo have moved together and fused, converting the neural plate into a *neural tube* (Figs. 5–5F and 5–6).

THE NEURAL CREST

As the neural folds fuse, some ectodermal cells lying along the crest of each neural fold

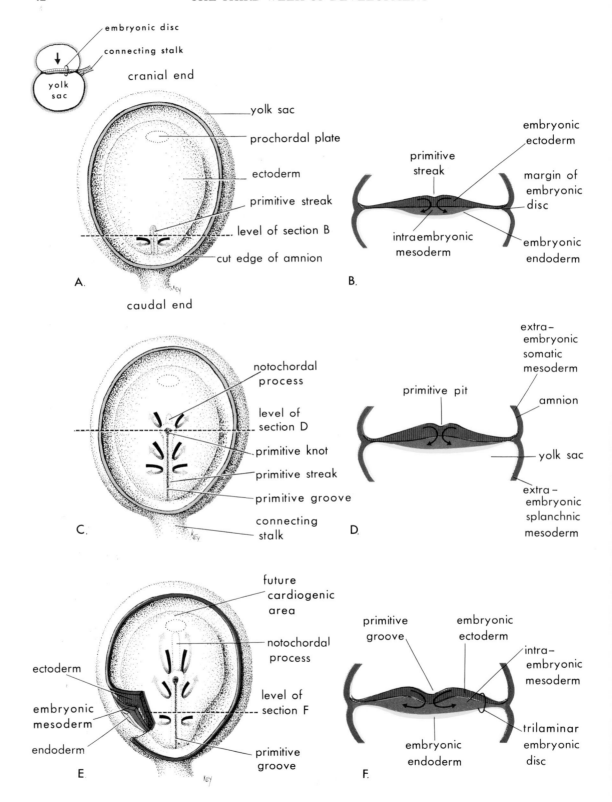

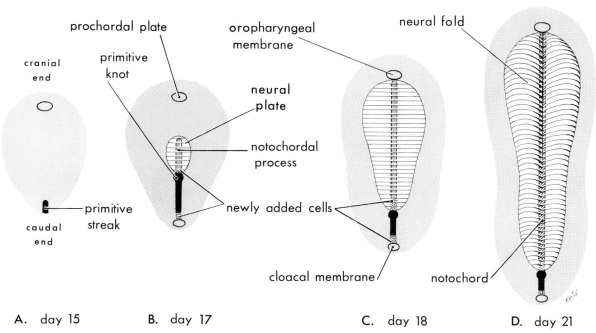

Figure 5–3 Sketches of dorsal views of the embryonic disc showing how it lengthens and changes shape during the third week. The primitive streak lengthens by addition of cells to its caudal end; the notochordal process lengthens by migration of cells from the primitive knot. The notochordal process and adjacent mesoderm induce the overlying embryonic ectoderm to form the neural plate, the primordium of the central nervous system.

lose their epithelial affinities and attachments to the neighboring cells. As the neural tube separates from the surface ectoderm (Fig. 5–6C), these neural crest cells migrate inwardly and invade the mesoblast on each side of the neural tube. They soon form an irregular flattened mass, called the *neural crest* (Fig. 5–6D), between the neural tube and the overlying surface ectoderm. Initially continuous across the midline, it soon separates into right and left parts that migrate to the dorsolateral aspect of the neural tube, where they give rise to the *sensory ganglia* of the

spinal and cranial nerves. Many neural crest cells begin to migrate in lateral and ventral directions and disperse. Although these cells are difficult to identify, special tracer techniques have revealed that they disseminate widely and have important derivatives.

Neural crest cells give rise to the spinal ganglia and the ganglia of the autonomic nervous system. The ganglia of the cranial nerves (V, VII, IX, and X) are also partly derived from the neural crest. In addition to forming ganglion cells, neural crest cells form the sheaths of nerves (Schwann cells) and the

---

Figure 5–2 Drawings illustrating formation of the trilaminar embryonic disc (three-layered embryo). The small sketch at the upper left is for orientation; the arrow indicates the dorsal aspect of the embryonic disc as shown in A. The arrows in all other drawings indicate migration of mesenchymal cells between the ectoderm and endoderm. A, C, and E, Dorsal views of the embryonic disc early in the third week, exposed by removal of the amnion. B, D, and F, Transverse sections through the embryonic disc at the levels indicated.

The intraembryonic mesoderm forms as follows: Cells of the epiblast move medially toward the primitive streak and enter the primitive groove. These cells lose their attachment to the cells of the epiblast and migrate inwardly between the epiblast and the hypoblast (Fig. 5–1). These wandering *mesoblastic cells* immediately begin to pass laterally and form a network of cells called the *mesoblast*. Some mesoblastic cells become organized into a layer called the *intraembryonic mesoderm*.

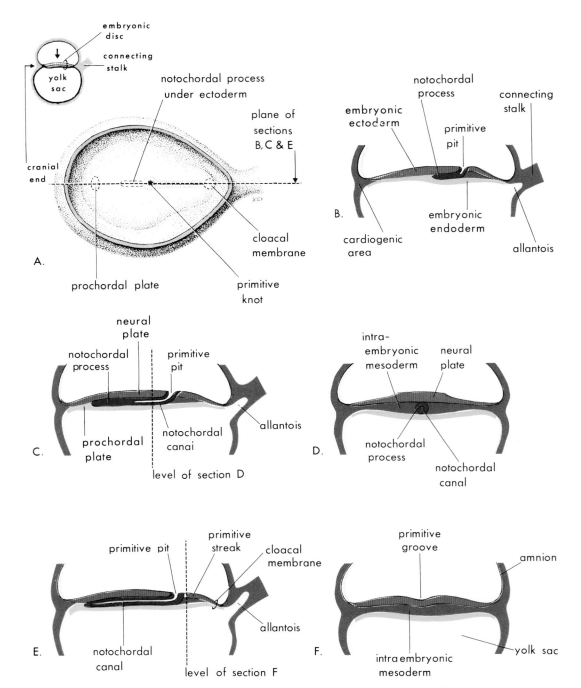

Figure 5–4 Drawings illustrating early stages of notochord development. The small sketch at the upper left is for orientation; the short arrow indicates the dorsal aspect of the embryonic disc. *A*, Dorsal view of the embryonic disc (about 16 days), exposed by removal of the amnion. The notochordal process is shown as if it were visible through the embryonic ectoderm. *B*, *C*, and *E*, Sagittal sections at the plane shown in *A*, illustrating successive stages in the development of the notochordal process and canal. Stages shown in *C* and *E* occur at about 18 days. *D* and *F*, Transverse sections through the embryonic disc at the levels shown. With further development the notochordal cells proliferate and form a solid cord known as the notochord (see Figs. 5–5*F*).

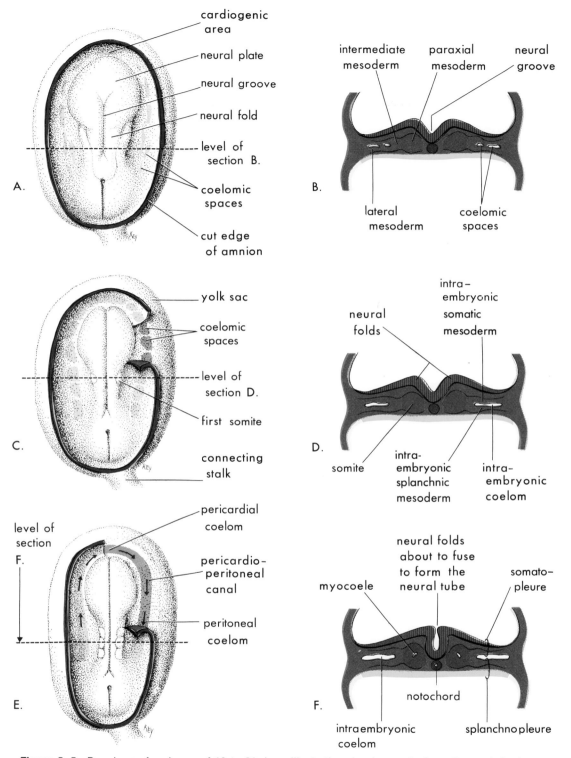

Figure 5–5 Drawings of embryos of 19 to 21 days, illustrating development of somites and the intraembryonic coelom. *A, C,* and *E,* Dorsal views of the embryonic disc exposed by removal of the amnion. *B, D,* and *F,* Transverse sections through the embryonic disc at the levels shown. Note the notochord in *F,* the cellular structure around which the vertebral column subsequently forms (see Chapter 11). *A,* Presomite embryo of about 19 days. *C,* An embryo of about 20 days showing the first pair of somites. A portion of the ectoderm and mesoderm on the right side has been removed to show the coelomic spaces in the lateral mesoderm. *E,* A three-somite embryo of about 21 days showing the horseshoe-shaped intraembryonic coelom, exposed on the right by removal of the ectoderm and mesoderm of the embryo.

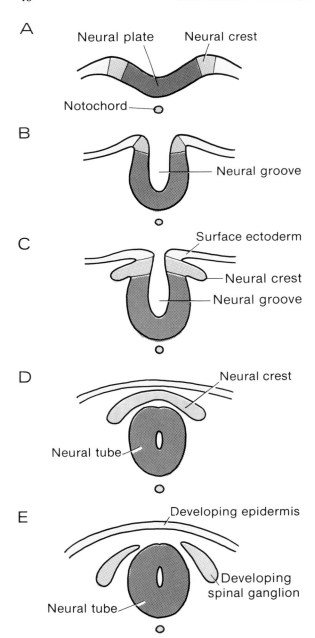

A

Neural plate   Neural crest

Notochord

B

Neural groove

C

Surface ectoderm

Neural crest

Neural groove

Figure 5–6 Diagrammatic transverse sections through progressively older embryos, illustrating formation of the neural groove, the neural tube, and the neural crest up to the end of the fourth week.

D

Neural crest

Neural tube

E

Developing epidermis

Developing spinal ganglion

Neural tube

meningeal covering of the brain and the spinal cord (at least the pia mater and arachnoid). They also contribute to the formation of pigment cells, the suprarenal (adrenal) medulla, and several skeletal and muscular components in the head (see Chapter 11).

Congenital Malformations of the Central Nervous System. Because the primordium of the central nervous system (neural plate) appears during the third week and gives rise to the neural folds, disturbance of neurulation may result in severe abnormalities of the brain and spinal cord (see Chapter 17).

Available evidence suggests that the primary disturbances (e.g., a teratogenic drug) affect the neural epithelium itself and result in *failure of closure of the neural tube* in the brain and/or the spinal cord regions. Extroversion of the neural tissue then occurs, and the exposed tissue degenerates. In *anencephaly,* the brain is represented by a mass of degenerated neural tissue exposed on the surface of the head (see Fig. 16–17).

THE ALLANTOIS

The allantois (Gr. *allantos,* "sausage") appears early in the third week as a relatively small, finger-like outpouching or diverticulum from the caudal wall of the yolk sac (Fig. 5–4B). The allantois remains very small in the human embryo, but it is involved with early blood and blood vessel formation and is associated with development of the urinary bladder (see Fig. 14–5). As the bladder enlarges, the allantois becomes the *urachus.*

DEVELOPMENT OF SOMITES

By the end of the third week, as the notochord and neural tube form, the mesoderm beside the neural tube and the notochord called *paraxial mesoderm* (Fig. 5–5B) begins to divide into paired cuboidal bodies called *somites* (Fig. 5–5C and D). The first pair of somites develops a short distance caudal to the cranial end of the notochord, and subsequent pairs form in a craniocaudal sequence. About 38 pairs of somites form during the so-called *somite period* (days 20 to 30); eventually 42 to 44 pairs develop. During the somite period the somites are used as one of the criteria for determining the embryo's age (see Table 6–1).

The somites form distinct surface elevations (Fig. 5–5E) and are somewhat triangular in transverse section. A transitory slit-like cavity, the *myocoele,* appears within each somite (Fig. 5–5F). The word somite is from the Greek *soma,* meaning "a body." The somites give rise to most of the axial skeleton (vertebral column, ribs, sternum, and skull) and associated musculature as well as much of the dermis of the skin (see Chapters 16 and 19).

DEVELOPMENT OF THE INTRAEMBRYONIC COELOM

The intraembryonic coelom (embryonic body cavity) first appears as a number of isolated *coelomic spaces* within the lateral mes-

oderm and the mesoderm that will form the heart, called the *cardiogenic mesoderm* (Fig. 5–5A and B). These spaces soon coalesce to form a horseshoe-shaped cavity, the *intraembryonic coelom* (Fig. 5–5E).

The intraembryonic coelom divides the lateral mesoderm into two layers (Fig. 5–5D): a *somatic (parietal) layer* continuous with the extraembryonic mesoderm covering the amnion, and a *splanchnic (visceral) layer* continuous with the extraembryonic mesoderm covering the yolk sac. The somatic mesoderm and the overlying embryonic ectoderm form the body wall or *somatopleure* (Fig. 5–5F), whereas the splanchnic mesoderm and the embryonic endoderm form the *splanchnopleure* or wall of the future primitive gut (see Fig. 6–1).

During the second month, the intraembryonic coelom is divided into three body cavities (see Chapter 10): (1) the *pericardial cavity* containing the heart, (2) the *pleural cavities* containing the lungs, and (3) the *peritoneal cavity* associated with the abdominal and pelvic viscera.

PRIMITIVE CARDIOVASCULAR SYSTEM

Blood vessel formation (*angiogenesis*) begins early in the third week in the extraembryonic mesoderm of the yolk sac, connecting stalk, and chorion (Fig. 5–7). Embryonic vessels develop about two days later. The early formation of the cardiovascular system is correlated with the absence of a significant amount of yolk in the ovum and yolk sac. Consequently, there is a need for vessels to bring nourishment and oxygen to the embryo from the maternal circulation (Fig. 5–8).

Blood and blood vessel formation may be summarized as follows: (1) mesenchymal cells, known as *angioblasts*, aggregate to form isolated masses and cords known as *blood islands* (Fig. 5–7A to C); (2) spaces appear within these islands (Fig. 5–7D); (3) cells arrange themselves around the cavity to form the primitive *endothelium* (Fig. 5–7E); (4) isolated vessels fuse to form networks of endothelial channels (Fig. 5–7F); and (5) vessels extend into adjacent areas by fusing with other vessels formed independently.

Primitive plasma and blood cells develop from the endothelial cells of the vessels (Fig. 5–7E). Blood formation does not begin within the embryo until the fifth week, where

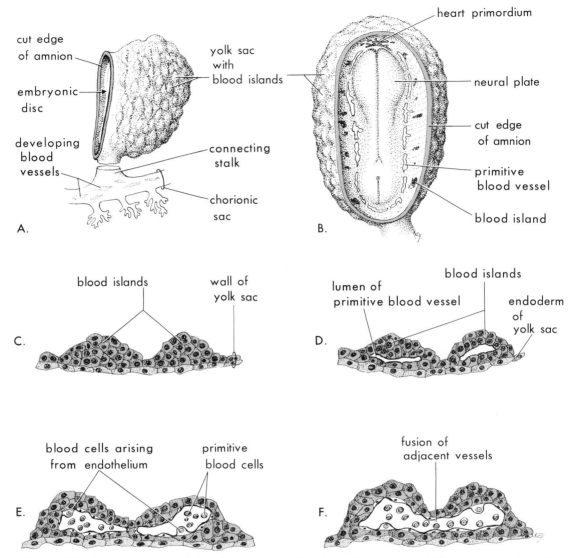

Figure 5–7   Successive stages in the development of blood and blood vessels. *A*, The yolk sac and a portion of the chorionic sac at about 18 days. *B*, Dorsal view of an embryo of about 19 days, exposed by removing the amnion. *C* to *F*, Sections of blood islands showing progressive stages of development of blood and blood vessels.

it first occurs in the liver and later in the spleen, bone marrow, and lymph nodes. Mesenchymal cells surrounding the primitive endothelial vessels differentiate into the muscular and connective tissue elements of the vessels.

The *primitive heart* forms in a similar manner from mesenchymal cells in the *cardiogenic area* (Fig. 5–7*B*). Paired *endocardial*

heart tubes develop before the end of the third week and begin to fuse into the primitive heart tube. By the twenty-first day, the heart tubes have linked up with blood vessels in the embryo, connecting stalk, chorion, and yolk sac to form a primitive cardiovascular system (Fig. 5–8). The circulation of blood has almost certainly started by the end of the third week; hence *the cardiovascular system*

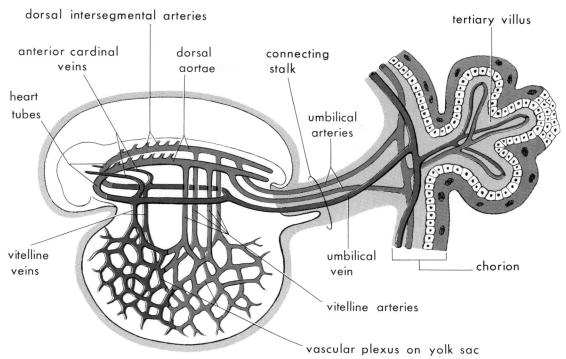

Figure 5–8 Diagram of the primitive cardiovascular system in a 21-day embryo viewed from the left side, showing the transitory stage of paired symmetrical vessels. Each heart tube continues dorsally into a *dorsal aorta* which passes caudally. Branches of the aortae are: (1) *umbilical arteries,* establishing connections with vessels in the chorion, (2) *vitelline arteries* to the yolk sac, and (3) *dorsal intersegmental arteries* to the body of the embryo. An *umbilical vein* returns blood from the chorion and divides into right and left umbilical veins within the embryo. Vessels on the yolk sac form a *vascular plexus* which is connected to the heart by *vitelline veins.* The *anterior cardinal veins* return blood from the head region.

is the first organ system to reach a functional state.

DEVELOPMENT OF CHORIONIC VILLI

Shortly after the primary chorionic villi appear (see Figs. 4–4 and 4–5), they begin to branch. By the end of this stage (about 15 days), mesenchyme has grown into the villi, forming a core of loose connective tissue. The villi at this stage, called *secondary chorionic villi,* cover the entire surface of the chorion (Fig. 5–9*A* and *B*). Soon mesenchymal cells within the villi begin to differentiate into blood capillaries, forming an *arteriocapillary venous network* (about 15 to 20 days). After blood vessels have developed in the villi, they are called *tertiary chorionic villi* (Fig. 5–9*D*). Vessels in these villi soon become connected with the embryonic heart via

vessels that differentiate in the mesenchyme of the chorion and in the connecting stalk (Fig. 5–8). By about 21 days, embryonic blood begins to circulate through the capillaries of the chorionic villi. The villi absorb nutriments from the maternal blood in the intervillous spaces and excrete wastes from the embryo into them.

Concurrently, the cytotrophoblast cells of the chorionic villi penetrate the syncytiotrophoblastic layer and join to form a *cytotrophoblastic shell* (Fig. 5–9*C*), which attaches the chorionic sac to the endometrial tissues. Villi that are attached to the maternal tissues via the cytotrophoblastic shell are called *stem* or *anchoring villi.* The villi that grow from the sides of the stem villi are called *branch villi,* and it is through them that the main exchange of material between the blood of the mother and the embryo takes place.

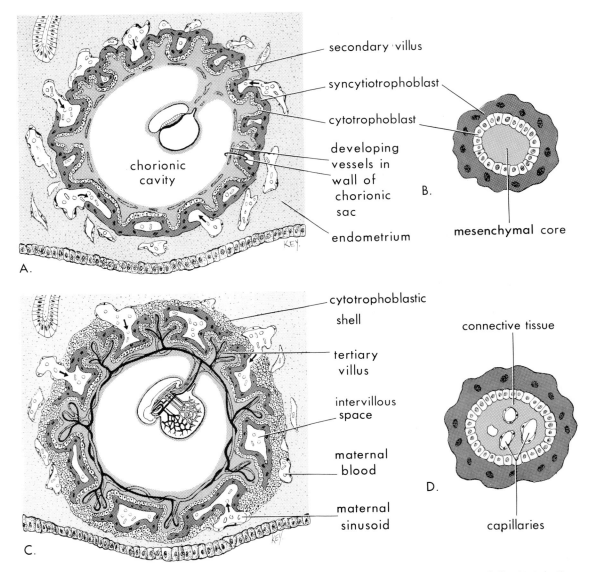

Figure 5–9   Diagrams illustrating further development of the chorionic villi and placenta. *A*, Sagittal section of an embryo (about 16 days). *B*, Section of a secondary chorionic villus. *C*, Section of an implanted embryo (about 21 days). *D*, Section of a tertiary chorionic villus. The fetal blood in the capillaries is separated from the maternal blood surrounding the villus by the placental membrane, composed of the endothelium of the capillary, mesenchyme, cytotrophoblast, and syncytiotrophoblast.

SUMMARY

As the *primitive streak* forms intraembryonic mesoderm, the bilaminar embryonic disc is converted into a trilaminar embryo composed of three *primary germ layers* (ectoderm, mesoderm, and endoderm). These layers will later give rise to all tissues and organs in the embryo (see Fig. 6–2).

The *primitive streak* appears early in the third week as a midline thickening of the embryonic *epiblast*. It gives rise to mesenchymal cells which migrate laterally and cranially between the epiblast and the hypoblast. As soon as the primitive streak has begun to produce these mesenchymal cells, the epiblast layer is known as the *embryonic ectoderm*, and the hypoblast is known as the *embryonic endoderm*. The cells produced by the primitive streak soon organize into a *third germ layer*, the *intraembryonic mesoderm*. The primitive knot gives rise to the *notochordal process*.

The *notochord* develops from the notochordal process and forms the primitive skeletal support of the embryo around which the axial skeleton later forms.

The *neural plate* appears as a midline thickening of the embryonic ectoderm, cranial to the primitive knot. A longitudinal *neural groove* develops which is flanked by *neural folds*; these folds meet and fuse to form the *neural tube*. As this process occurs, some cells migrate ventrolaterally to form the *neural crest*.

The mesoderm on each side of the notochord thickens to form longitudinal columns of *paraxial mesoderm*. Division of the paraxial mesoderm into pairs of *somites* begins cranially by the end of the third week.

The intraembryonic coelom arises as isolated spaces in the *lateral mesoderm* and *cardiogenic mesoderm*. These coelomic spaces subsequently coalesce to form a single, horseshoe-shaped cavity which eventually gives rise to the body cavities.

Blood vessels first appear on the yolk sac, on the allantois, and in the chorion and develop within the embryo shortly thereafter. Spaces appear within aggregations of mesenchyme (*blood islands*) which soon become lined with endothelium and unite with other spaces to form a *primitive cardiovascular system*. At the end of the third week, the heart is represented by paired *heart tubes* which are joined to blood vessels in the extraembryonic membranes. The primitive blood cells are derived mainly from the endothelial cells of blood vessels in the yolk sac and allantois.

Primary chorionic villi become *secondary chorionic villi* as they acquire mesenchymal cores. Before the end of the third week, capillaries develop in the villi, transforming them into *tertiary chorionic villi*. Cytotrophoblastic extensions from the villi mushroom out and join to form a *cytotrophoblastic shell* that anchors the chorionic sac to the endometrium. The rapid development of chorionic villi during the third week greatly increases the surface area of the chorion for the exchange of nutrients and other substances between the maternal and embryonic circulations.

SUGGESTED SUPPLEMENTARY READING

Boué, J., Boué, A., and Lazar, P.: Retrospective and prospective epidemiological studies of 1500 karyotyped spontaneous abortions. *Teratology* 12:11, 1975.
Chromosome abnormalities are an important cause of spontaneous abortion. The incidence of chromosomal abnormalities in early abortion is about 61.1 per cent, and about 5 per cent in later ones.
Tuchmann-Duplesis, H., and Haegal, P. (translated by L. S. Hurley): *Illustrated Human Embryology*, Vol. 1. New York, Springer-Verlag, 1972.
Students who have difficulty visualizing the early stages of embryos in three dimensions should consult this excellent atlas.

6

THE FOURTH TO EIGHTH WEEKS

THE EMBRYONIC PERIOD

The embryonic period is a very important period of human development because the beginnings of all major external and internal structures develop during these five weeks. *By the end of the embryonic period, all the main organ systems have begun to develop,* but the function of most organs is minimal. As the organs develop, the shape of the embryo gradually changes.

Because the beginnings of all major external and internal structures develop during the embryonic period, exposure of an embryo to certain agents (drugs, viruses, etc.) during this *critical period of development* may cause major congenital malformations (see Chapter 9).

FOLDING OF THE EMBRYO

The significant event in the establishment of general body form is folding of the flat trilaminar embryonic disc into a somewhat cylindrical embryo (Fig. 6–1).

During the fourth week, the embryo grows rapidly (tripling its size), and its shape changes significantly as the result of folding. The gradual establishment of body form results from folding of the flat embryonic disc into a somewhat cylindrical embryo and the development of the organs (e.g., the heart). The infolding in both longitudinal and transverse planes is mainly caused by rapid growth of the neural tube. The formation of longitudinal and transverse folds is a simultaneous process of constriction at the junction of the embryo and yolk sac and not a separate sequence of events. Folding in the longitudinal plane produces head and tail folds that result in the cranial and caudal regions "swinging" ventrally as if on a hinge (Fig. 6–1A_2 to D_2). During folding, part of the yolk sac is incorporated into the embryo.

The Head Fold (Fig. 6–1A_2). The developing brain grows cranially beyond the oropharyngeal membrane and soon overhangs the primitive heart. The heart and oropharyngeal membrane also turn under onto the ventral surface. After folding, the mass of mesoderm cranial to the pericardial coelom, called the *septum transversum,* lies caudal to the heart. Subsequently, this septum develops into a major part of the diaphragm (see Chapter 10).

During folding, part of the yolk sac is incorporated into the embryo as the *foregut;* it lies between the brain and the heart and ends blindly at the *oropharyngeal membrane.* This membrane separates the foregut from the *stomodeum,* or primitive mouth cavity.

The Tail Fold (Fig. 6–1B_2). Folding of the caudal end of the embryo occurs a little later than that of the cranial end. As the embryo grows, the tail region projects over the *cloacal membrane.* The *connecting stalk* later attaches to the ventral surface of the embryo as the *umbilical cord* forms (Fig. 6–1D_2).

The Lateral Folds (Fig. 6–1A_3 to 6–1D_3). Folding of the embryo in the transverse plane produces right and left *lateral folds.* Each lateral body wall folds toward the midline, rolling the edges of the embryonic disc ventrally and forming a roughly cylindrical embryo. As the lateral and ventral body walls form, part of the yolk sac is incorporated into the embryo as the *midgut.* Concurrently, the connection of the midgut with the yolk sac is reduced to a narrow *yolk stalk* (Fig. 6–1C_2). After folding, the region of the attachment of the amnion to the embryo is reduced to a relatively narrow region where the umbilical cord attaches on the ventral surface (Fig. 6–1D_2). As the midgut is separated from the yolk sac, it becomes attached to the dorsal abdominal wall by a thin *dorsal mesentery* (Fig. 6–1D_3). As the am-

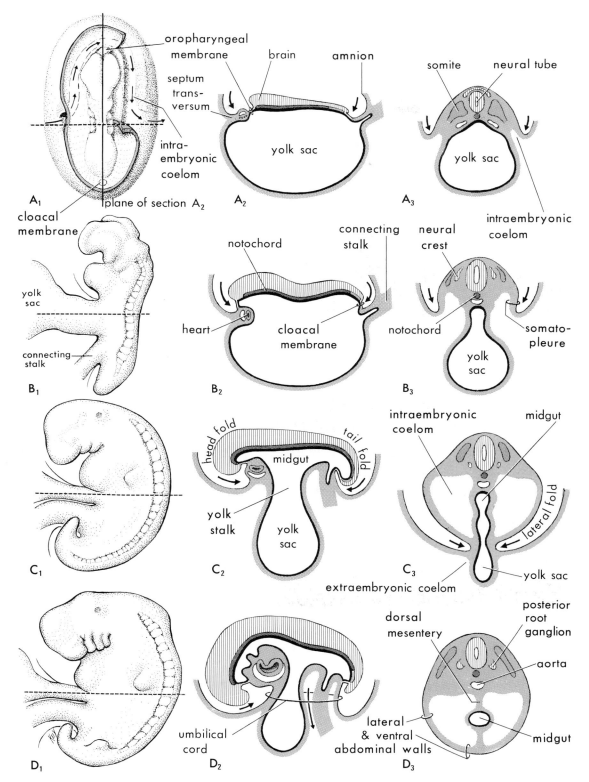

Figure 6–1 Drawings of four-week embryos illustrating folding in both longitudinal and transverse planes. A_1, Dorsal view of a 22-day embryo. The continuity of the intraembryonic coelom and extraembryonic coelom is illustrated on the right side by removal of a portion of the embryonic ectoderm and mesoderm. B_1, C_1, and D_1, Lateral views of embryos of about 24, 26, and 28 days, respectively. A_2 to D_2, Longitudinal sections at the plane shown in A_1. A_3 to D_3, Transverse sections at the levels indicated in A_1 to D_1.

53

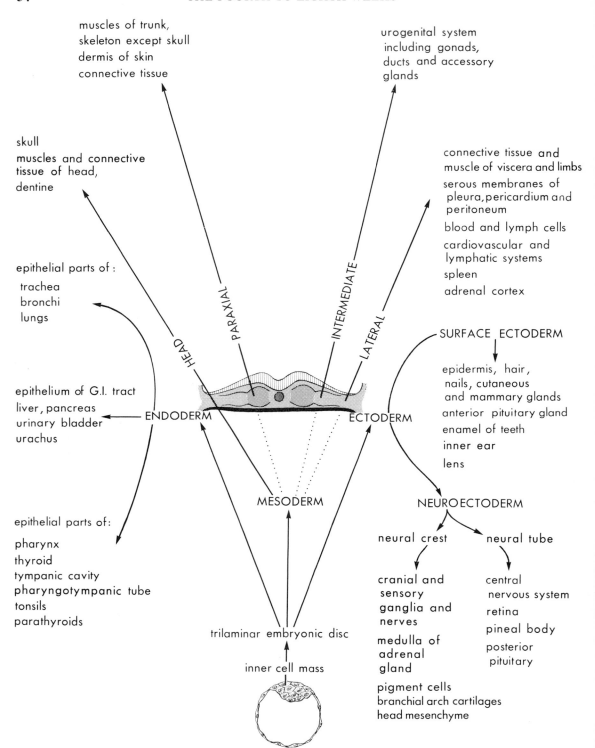

muscles of trunk,
skeleton except skull
dermis of skin
connective tissue

urogenital system
including gonads,
ducts and accessory
glands

skull
muscles and connective
tissue of head,
dentine

connective tissue and
muscle of viscera and limbs
serous membranes of
pleura, pericardium and
peritoneum
blood and lymph cells
cardiovascular and
lymphatic systems
spleen
adrenal cortex

epithelial parts of :
trachea
bronchi
lungs

SURFACE ECTODERM

PARAXIAL

INTERMEDIATE

LATERAL

HEAD

epithelium of G.I. tract
liver, pancreas
urinary bladder
urachus

epidermis, hair,
nails, cutaneous
and mammary glands
anterior pituitary gland
enamel of teeth
inner ear
lens

ENDODERM

ECTODERM

MESODERM

NEUROECTODERM

epithelial parts of:
pharynx
thyroid
tympanic cavity
pharyngotympanic tube
tonsils
parathyroids

neural crest

neural tube

cranial and
sensory
ganglia and
nerves
medulla of
adrenal
gland
pigment cells
branchial arch cartilages
head mesenchyme

central
nervous system
retina
pineal body
posterior
pituitary

trilaminar embryonic disc

inner cell mass

Figure 6–2 Scheme illustrating the origin and derivatives of the three primary germ layers. The cells of these layers make specific contributions to the formation of the different tissues and organs, e.g., the endoderm forms the epithelial lining of the gastrointestinal tract and the mesoderm gives rise to its connective tissues and muscles.

niotic cavity expands it almost obliterates the extraembryonic coelom. The amnion forms the epithelial covering for the *umbilical cord* (Fig. 6–1D$_2$). Development of the umbilical cord is also discussed in Chapter 8.

GERM LAYER DERIVATIVES

The three germ layers (embryonic ectoderm, mesoderm, and endoderm), formed during the third week, give rise to all the tissues and organs of the embryo. In addition to the derivatives shown in Figure 6–2, other tissues may originate from these germ layers under different normal or experimental influences; i.e., the specificity of the germ layers is not rigidly fixed. The cells of each germ layer divide, migrate, aggregate, and differentiate in rather precise patterns as they form the various organ systems. Tissues that develop from the different germ layers are commonly associated in the formation of an organ (*organogenesis*).

The main germ layer derivatives are as follows:

ECTODERM. This layer gives rise to the central nervous system (brain and spinal cord), the peripheral nervous system, the sensory epithelia of the eye, the ear, and the nose, the epidermis and its appendages (hair and nails), the mammary glands, the hypophysis (pituitary gland), the subcutaneous glands, and the enamel of teeth.

Neural crest cells, derived from ectoderm, give rise to the following: cells of the *spinal, cranial,* and *autonomic ganglia*; ensheathing cells of the peripheral nervous system; *pigment cells* of the dermis; muscle, connective tissues, and *bone of branchial arch origin* (see Chapter 11); the *suprarenal (adrenal)* medulla, and the pia-arachnoid (*leptomeninges*).

MESODERM. This layer gives rise to cartilage, bone, and connective tissue, striated and smooth muscles, the heart, blood and lymph vessels and cells, the kidneys, the gonads (ovaries and testes), and the genital ducts, the serous membranes lining the body cavities (pericardial, pleural, and peritoneal), the spleen, and the cortex of the suprarenal (adrenal) gland.

ENDODERM. This layer gives rise to the epithelial lining of the gastrointestinal and respiratory tracts, the paraenchyma of the tonsils, the thyroid gland, the parathyroid glands, the thymus, the liver, and the pancreas, the epithelial lining of the urinary bladder and the urethra, and the epithelial lining of the tympanic cavity, the tympanic antrum, and the auditory tube.

CONTROL OF DEVELOPMENT

Development results from genetic plans contained in the chromosomes. The individuality of each person is largely determined at fertilization by the genes contained in the chromosomes of the sperm and the ovum. These genes control the processes by which the body develops before and after birth.

Most developmental processes depend upon a precisely coordinated interaction of genetic and environmental factors. There are several control mechanisms that guide differentiation and ensure synchronized development, e.g., tissue interactions, regulated migrations of cells and cell colonies, controlled proliferations, and cell death. Each system of the body has its own developmental pattern, but most processes of morphogenesis are similar.

Defective genetic plans (abnormal number of chromosomes, gene mutations, and so forth) result in maldevelopment. Abnormal development may also be caused by environmental factors (discussed in Chapter 9). Most developmental processes depend upon a precisely coordinated interaction of genetic and environmental factors.

INDUCTION

For a limited time during early development, certain embryonic tissues markedly influence the development of adjacent tissues. The tissues producing these influences or effects are called *inductors* or organizers. In order to induce, an inductor must be close to but not necessarily in contact with the tissue to be induced. In birds, and probably in humans, the primitive streak, notochordal process, and paraxial mesoderm act as primary organizers of the central nervous system.

Once the basic embryonic plan has been established by primary organizers, a chain of *secondary inductions* occurs. The nature of the inductive agents is not clearly understood, but it is generally accepted that some substance (protein in nature) passes from the inducing tissue to the induced tissue.

HIGHLIGHTS OF THE EMBRYONIC PERIOD

The following descriptions summarize the main developmental events and changes in external form. The details of organ formation are given with discussions of the various systems (Chapters 12 to 19). Useful criteria for estimating developmental stages in human embryos are listed in Table 6–1.

The Fourth Week (Figs. 6–3 to 6–6). Initially the embryo is almost straight

TABLE 6–1   CRITERIA FOR ESTIMATING DEVELOPMENTAL STAGES IN HUMAN EMBRYOS

Age* (Days)	Carnegie Stage	No. of Somites	Length (mm)†	Main Characteristics‡
20–21	9	1–3	1.5–3.0	*Deep neural groove and first somites present.* Head fold evident.
22–23	10	4–12	2.0–3.5	*Embryo straight or slightly curved.* Neural tube forming or formed opposite somites, but widely open at rostral and caudal neuropores. First and second pairs of branchial arches visible.
24–25	11	13–20	2.5–4.5	*Embryo curved owing to head and tail folds.* Rostral neuropore closing. Otic placodes present. Optic vesicles formed.
26–27	12	21–29	3.0–5.0	*Upper limb buds appear.* Caudal neuropore closing or closed. Three pairs of branchial arches visible. Heart prominence distinct. Otic pits present.
28–30	13	30–35	4.0–6.0	*Embryo has C-shaped curve. Upper limb buds are flipper-like.* Four pairs of branchial arches visible. Lower limb buds appear. *Otic vesicles* present. Lens placodes distinct. Attenuated *tail* present.
31–32	14	§	5.0–7.0	*Upper limbs are paddle-shaped.* Lens pits and nasal pits visible. Optic cups present.
33–36	15		7.0–9.0	*Hand plates formed.* Lens vesicles present. Nasal pits prominent. *Lower limbs are paddle-shaped.* Cervical sinuses visible.
37–40	16		8.0–11.0	*Foot plates formed.* Pigment visible in retina. Auricular hillocks developing.
41–43	17		11.0–14.0	*Digital, or finger, rays appear.* Auricular hillocks outline future auricle of external ear. Trunk beginning to straighten. Cerebral vesicles prominent.
44–46	18		13.0–17.0	*Digital, or toe, rays appearing.* Elbow region visible. Eyelids forming. Notches between finger rays. Nipples visible.
47–48	19		16.0–18.0	*Limbs extend ventrally.* Trunk elongating and straightening. Midgut herniation prominent.
49–51	20		18.0–22.0	*Upper limbs longer and bent at elbows. Fingers distinct but webbed.* Notches between toe rays. Scalp vascular plexus appears.
52–53	21		22.0–24.0	*Hands and feet approach each other. Fingers are free and longer.* Toes *distinct* but webbed. Stubby tail present.
54–55	22		23.0–28.0	*Toes free and longer.* Eyelids and auricles of external ears are more developed.
56	23		27.0–31.0	*Head more rounded and shows human characteristics.* External genitalia still have sexless appearance. Distinct bulge still present in umbilical cord; caused by herniation of intestines. *Tail has disappeared.*

* There is still uncertainty about the age of embryos in some embryonic stages. The age given by Streeter (1951) were based on comparison with macaque embryos and are now known to be inaccurate for stages 14 to 23. For example, embryos at stage 23 are now generally believed to be at least 56 days and not 47 ± 1 days as described by Streeter.

† The embryonic lengths indicate the usual range, but do not indicate the full range within a given stage, especially when specimens of poor quality are included (O'Rahilly, 1973). In stages 10 and 11, the measurement is greatest length (*GL*); in subsequent stages crown-rump (*CR*) measurements are given (Fig. 6–14).

‡ Based on Streeter (1942, 1945, 1948, and 1951), O'Rahilly (1973), and Nishimura et al. (1974).

§ At this and subsequent stages, the number of somites is difficult to determine and so is not a useful criterion.

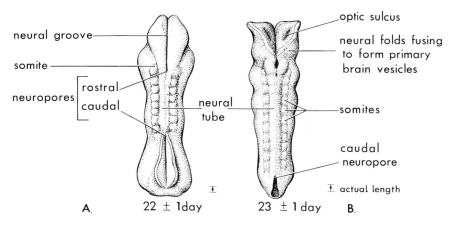

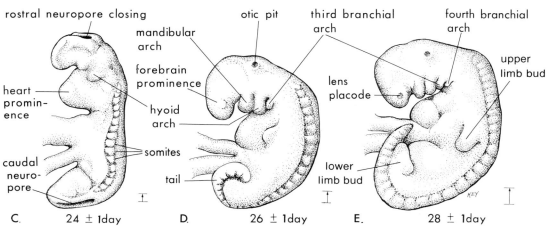

Figure 6–3 Drawings of four-week embryos. *A* and *B,* Dorsal views of embryos with 8 and 12 somites, respectively. *C, D,* and *E,* Lateral views of embryos with 16, 27, and 33 somites, respectively.

and the *somites* (beginnings of muscles and vertebrae) produce conspicuous surface elevations. The neural tube is closed opposite the somites, but is widely open at rostral and caudal openings called *neuropores.*

By 24 days the first (or mandibular) and the second (or hyoid) *branchial arches* are visible (Fig. 6–3C).

The major portion, or mandibular prominence (process), of the first arch forms the mandible or lower jaw, and an extension of it, the maxillary prominence (process), contributes to the maxilla or upper jaw (see Chapter 11). A slight curve is produced in the embryo by the head and tail folds, and the heart produces a large ventral prominence.

Three branchial arches are visible by 26 days (Figs. 6–3D and 6–5), and the forebrain produces a prominent elevation on the head.

Continued longitudinal folding has given the embryo a characteristic C-shaped curvature. The *upper limb buds* become recognizable as small swellings on the lateral body walls (Figs. 6–3D and 6–6). The *otic pits,* the primordia of the internal ears, are also clearly visible. The *lower limb buds* are present by 28 days (Fig. 6–3E). Lens placodes, ectodermal thickenings indicating the future lenses, are visible on the sides of the head. The fourth pair of branchial arches is also visible by the end of the fourth week.

The Fifth Week (Fig. 6–7A). Changes in body form are minor compared with the fourth week. Extensive head growth is caused mainly by the rapid development of the brain. The *upper limbs become paddle-shaped* and the lens pits and nasal pits become visible. By the end of the fifth week the

Text continued on page 63

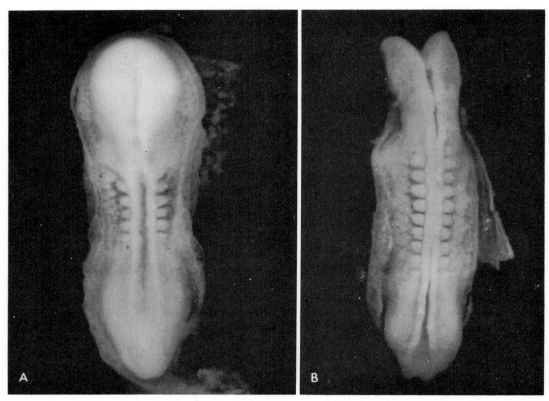

Figure 6–4 Photographs of embryos 22 to 23 days old. In *A*, the embryo is essentially straight, whereas the embryo in *B* is slightly curved. In *A*, the neural groove is deep and is open throughout its entire extent. About one half of the longitudinal extent of the groove represents the future brain. In *B*, the neural tube has formed opposite the somites but is widely open at the rostral and caudal neuropores. Compare with Figure 6–3*A*. (Courtesy of Professor Hideo Nishimura, Kyoto University, Kyoto, Japan.)

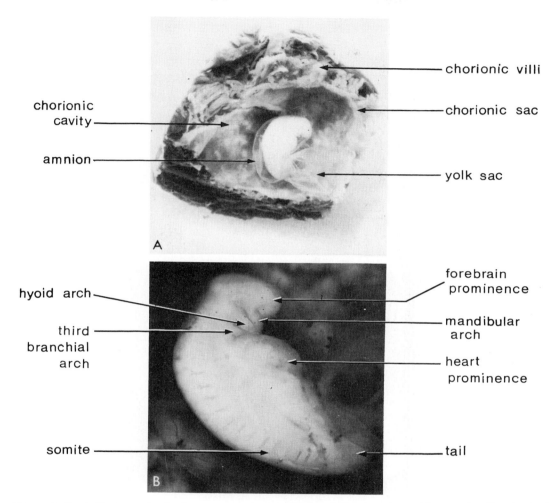

Figure 6–5 *A*, Photograph of a four-week embryo in the amniotic sac, exposed by opening the chorionic sac (×5). *B*, Higher magnification of the embryo of 26 to 27 days (×18). For a discussion of the branchial arches and other parts of the branchial apparatus, see Chapter 11. Although present, the upper limb bud is not visible in this photograph. (Photgraphed by Professor Jean Hay, Department of Anatomy, University of Manitoba.)

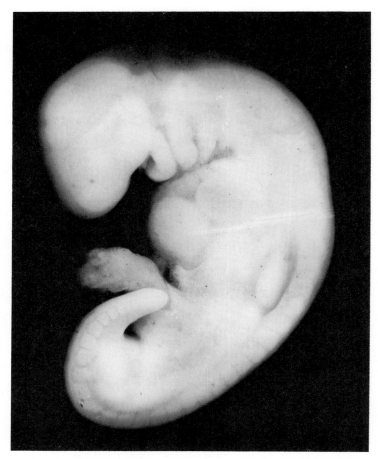

Figure 6–6   Photograph of an embryo 28 days old. The embryo has a characteristic C-shaped curvature, four branchial arches, and upper and lower limb buds. The lower limb bud is not recognizable in this photograph. The heart prominence is easily recognized. The ventrally curled attenuated tail, with its somites, is a characteristic feature of this stage. Compare with Figure 6–3E. (Courtesy of Professor Hideo Nishimura, Kyoto University, Kyoto, Japan.)

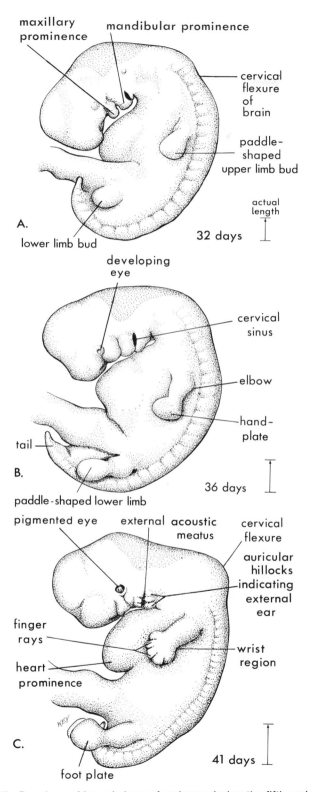

Figure 6–7 Drawings of lateral views of embryos during the fifth and sixth weeks.

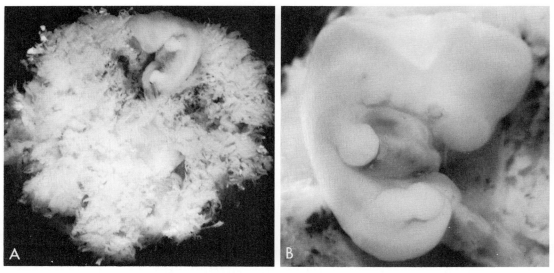

Figure 6–8 *A*, Photograph of a six-week embryo in the amniotic sac, exposed by opening the chorionic sac (×2). *B*, Higher magnification of the embryo of about 41 days (×6). Compare with Figure 6–7*C*. Note the large size of the head compared with the rest of the body, and the prominence of the cerebral vesicles, the primordia of the cerebral hemispheres. (Photographed by Professor Jean Hay, Department of Anatomy, University of Manitoba.)

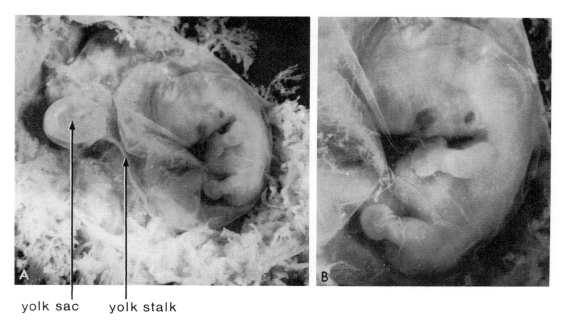

yolk sac   yolk stalk

Figure 6–9 *A*, Photograph of a seven-week embryo in the amniotic sac, exposed by opening the chorionic sac (×2.8). *B*, Higher magnification of the embryo of 44 to 46 days (×5). Note the low position of the ear at this stage and the notches between the finger rays.

hand plates have formed and the lower limbs have become paddle-shaped. Note that development of the lower limb occurs somewhat later than that of the upper limb.

The Sixth Week (Figs. 6–7B and C and 6–8). The head is now much larger relative to the trunk and is more bent over the *heart prominence*. This head position results from bending of the brain in the cervical region.

The limbs show considerable regional differentiation, especially the upper limbs. The elbow and wrist regions become identifiable, and the paddle-shaped hand plates develop ridges, called *digital*, or *finger, rays*, indicating the future *digits* (fingers and thumb). Note that development of the lower limb still occurs somewhat later than that of the upper limb.

Several small swellings develop around the branchial groove between the first two branchial arches (Fig. 6–7C); this groove becomes the *external acoustic meatus*, and the swellings eventually fuse to form the auricle of the external ear. Largely because retinal pigment begins to appear, the eye becomes more obvious.

By the end of the sixth week, the trunk and neck have begun to straighten. The somites are visible in the lumbosacral region until the middle of the week, but are not useful criteria for estimating age at this time.

The Seventh Week (Figs. 6–9, 6–10A, and 6–11C). The communication between the primitive gut and the yolk sac has been reduced to a relatively small duct, the *yolk stalk*. The intestines enter the extraembryonic coelom in the proximal portion of the umbilical cord; this is called *umbilical herniation* (Fig. 6–10B).

The limbs undergo considerable change during the seventh week. The upper limbs project over the heart. Notches appear between the digital rays in the hand plates, indicating the future digits.

The Eighth Week (Figs. 6–10B, 6–12, and 6–13). At the beginning of the final week of the embryonic period, the digits of the hand are short and noticeably webbed (Fig. 6–10B). Notches are visible between the digital, or toe, rays, and the tail is still visible, but it is stubby (Fig. 6–12A). The scalp vascular plexus has appeared and forms a characteristic band around the head.

By the end of the eighth week, the regions of the limbs are apparent, the fingers have lengthened, and the toes are distinct. All evidence of the tail disappears by the end of the eighth week (Figs. 6–12B and 6–13). The scalp vascular plexus now forms a band near the vertex (crown) of the head.

The embryo now has unquestionably human characteristics. The head is more round and erect, but is still disproportionately large, constituting almost half of the embryo. The neck region has become established, and the eyelids are more obvious. The

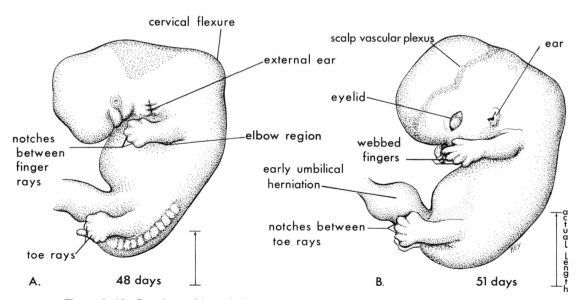

Figure 6–10 Drawings of lateral views of embryos during the seventh and eighth weeks.

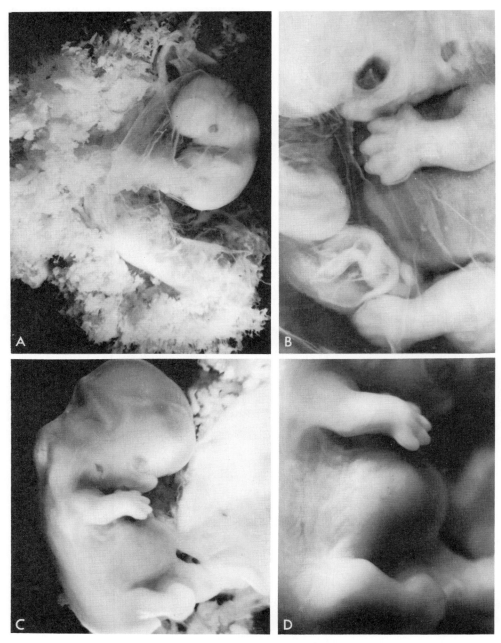

Figure 6–11   *A*, Photograph of an embryo in the amniotic sac, exposed by opening the chorionic sac (×2). *B*, Higher magnification of this embryo of 49 to 51 days (×7). Note the webbed fingers and the notches between the toe rays. *C*, Photograph of a slightly younger embryo, exposed by removal from the chorionic and amniotic sacs (×4). *D*, Higher magnification of this embryo of 47 to 48 days (×7). The large abdominal prominence is caused mainly by the liver; most of the intestine is in the umbilical cord. (Photographed by Professor Jean Hay, Department of Anatomy, University of Manitoba.)

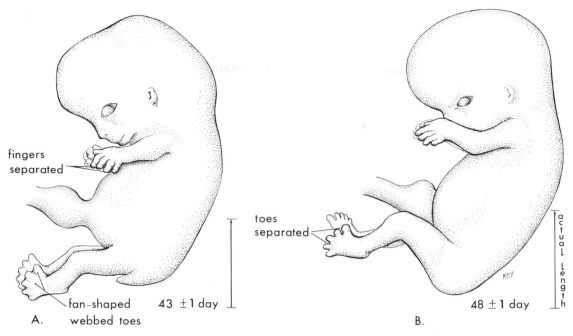

fingers
separated

toes
separated

actual length

fan-shaped
A.   webbed toes   43 ± 1 day

B.   48 ± 1 day

Figure 6–12   Drawings of lateral views of embryos during the eighth week.

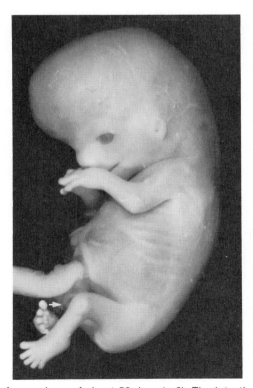

Figure 6–13   Photograph of an embryo of about 56 days (×2). The intestine is still in the umbilical cord (arrow). The digits (fingers and toes) are clearly defined. Note the relatively large head and that the tail has disappeared. (Photographed by Professor Jean Hay, Department of Anatomy, University of Manitoba.)

abdomen is less protuberant, and the umbilical cord is relatively reduced in size. The intestines are still within the proximal portion of the cord (Fig. 6–13).

During the eighth week, the eyes are usually open, but toward the end of the week, the eyelids may begin to meet and become united by epithelial fusion. The auricles of the external ears begin to assume their final shape, but they are still low-set. Although sex differences exist in the appearance of the external genitalia, they are not distinct enough to permit accurate sexual identification to be made by lay persons.

ESTIMATION OF EMBRYONIC AGE

Information about the starting date of pregnancies may be unreliable, partly because it depends on the mother's memory. Two reference points are commonly used for estimating age: the onset of the *last menstrual period* (*LMP*), and the time of *fertilization*. The probability of error in establishing the last normal menses is highest in women who become pregnant after discontinuing oral contraceptives. This is because the interval between stopping the hormones and ovulation is highly variable. In addition, uterine bleeding or "spotting" sometimes occurs after implantation of the blastocyst and is incorrectly regarded as menstruation.

It must be emphasized that the zygote does not form until about two weeks after the onset of the last menstrual period (see Fig. 1–1). Consequently, 14 ± 2 days must be deducted from the menstrual age to obtain the actual or *fertilization age* of an embryo. The day fertilization occurs is the most accurate reference point for estimating age. This is commonly calculated from the estimated time of ovulation because the ovum is usually fertilized within 12 hours after ovulation.

Because it may be important to know the actual or fertilization age of an embryo, e.g., for determining its sensitivity to drugs (Chapter 9), all statements about age should indicate the reference point used, i.e., weeks after LMP or the estimated time of fertilization.

Estimates of the age of recovered embryos (e.g., after abortion) are determined from external characteristics and measurements of length (Table 6–1). The changing appearance of the developing limbs is also a very useful criterion. Size alone may be an unreliable criterion because some embryos probably undergo a progressively slower rate of growth prior to death.

Methods of Measurement (Fig. 6–14). Because embryos of the third and early fourth weeks are nearly straight, measurements indicate the *greatest length* (GL). The sitting height or *crown-rump length* (CR) is most frequently used for older embryos. Standing height or *crown-heel length* (CH) is sometimes used for eight-week-old and older specimens.

The size of the embryo in a pregnant

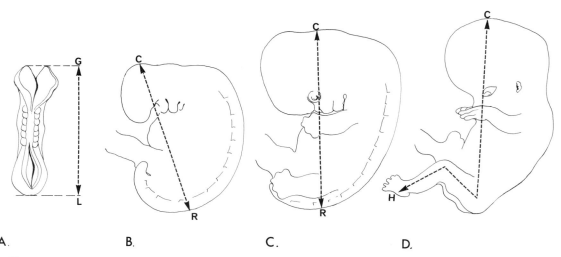

Figure 6–14 Sketches showing methods of measuring the length of embryos. *A*, Greatest length. *B* and *C*, Crown-rump length. *D*, Crown-heel length.

woman can be estimated using gray-scale ultrasound measurements. At four weeks (six weeks after LMP), the embryo, the amnion, and the yolk sac compose a structure more than 5 mm long that is detectable with careful scanning. After the fifth week (seven weeks after LMP), discrete embryonic structures can be visualized, and "crown-rump" measurements are predictive of embryonic age with an accuracy of ± one to four days. Furthermore, after the sixth week (eight weeks after LMP), dimensions of the head and trunk can be obtained and used for assessment of embryonic size.

SUMMARY

Early in the embryonic period, *longitudinal and transverse folding* converts the flat trilaminar embryonic disc into a C-shaped cylindrical embryo. The dorsal part of the yolk sac is incorporated into the embryo during folding and gives rise to the *primitive gut*. The gut becomes pinched off from the yolk sac but remains attached to it by the narrow *yolk stalk*. As the amnion expands, it forms an external investment for the *umbilical cord*. The head fold results in the heart coming to lie ventrally and the brain becoming the most cranial part of the embryo. The tail fold causes the connecting stalk (future umbilical cord) and allantois to move to the ventral surface of the embryo.

The three germ layers differentiate into various tissues and organs, so that by the end of the embryonic period, the beginnings of all the main organ systems have been established. The external appearance of the embryo is greatly affected by the formation of the brain, the heart, the liver, the somites, the limbs, the ears, the nose, and the eyes. As these structures develop, they affect the appearance of the embryo by forming characteristics that mark the embryo as unquestionably human. Because the beginnings of all essential external and internal structures are formed during the embryonic period, *the fourth to eighth weeks constitute the most critical period of development*. Developmental disturbances during this period may give rise to major congenital malformations.

Reasonable estimates of the age of embryos can be determined from (1) the day of onset of the last normal menstrual period, (2) the estimated time of fertilization, (3) measurements of length, and (4) external characteristics. The age of an embryo can also be estimated by using gray-scale ultrasound measurements.

SUGGESTED SUPPLEMENTARY READING

Balinsky, B. I.: *An Introduction to Embryology*, 5th ed. Philadelphia, Saunders College Publishing, 1981, pp. 271–283.
The pages referred to give a good description of the fascinating process of induction.
Gasser, F.: *Atlas of Human Embryos*. Hagerstown, MD, Harper & Row, Publishers, 1975.
An excellent atlas describing embryos in the world renowned Carnegie Embryological Collection.
Chilcote, W. S., and Asokan, S.: Evaluations of first trimester pregnancy by ultrasound. *Clin. Obstet. Gynecol.* 20:273, 1977.
The ultrasound techniques used to examine early embryos are clearly described and illustrated.

7

THE NINTH WEEK TO BIRTH

THE FETAL PERIOD

At nine weeks the human embryo is referred to as a *fetus* (L. offspring), signifying that it has developed into a recognizable human being. In addition, the fetus is far less vulnerable than the embryo to the deforming effects of drugs, viruses, and radiation (see Chapter 9). The transition from embryo to fetus is not abrupt. You should be aware that some doctors commonly refer to the developing human as a "fetus" throughout the entire gestation, and routinely date developmental events from the last menstrual period (LMP). This should not cause confusion about the actual age of the developing human

if it is remembered that *development starts two weeks after LMP* and that the developing human is not called a fetus until nine weeks after fertilization (i.e., 11 weeks after LMP).

Development during the fetal period is primarily concerned with growth and differentiation of tissues and organs that appeared during the embryonic period. Very few new structures appear during the fetal period.

The rate of body growth during the fetal period is remarkable, especially between the ninth and sixteenth weeks (Figs. 7–1 and 7–4), and weight gain is phenomenal during the terminal months (see Table 7–2 and Fig. 7–10).

Fetuses weighing less than 500 gm at birth

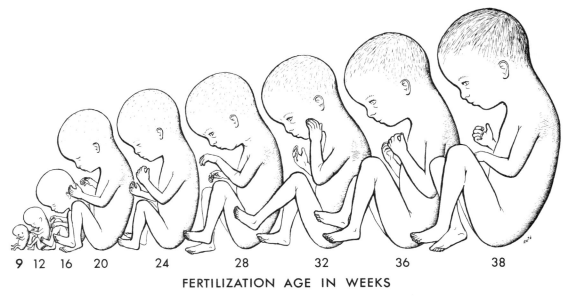

FERTILIZATION AGE IN WEEKS

Figure 7–1 Drawings of fetuses, about *one-fifth actual size.* Head hair begins to appear at about 20 weeks. Eyebrows and eyelashes are usually recognizable by 24 weeks, and the eyes reopen by 26 weeks. Fetuses born prematurely (22 weeks or more) may survive, but intensive care is required. The mean duration of pregnancy is 266 days (38 weeks) from fertilization, with a standard deviation of 12 days. *In clinical practice,* it is customary to refer to full term as 40 weeks from the first day of the last menstrual period (LMP), assuming that conception occurs two weeks after the onset of menses. Thus when a doctor refers to a pregnancy of 20 weeks, the true duration or actual age of the fetus is 18 weeks. The fetus begins to move by the twelfth week, but the mother does not usually feel the fetus move before the sixteenth week.

usually do not survive. The term *abortion* is applied to all pregnancies that terminate before the period of viability (see Table 7–2). If given expert postnatal care, fetuses weighing 500 to 1000 gm may survive and are referred to as *immature infants*. Fetuses weighing between 1000 and 2500 gm are called *premature infants,* and most of them survive. However, *prematurity is one of the most common causes of perinatal death.*

During a pregnant woman's first visit to a doctor, the age of the embryo or fetus is estimated. The date of the *last menstrual period* (*LMP*) is a time-honored guide to establishing *gestational age,* and it is reliable in most cases. To determine the actual age, or *fertilization age,* two weeks must be deducted from the gestational age because development does not begin until about two weeks after LMP.

ESTIMATION OF FETAL AGE

Pregnancy or the gestational period may be divided into days, weeks, or months (Table 7–1). Confusion arises if it is not stated whether a given time is calculated from the onset of the last menstrual period (LMP) or from the estimated day of fertilization. More uncertainty arises when months are used, particularly when it is not stated whether *calendar months* (28 to 31 days) or *lunar months* (28 days) are meant. Unless otherwise stated, age in this book is calculated from estimated time of fertilization, and months refer to calendar months. *It is best to express fetal age in weeks* and to state whether the beginning or the end of a week is meant.

Clinically, gestation is commonly divided into three parts, or trimesters, each lasting three calendar months. By the end of the first trimester, all major systems are developed and the crown-rump length of the fetus is about the width of one's palm (see Fig. 7–6). At the end of the second trimester, the fetus

is not likely to survive independently, even though its length is now equal to about the span of one's hand (see Fig. 7–8).

Various measurements and external characteristics are useful in *estimating fetal age* (Table 7–2). *Foot length* correlates well with CR length and is particularly useful for estimating the age of incomplete or macerated fetuses. *Fetal weight* is often a useful criterion, but there may be a discrepancy between the fertilization age and the weight of a fetus, particularly when the mother has had metabolic disturbances during pregnancy; e.g., in diabetes mellitus, fetal weight often exceeds values considered normal for the length.

The fetal dimensions obtained from measurements of fetuses using *ultrasound techniques* closely approximate the crown-rump measurements obtained from aborted fetuses (Table 7–2). In addition, the *biparietal diameter* of the head and the dimension of the trunk may be obtained. At 9 to 10 weeks (11 to 12 weeks after LMP), the head is still slightly larger (about 3 mm) than the trunk. Ultrasound crown-rump measurements of the fetus are predictive of fetal age with an accuracy of ± one to four days. Assessment of fetal size is enhanced when head and trunk dimensions are considered along with crown-rump measurements.

Determination of the size of the fetus, especially of its head, is of great value to the obstetrician for improving the management of patients (e.g., those women with small pelves and/or those fetuses with *intrauterine growth retardation*).

HIGHLIGHTS OF THE FETAL PERIOD

Nine to Twelve Weeks (Figs. 7–2 to 7–5). At the beginning of the ninth week, the head constitutes almost half the fetus. Thereafter, growth in body length accelerates rapidly so that by the end of 12 weeks fetal length has more than doubled (Table 7–2). Growth

TABLE 7–1 COMPARISON OF GESTATIONAL TIME UNITS

Reference Point	Days	Weeks	Calendar Months	Lunar Months
Fertilization*	266	38	8¾	9½
Last Menstrual Period	280	40	9	10

*The date of birth is calculated as about 266 days after fertilization, or 280 days after the onset of the last normal menstrual period. From fertilization to the end of the embryonic period, age is best expressed in days; thereafter age is commonly given in weeks. Because ovulation and fertilization are usually separated by not more than 12 hours, these events are more or less interchangeable in expressing prenatal age.

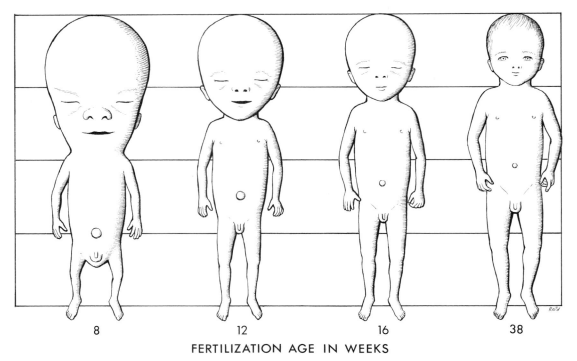

FERTILIZATION AGE IN WEEKS

8   12   16   38

Figure 7–2 Diagram illustrating the changing proportions of the body during the fetal period. By 36 weeks, the circumferences of the head and the abdomen are approximately equal. After this, the circumference of the abdomen may be greater. All stages are drawn to the same total height.

chorionic villi   amniotic sac

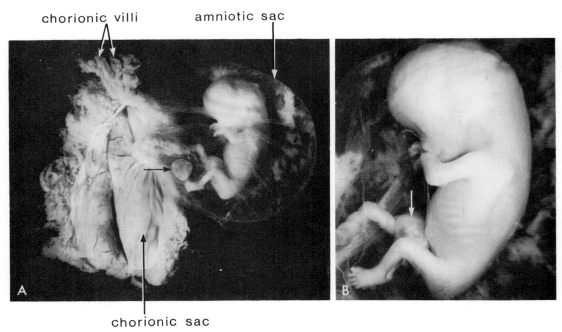

chorionic sac

Figure 7–3 Photographs of a nine-week fetus in the amniotic sac exposed by removal from its chorionic sac. *A, Actual size.* The remnant of the yolk sac is indicated by an arrow. *B,* Enlarged photograph of the fetus (×2). Note the following features: (1) large head, (2) cartilaginous ribs, and (3) intestines in the umbilical cord (arrow). Ultrasound crown-rump measurements of the fetus can ascertain fetal age with an accuracy of ± one to four days. Determination of fetal size, especially of the head, allows the obstetrician to improve the management of patients (e.g., women whose fetuses may have congenital malformations such as hydrocephalus; see chapter 17). (Photographed by Professor Jean Hay, Department of Anatomy, University of Manitoba.)

TABLE 7–2   CRITERIA FOR ESTIMATING FERTILIZATION AGE DURING THE FETAL PERIOD

Age (weeks)	CR Length (mm)*	Foot Length (mm)*	Fetal Weight (gm)†	Main External Characteristics
PREVIABLE FETUSES				
9	50	7	8	*Eyes closing or closed.* Head more rounded. External genitalia still not distinguishable as male or female. Intestines in umbilical cord.
10	61	9	14	*Intestine in abdomen.* Early fingernail development.
12	87	14	45	*Sex distinguishable externally.* Well-defined neck.
14	120	20	110	*Head erect.* Lower limbs well developed.
16	140	27	200	*Ears stand out from head.*
18	160	33	320	*Vernix caseosa present.* Early toenail development.
20	190	39	460	*Head and body hair (lanugo) visible.*
VIABLE FETUSES‡				
22	210	45	630	*Skin wrinkled* and red.
24	230	50	820	*Fingernails present.* Lean body.
26	250	55	1000	*Eyes partially open.* Eyelashes present.
28	270	59	1300	*Eyes open.* Good head of hair. Skin slightly wrinkled.
30	280	63	1700	*Toenails present.* Body filling out. Testes descending.
32	300	68	2100	*Fingernails reach finger tips.* Skin pink and smooth.
36	340	79	2900	*Body usually plump.* Lanugo hairs almost absent. Toenails reach toe tips. Flexed limbs; firm grasp.
38	360	83	3400	*Prominent chest;* breasts protrude. Testes in scrotum or palpable in inguinal canals. Fingernails extend beyond finger tips.

* These measurements are averages and so may not apply to specific cases; dimensional variations increase with age. The method for taking CR (crown-rump) measurements is illustrated in Figure 6–14.

† These weights refer to fetuses that have been fixed for about two weeks in 10 per cent formalin. Fresh specimens usually weigh about 5 per cent less.

‡ There is no sharp limit of development, age, or weight at which a fetus automatically becomes viable or beyond which survival is assured, but experience has shown that it is rare for a baby to survive whose weight is less than 500 gm or whose fertilization age is less than 22 weeks. Even fetuses born during the 26- to 28-week period have difficulty surviving, mainly because the respiratory and central nervous systems are not completely differentiated. The term *abortion* refers to all pregnancies that terminate before the period of viability.

of the head slows down considerably, however, compared with that of the rest of the body. The face is broad, the eyes widely separated, and the ears low-set. The eyes are usually closed during the ninth week.

At the beginning of the ninth week, the legs are short and the thighs are relatively small (Fig. 7–3). At the end of 12 weeks, the upper limbs have almost reached their final relative lengths, but the lower limbs are still not so well developed and are slightly shorter than their final relative length (Fig. 7–2).

The external genitalia of males and females appear somewhat similar until the end of the ninth week, and their mature form is not established until the twelfth week (see Chapter 14). Intestinal coils are visible within the proximal end of the umbilical cord (Fig. 7–3*B*) until the middle of the tenth week, when the intestines return to the abdomen.

At the beginning of the ninth week, the liver is the major site of *erythropoiesis.* By the end of the twelfth week, this activity decreases in the liver and begins in the spleen. *Urine starts to form* between the ninth and twelfth weeks and is excreted into the amniotic fluid. The fetus begins to move during the nine- to twelve-week period, but these movements cannot be detected by the mother.

Thirteen to Sixteen Weeks (Figs. 7–4 and 7–6).   Growth is very rapid during this period (Table 7–2). At the end of this period, the head is relatively small compared with that of the 12-week fetus, and the lower limbs have lengthened. The skeleton shows clearly on x-ray films toward the end of this period.

Seventeen to Twenty Weeks (Fig. 7–7).   Growth slows down during this period (Table 7–2). Fetal movements, known as

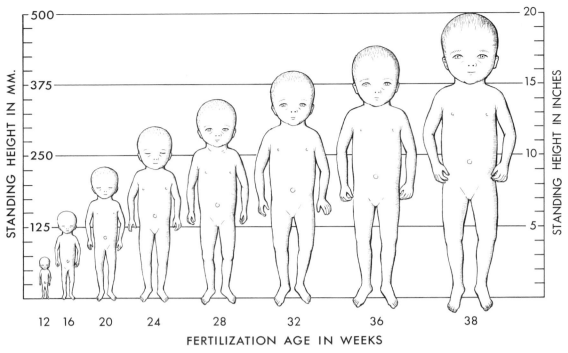

Figure 7–4 Diagram illustrating the changes in size of the human fetus when drawn to scale.

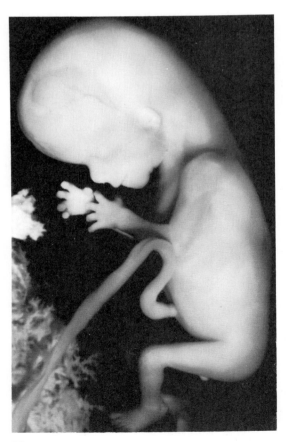

Figure 7–5 Photograph of an 11-week fetus exposed by removal from the chorionic and amniotic sacs ($\times 1.5$). Note the relatively large head and that the intestine is no longer in the umbilical cord. (Photographed by Professor Jean Hay, Department of Anatomy, University of Manitoba.)

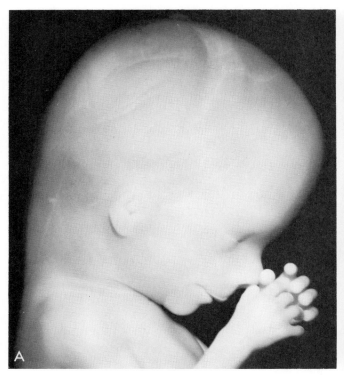
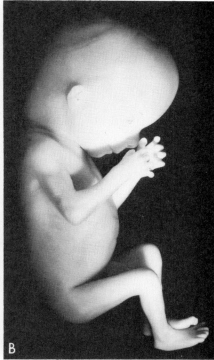

Figure 7–6 Photographs of a 13-week fetus. *A*, Enlarged photograph of the head and shoulders of this fetus (×2). Note that its eyes are closed at this stage. *B, Actual size*. Note that its crown-rump length is about the same as the width of your palm. (Photographed by Professor Jean Hay, Department of Anatomy, University of Manitoba.)

quickening, are commonly recognized by the mother. The skin is covered with a greasy cheeselike material known as *vernix caseosa.* It consists of a mixture of a fatty secretion from the fetal sebaceous glands and dead skin (see Chapter 19); it protects the fetus' delicate skin from abrasions, chapping, and hardening as a result of being bathed in amniotic fluid.

The bodies of 20-week fetuses are usually completely covered with fine downy hair called *lanugo*; this may help hold the vernix on the skin. Eyebrows and head hair are also visible at the end of this period.

Brown fat forms during this time and is the site of heat production, particularly in the newborn infant. This specialized adipose tissue produces heat by oxidizing fatty acids. Brown fat is chiefly found (1) on the floor of the anterior triangle of the neck surrounding the subclavian and carotid vessels, (2) posterior to the sternum, and (3) in the perirenal area. Brown fat has a high content of mitochondria, giving it a definite brown hue.

Twenty-one to Twenty-five Weeks (Fig. 7–8). There is a substantial weight gain during this period. Although the body is still somewhat lean, it is better proportioned. The skin is usually wrinkled and is pink to red in color because blood in the capillaries is now visible.

By 24 weeks, alveolar cells of the lung have begun to make *surfactant*, a surface-active lipid that maintains alveolar patency. Although all organs are rather well developed, a 22- to 25-week fetus may die within a few days if born prematurely, mainly because its respiratory system is still immature.

Twenty-six to Twenty-nine Weeks. A fetus could now survive if born prematurely (Table 7–2), because *the lungs are capable of breathing air,* and because the lungs and pulmonary vasculature have developed sufficiently to provide gas exchange. In addition, the central nervous system has matured to the stage at which it can direct rhythmic breathing movements and control body temperature.

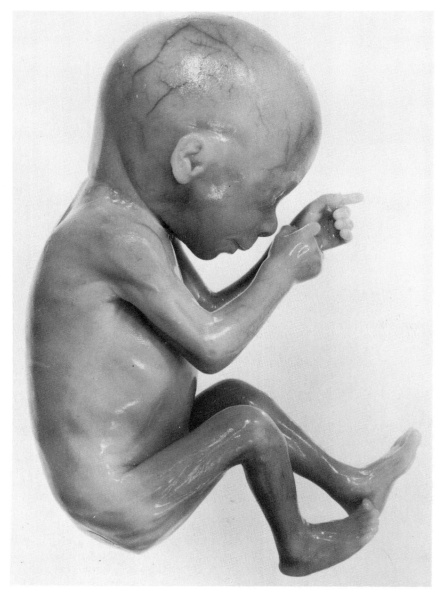

Figure 7–7   Photograph of a 17-week fetus. *Actual size.* Because the skin is very thin, the underlying scalp vessels are clearly visible. Movements of the fetus should be felt by the mother at this time (19 weeks after LMP).

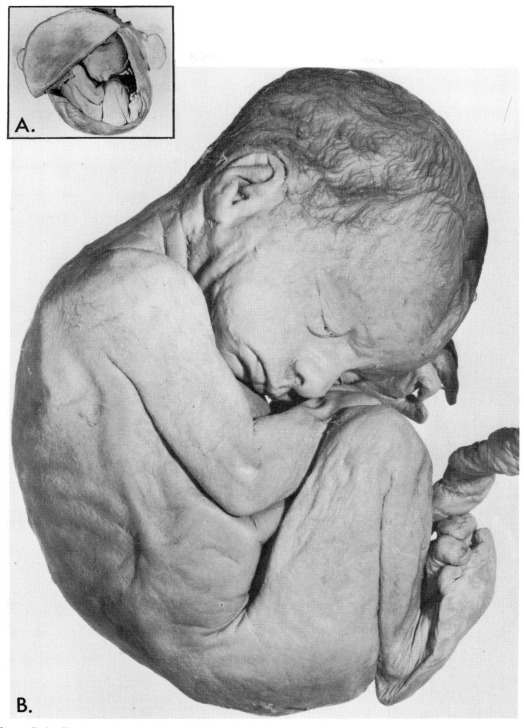

Figure 7–8   Photographs of a 25-week fetus. *A*, in the uterus. *B Actual size.* Note the wrinkled skin and rather lean body caused by the scarcity of subcutaneous fat. Observe that the eyes are beginning to open. A fetus of this size might survive if born prematurely; hence it is considered a viable fetus. Termination of pregnancy is illegal after the period of viability (Table 7–2).

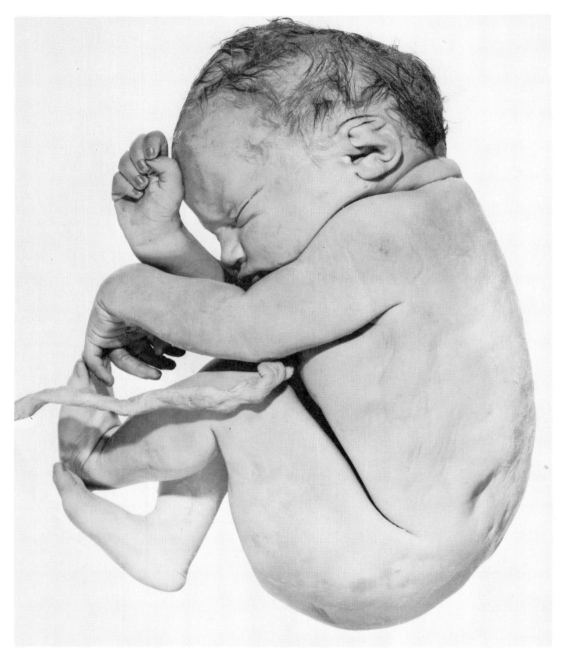

Figure 7–9   Photograph of a 36-week fetus. *Half actual size.* Fetuses at this size and age usually survive. Note the plump body resulting from the deposition of subcutaneous fat. This fetus' mother was killed in an automobile accident, and the fetus died before it could be delivered by cesarean section.

The eyes reopen during this period, and head and lanugo hair are well developed. Considerable subcutaneous fat has now formed under the skin, smoothing out many of the wrinkles. During this period, the quantity of white fat in the body increases to about 3.5 per cent of body weight. *Erythropoiesis in the spleen* ends by 28 weeks, and the bone marrow becomes the major site of this process.

The fetus usually assumes an upside-down position as the time of birth approaches; this positioning results partly from the shape of the uterus and partly because the head is heavier than the feet.

Thirty to Thirty-four Weeks. *The pupillary light reflex is present by 30 weeks.* Usually by the end of this period, the skin is pink and smooth, and the upper and lower limbs often have a chubby appearance. At this stage, the quantity of white fat in the body is about 7 to 8 per cent of body weight.

Thirty-five to Thirty-eight Weeks (Fig. 7–9). Fetuses at 35 weeks have a firm grasp and exhibit a spontaneous orientation to light. Most fetuses during this "finishing" period are plump.

At 36 weeks, the circumference of the head and the abdomen are approximately equal. After this, the circumference of the abdomen is greater than that of the head.

There is a slowing of growth as the time of birth approaches (Fig. 7–10). Fetuses usually reach a CR length of 360 mm and weigh about 3400 gm. By full term, the amount of white fat in the body is about 16 per cent of body weight. The fetus lays down about 14 gm of fat a day during the last few weeks of gestation. In general, male fetuses grow faster than females, and male infants generally weigh more than female infants at birth. Succeeding pregnancies tend to last slightly longer, and result in larger babies.

By *full term* (38 weeks after fertilization, or 40 weeks after LMP), the skin is usually white or bluish-pink in color. The chest is prominent and the breasts protrude in both sexes. The testes are usually in the scrotum in full-term male infants; descent begins at about 28 to 32 weeks. Thus premature male infants commonly have undescended testes. Usually, the testes descend during early infancy.

Time of Birth. The expected time of birth is roughly calculated as 266 days or 38 weeks after fertilization, or 280 days or 40 weeks

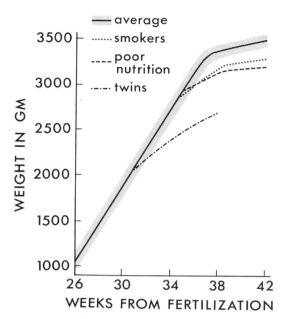

Figure 7–10 Graph showing the rate of fetal growth during the last trimester. Average refers to babies born in the United States. After 36 weeks the growth rate deviates from the straight line. The decline, particularly after full term (38 weeks), probably reflects inadequate fetal nutrition caused by placental changes. Note the adverse effect on fetal weight created by mothers who smoke heavily or eat a poor-quality diet. (Adapted from Gruenwald, P.: Growth of the human fetus. I. Normal growth and its variation. *Amer. J. Obstet. Gynec.* 94:1112, 1966.)

from the onset of the last menstrual period (Table 7–1). Most fetuses are born within 10 to 15 days of this time, but occasionally birth does not occur until 276 to 286 days after fertilization. A common way of setting the expected date of delivery is to count back three calendar months from the first day of the last menstrual period and then add a year and one week.

FACTORS INFLUENCING FETAL GROWTH

Glucose, Insulin, and Amino Acids. Glucose is the primary source of energy for fetal metabolism and growth, but amino acids are also required. These substances are derived from the mother via the placenta (see Chapter 8). The insulin required for the metabolism of glucose is secreted by the fetal pancreas. No significant quantities of maternal insulin reach the fetus.

FACTORS CAUSING FETAL GROWTH RETARDATION

Maternal Malnutrition. Severe maternal malnutrition resulting from a poor-quality diet is known to cause reduced fetal growth (Fig. 7–10). Poor nutrition and faulty food habits are common and they are not restricted to mothers belonging to poverty groups.

Smoking. The growth rate of fetuses of mothers who smoke cigarettes is less than normal during the last six to eight weeks of pregnancy (Fig. 7–10). The effect is greater on fetuses whose mothers also eat a poor-quality diet.

Multiple Pregnancy. Individuals of twins, triplets, and other multiple births usually weigh considerably less than infants resulting from a single pregnancy. It is evident that the total requirements of twins (Fig. 7–10), triplets, and so forth exceed the nutritional supply available from the placenta during the third trimester.

Socially Used Drugs. Infants born to alcoholic mothers often exhibit intrauterine growth retardation (IUGR) as part of the *fetal alcohol syndrome* (see Chapter 9). Similarly, narcotic addiction can cause IUGR and other obstetrical complications.

Impaired Uteroplacental Blood Flow. Maternal placental circulation may be reduced by a variety of conditions which decrease uterine blood flow (e.g., severe hypotension and renal disease). Chronic reduction of uterine blood flow can cause fetal starvation and result in fetal growth retardation.

Placental Insufficiency. Placental defects can also cause intrauterine fetal growth retardation. These placental changes reduce the total surface area available for exchange of nutrients between the fetal and maternal blood streams (Chapter 8).

Genetic Factors and Chromosomal Aberrations. It is well established that genetic factors can lead to retarded fetal growth. In recent years structural and numerical chromosomal aberrations (Chapter 9) have also been associated with cases of retarded fetal growth. Intrauterine growth retardation is pronounced in Down syndrome and is very characteristic of trisomy 18 syndrome (see Chapter 9).

PERINATOLOGY

Perinatology is the branch of medicine which is primarily concerned with the health of the fetus and newborn infant, generally covering the *perinatal period* from about 26 weeks after fertilization to about four weeks after birth. The subspecialty known as *perinatal medicine* combines certain aspects of obstetrics and pediatrics.

The fetus is now commonly regarded as a patient on whom diagnostic and therapeutic procedures may be performed. Studies concerned with the fetus are sometimes called *fetology*. Several techniques are now avail-

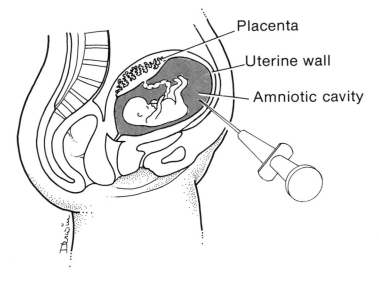

Figure 7–11 Drawing illustrating the technique of amniocentesis. A needle is inserted through the lower abdominal wall and the uterine wall into the amniotic cavity. A syringe is attached and amniotic fluid is withdrawn for diagnostic purposes (e.g., for cell cultures or protein studies). Amniocentesis is relatively devoid of risk, especially when combined with ultrasonography for placental localization. The risk of injuring the fetus with the needle is also minimized by using ultrasound. The technique is usually performed at 15 to 16 weeks of gestation. Prior to this stage of development, there is relatively little amniotic fluid, and the difficulties in obtaining it without endangering the mother or the fetus are consequently greater. There is an excessive amount of amniotic fluid (polyhydramnios) in the case illustrated in this figure.

Placenta

Uterine wall

Amniotic cavity

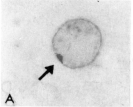 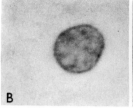 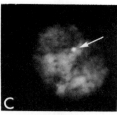

Figure 7–12 Nuclei of cells in amniotic fluid obtained by amniocentesis. *A*, Chromatin-positive nucleus indicating the presence of a female fetus; the sex chromatin is indicated by an arrow. *B*, Chromatin-negative nucleus indicating the presence of a male fetus. No sex chromatin is visible. Cresylecht violet stain (× 1000). *C*, Y-chromatin-positive nucleus indicating the presence of a male fetus. The arrow indicates the Y-chromatin as an intensely fluorescent body obtained after staining the cell in quinacrine mustard. (*A* and *B* from Riis, M., and Fuchs, F.: Sex chromatin and antenatal sex diagnosis; *in* K. L. Moore [Ed.]: *The Sex Chromatin.* Philadelphia, W. B. Saunders Company, 1966. *C* courtesy of Dr. M. Ray, Department of Pediatrics, Division of Genetics and Department of Anatomy, University of Manitoba and Health Sciences Centre, Winnipeg, Canada.)

able for assessing the status of the human fetus and for providing prenatal treatment.

Amniocentesis (Fig. 7–11). Amniotic fluid is sampled by inserting a hollow needle through the mother's abdominal wall into the amniotic cavity. A syringe is then attached and amniotic fluid withdrawn. Because there is relatively little amniotic fluid, amniocentesis is difficult to perform prior to the fourteenth week.

Amniocentesis is relatively devoid of risk, especially when the procedure is performed by an experienced obstetrician who is guided by ultrasonography for placental localization. Amniocentesis is the most common technique for detecting genetic disorders and is usually performed at 15 to 16 weeks of gestation (i.e., after LMP).

Sex Chromatin Patterns. Fetal sex can be diagnosed by noting the presence or absence of sex chromatin in cells recovered from amniotic fluid (Fig. 7–12). Knowledge of fetal sex can be useful in diagnosing the presence of severe sex-linked hereditary diseases such as hemophilia or muscular dystrophy. *These tests are not done merely to diagnose fetal sex for curious parents.*

Cell Cultures. Fetal sex can also be determined by studying the sex chromosomes of cultured amniotic cells. These studies are more commonly done when an autosomal abnormality is suspected, such as occurs in Down syndrome (discussed in Chapter 9). Inborn errors of metabolism and enzyme deficiencies in fetuses can also be detected by studying cell cultures. Cell cultures permit prenatal diagnosis of severe diseases for which there is no effective treatment and af-

ford the opportunity to interrupt the pregnancy.

Fetoprotein Measurements. Chemical components are known to leak from skin defects of fetuses with neural tube defects into the amniotic fluid (see Chapter 17). The concentration of α-*fetoprotein* (*AFP*) in the amniotic fluid surrounding fetuses with spina bifida cystica and anencephaly is remarkably high. Thus, it is possible to detect the presence of these severe abnormalities by measuring the concentration of α-fetoprotein in amniotic fluid.

Detection of an increased concentration of α-fetoprotein in amniotic fluid is likely to be a useful diagnostic tool for detecting the presence or absence of *open neural tube defects,* e.g., anencephaly and severe types of spina bifida in fetuses of mothers who have already had a child with a neural tube defect. The findings would help to decide whether the pregnancy should be terminated.

Intrauterine Fetal Transfusion. Some fetuses with erythroblastosis fetalis can be saved by giving them intrauterine blood transfusions. The blood is injected through a needle inserted into the fetal peritoneal cavity. Over a period of five to six days, most of the cells pass into the fetal circulation via the lymphatics of the diaphragm.

Fetoscopy. Using fiberoptic lighting instruments, one may directly visualize parts of the fetal body. It is possible to scan the entire fetus, looking for congenital malformations such as cleft lip. The fetoscope is usually introduced through the anterior abdominal wall and the uterine wall into the amniotic cavity, similar to the way the needle

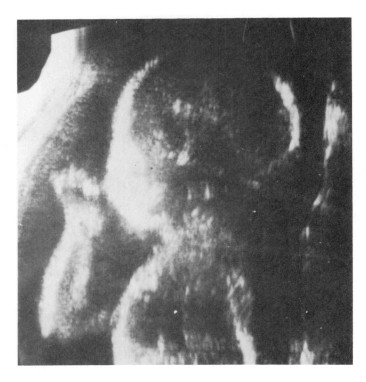

Figure 7–13 Ultrasound scan of a 30-week fetus that is sucking its thumb. Observe that its forearm bones are visible. The biparietal diameter of the head can be determined and compared with the abdominal diameter. Determination of these measurements facilitates estimation of the age and weight of the fetus. (From Thompson, J. S., and Thompson, M. W.: *Genetics in Medicine.* 3rd ed. Philadelphia, W. B. Saunders Co., 1980. Courtesy of Stuart Campbell.)

is inserted during amniocentesis (Fig. 7–11). One can not only see the fetus, but also take biopsies of skin or blood samples. Probably the optimal time for doing this procedure is at 18 weeks of pregnancy, because the amniotic sac is large enough to allow easy entry of the trochar, and the fetus can be maneuvered for inspection.

Ultrasonography. (Fig. 7–13). Chorionic sacs may be visualized during the embryonic period by using ultrasound techniques; placental and fetal size, multiple births, and abnormal presentations can also be determined.

Ultrasonic scans give accurate measurements of the biparietal diameter of the fetal skull, from which close estimates of fetal length can be made. Thus "small for date" fetuses can be detected. In most cases, the male genitalia can be visualized by ultrasound.

Recent advances in ultrasonography have made this technique a major tool for prenatal diagnosis of fetal abnormalities such as the following: anencephaly, hydrocephaly, microcephaly, fetal ascites, and renal agenesis. Because of the cost, ultrasonography for estimation of gestational age and for the determination of congenital malformations is not routine. It is indicated in *high-risk obstetrical patients* (e.g., when there is a medical indication for induction of labor).

SUMMARY

The fetal period begins nine weeks after fertilization and ends at birth. It is primarily *characterized by rapid body growth and differentiation of organ systems.* An obvious change is the relative slowing of head growth compared with that of the rest of the body. Lanugo and head hair appear, and the skin is coated with *vernix caseosa* by the beginning of the twentieth week. The eyelids are closed during much of the fetal period but reopen at about 26 weeks. Until this time the fetus is usually incapable of extrauterine existence, mainly because of the immaturity of the respiratory system.

Until about 30 weeks the fetus appears reddish and wizened because of the thinness of its skin and the relative absence of subcutaneous fat. Fat usually develops rapidly during the last six to eight weeks, making the fetus smooth and plump. This terminal period is devoted mainly to building up of tissues and preparation of systems involved in the transition from intrauterine to extrauterine environments.

Changes occurring during the fetal period are not so dramatic as those in the embryonic period, but they are very important. The fetus is far less vulnerable to the teratogenic or deforming effects of drugs, viruses, and radiation, but these agents may interfere with normal functional development, especially of the brain and the eyes. Various techniques are available for assessing the status of the fetus and for diagnosing certain diseases and developmental abnormalities before birth.

SUGGESTED SUPPLEMENTARY READING

Gosink, B. B.: *Diagnostic Ultrasound,* 2nd ed. Philadelphia, W. B. Saunders Company, 1981.
A good introduction to the applications of ultrasound in clinical practice.
Page, E. W., Villee, C. A., and Villee, D. B.: *Human Reproduction. Essentials of Reproductive and Perinatal Medicine,* 3rd ed. Philadelphia, W. B. Saunders Company, 1981, pp. 249–276.
Describes the prenatal development of the organ systems which prepare the fetus for extrauterine existence.
Persaud, T. V. N.: *Prenatal Pathology. Fetal Medicine.* Springfield, IL, Charles C Thomas, 1979.
A very good account of the methods used for the prenatal detection of birth defects.

8

THE PLACENTA AND FETAL MEMBRANES

The *placenta* is a *fetomaternal organ* that consists of fetal and maternal portions. It functions primarily as an organ that *permits the exchange of materials* carried in the bloodstreams of the mother and the embryo or fetus (see Fig. 8–5).

The *chorion*, the *amnion*, the *yolk sac*, and the *allantois* constitute the fetal membranes. These membranes develop from the zygote but do not form embryonic structures, except for portions of the yolk sac and allantois.

Before birth, the placenta and fetal membranes perform the following functions and activities: *protection, nutrition, respiration, excretion* and *hormone production*. At birth, the placenta and fetal membranes separate from the fetus and are expelled from the uterus as the *afterbirth*.

THE DECIDUA

The term *decidua*[1] is applied to the functional layer of the gravid or pregnant endometrium (see Fig. 2–2B), indicating that it is shed at *parturition* (birth).

Three regions of decidua are designated according to their relation to the implantation site (Fig. 8–1): (1) the part underlying the conceptus and forming the maternal component of the placenta is the *decidua basalis*; (2) the superficial portion overlying the conceptus is the *decidua capsularis*; and (3) all the remaining uterine mucosa is the *decidua parietalis*. As the conceptus enlarges, the decidua capsularis bulges into the uterine cavity and eventually fuses with the decidua parietalis, thus obliterating the uterine cavity (Fig. 8–1F). By about 22 weeks, the decidua capsularis degenerates and disappears.

DEVELOPMENT OF THE PLACENTA

The rapid proliferation of the trophoblast and development of the chorionic sac were

---

[1] From Latin *deciduus*, "a falling-off," as of the leaves of deciduous trees in the autumn.

described in Chapters 4 and 5. By the fourth week, the essential arrangements necessary for physiological exchanges between the mother and embryo are established.

Chorionic villi cover the entire surface of the chorionic sac until about the eighth week (Figs. 8–1C and 8–2A). As the sac grows, the villi associated with the decidua capsularis become compressed and their blood supply is reduced. Subsequently, these villi degenerate, producing a bare area known as the chorion laeve (L. *levis*, smooth) or *smooth chorion* (Figs. 8–1D and 8–2B). As this occurs, the chorionic villi associated with the decidua basalis rapidly increase in number, branch profusely, and enlarge. This portion of the chorionic sac, known as the chorion frondosum (L. *frondosus*, leafy) or *villous chorion*, forms the fetal component of the placenta (Figs. 8–1F and 8–3).

The final shape of the placenta is determined by the form of the persistent area of chorionic villi; usually this is circular, giving the placenta a discoid shape (Figs. 8–3 and 8–11). As the villi erode the decidua basalis, they leave several wedge-shaped areas of decidual tissue called *placental septa* (see Fig. 8–5). These septa divide the fetal part of the placenta into 10 to 38 irregular areas called *cotyledons* (see Fig. 8–11A). Each cotyledon consists of two or more main stem villi and their many branches.

The fetal portion of the placenta (or villous chorion) is anchored to the maternal portion of the placenta (decidua basalis) by *anchoring villi* (see Fig. 8–5).

The Intervillous Space (Figs. 8–1D and 8–4). The blood-filled intervillous spaces are derived mainly from the lacunae which developed in the syncytiotrophoblast during the second week. During erosion by the syncytiotrophoblast, these spaces enlarge at the expense of the decidua basalis. Collectively, the spaces form a large blood sinus, the *intervillous space*, which is bounded by the

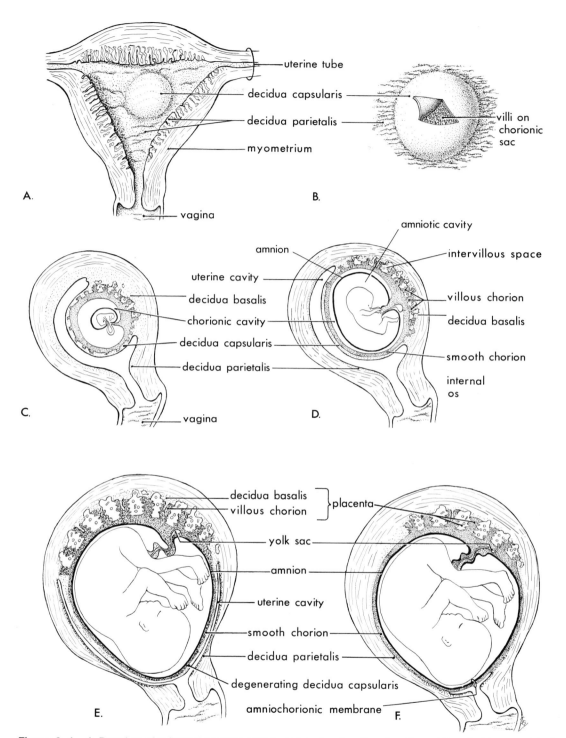

Figure 8–1 *A*, Drawing of a frontal section of the uterus showing the elevation of the decidua capsularis caused by the expanding chorionic sac of an implanted four-week embryo. *B*, Enlarged drawing of the implantation site; the chorionic villi have been exposed by cutting an opening in the decidua capsularis. *C* to *F*, Drawings of sagittal sections of the gravid uterus from the fourth to twenty-second weeks, showing the changing relations of the fetal membranes to the decidua. In *F*, the amnion and chorion are fused with each other and the decidua parietalis, thus obliterating the uterine cavity. Note that the villi persist only where the chorion is associated with the decidua basalis; here they form the villous chorion. Initially the placenta is larger than the fetus, but during the last half of pregnancy the fetus grows faster than the placenta.

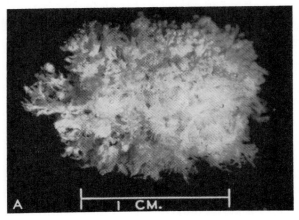

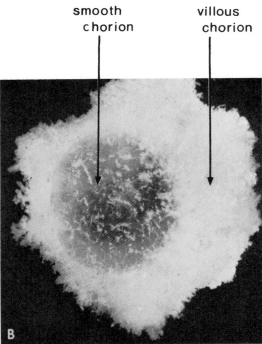

smooth
chorion

villous
chorion

Figure 8–2 Photographs of human chorionic sacs. *A*, 21 days. The entire sac is covered with chorionic villi (×4). *B*, Eight weeks. *Actual size.* Note that some villi have degenerated, leaving the chorion smooth. The remaining villous chorion forms the fetal contribution to the placenta. (Reproduced with permission from Potter, E. L.: *Pathology of the Fetus and Infant*, 2nd ed. Copyright © 1961 by Year Book Medical Publishers, Inc., Chicago.)

chorionic plate and decidua basalis (Figs. 8–4 and 8–5). The intervillous space is divided into compartments by the placental septa, but, because the septa do not reach the *chorionic plate*, there is communication between the intervillous spaces of different compartments. The intervillous space is drained by *endometrial veins* which open over the entire surface of the decidua basalis (Fig. 8–5).

Maternal blood circulates through the intervillous spaces, bringing nutritive and other substances necessary for embryonic and fetal development, and taking away the waste products of fetal metabolism.

PLACENTAL CIRCULATION

The placenta essentially provides a large area where materials may be exchanged across the *placental membrane* interposed between the fetal and maternal circulations (see Fig. 8–7). From the maternal blood the fetal blood acquires nutrients and oxygen. Waste products formed within the embryo

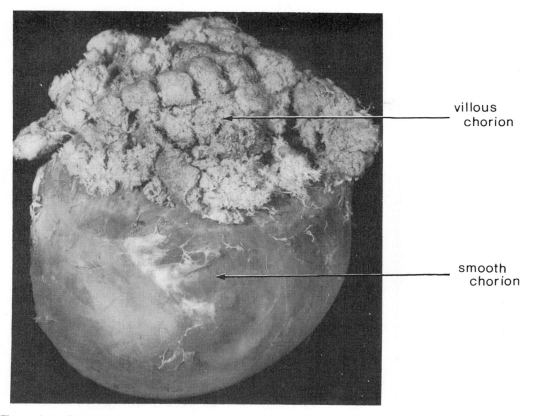

Figure 8–3 Photograph of a human chorionic sac containing a 13-week fetus showing the smooth and villous areas of the chorion. *Actual size.* To visualize how this chorionic sac was situated in the uterus prior to abortion, see Figures 8–1*E* and 8–4.

villous
chorion

smooth
chorion

Figure 8–4 Drawing of a sagittal section of the gravid uterus at 22 weeks showing the relations of the fetal membranes to each other and to the decidua. The fetus has been removed, and the amnion and smooth chorion have been cut and reflected. The fetal component of the placenta consists of the chorionic plate and the chorionic villi that arise from it and project into the intervillous spaces containing maternal blood. The maternal component of the placenta is formed by the decidua basalis. This comprises all the endometrium beneath the fetal component of the placenta.

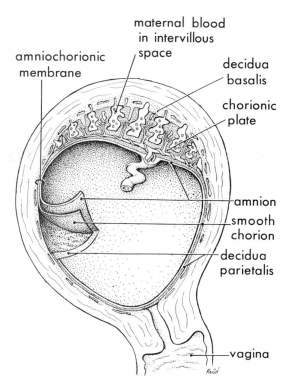

amniochorionic
membrane

maternal blood
in intervillous
space

decidua
basalis

chorionic
plate

amnion

smooth
chorion

decidua
parietalis

vagina

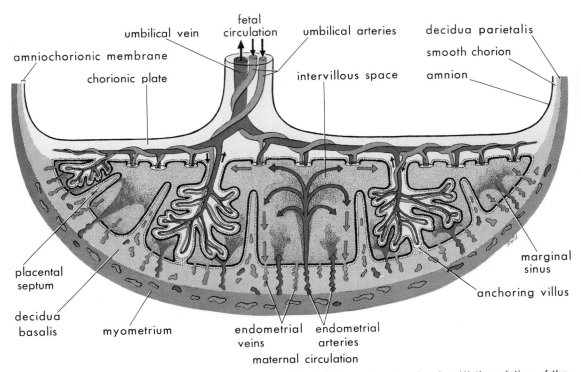

Figure 8–5 Schematic drawing of a section through a full-term placenta, showing (1) the relation of the villous chorion (fetal placenta) to the decidua basalis (maternal placenta), (2) the fetal placental circulation, and (3) the maternal placental circulation. Maternal blood flows into the intervillous spaces in funnel-shaped spurts, and exchanges occur with the fetal blood as the maternal blood flows around the villi. The inflowing arterial blood pushes venous blood out into the endometrial veins, which are scattered over the entire surface of the decidua basalis. Note that the umbilical arteries carry deoxygenated fetal blood (shown in blue) to the placenta and that the umbilical vein carries oxygenated blood (shown in red) to the fetus. Note that the cotyledons are separated from each other by decidual septa of the maternal portion of the placenta. Each cotyledon consists of two or more main stem villi and their many branches. In this drawing only one main stem villus is shown in each cotyledon, but the stumps of those that have been removed are indicated. (Based on Ramsey, E. M.: The placenta and fetal membranes; *in* Greenhill, J. P. (Ed.): *Obstetrics*, 13th ed. Philadelphia, W. B. Saunders Company, 1965.)

are carried to the placenta and transferred to the maternal blood. Within the placenta, the maternal and fetal bloodstreams flow close to each other, but they do not normally mix.

The Placental Membrane (Figs. 8–6 and 8–7). This membrane consists of the fetal tissues separating the maternal and fetal blood. Until about 20 weeks, it consists of four layers (Fig. 8–6B): (1) the syncytiotrophoblast, (2) the cytotrophoblast, (3) the connective tissue core of the villus, and (4) the endothelium of the fetal capillary.

As pregnancy advances, the placental membrane ("barrier") becomes progressively thinner and many capillaries come to lie very close to the syncytiotrophoblast (Fig. 8–6C). At some sites the syncytiotrophoblastic nuclei form nuclear aggregations or *syncytial knots*. Toward the end of pregnancy, *fibrinoid material* forms on the sur-

faces of villi; it consists of fibrin and other substances. These changes result mainly from aging.

Fetal Placental Circulation (Fig. 8–5). The deoxygenated blood leaves the fetus and passes in the umbilical arteries to the placenta. The blood vessels form an extensive *arterio-capillary-venous system* within the chorionic villus (Fig. 8–6A), bringing the fetal blood very close to the maternal blood. The oxygenated fetal blood passes into thin-walled veins which converge to form the umbilical vein. This large vessel carries the oxygenated blood to the fetus.

Maternal Placental Circulation (Fig. 8–5). The blood in the intervillous space is temporarily outside the maternal circulatory system; it enters the intervillous space through 80 to 100 *spiral arteries* or endometrial arteries (see Fig. 2–2B). The blood is propelled

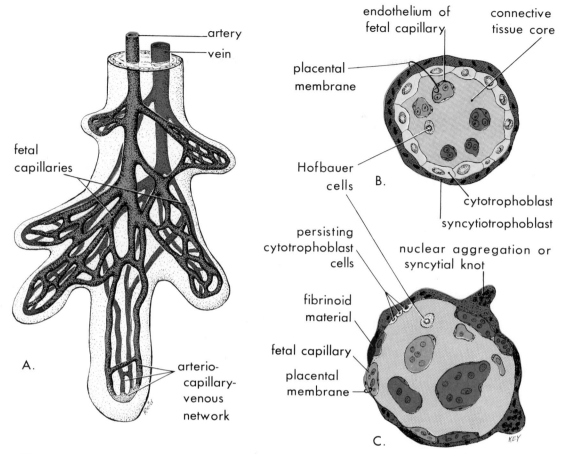

Figure 8–6 *A,* Drawing of a chorionic villus showing the arterio-capillary-venous system carrying fetal blood. The artery carries deoxygenated blood and waste products from the fetus, whereas the vein carries oxygenated blood and nutrients to the fetus. *B* and *C,* Drawings of sections through a chorionic villus at 10 weeks and at full term, respectively. The villi are bathed externally in maternal blood. The placental membrane, composed of fetal tissues, separates the maternal blood from the fetal blood. Hofbauer cells have the general qualities of macrophages.

in jetlike streams by the maternal blood pressure and spurts toward the chorionic plate or "roof" of the intervillous space. The blood slowly flows around and over the surface of the villi, allowing an exchange of metabolic and gaseous products with the fetal blood. The maternal blood eventually reaches the floor of the intervillous space, where it enters the endometrial veins.

The welfare of the embryo and fetus depends more on the adequate bathing of the chorionic villi by maternal blood than on any other factor. Acute reductions of uteroplacental circulation result in *fetal hypoxia,* or fetal death. Chronic reductions of uteroplacental circulation result in disturbances of growth and development that constitute a syndrome known as *intrauterine growth retardation.*

PLACENTAL ACTIVITIVES

The placenta has three main activities: (1) metabolism, (2) transfer, and (3) endocrine secretion that are essential for maintaining pregnancy and promoting normal embryonic development. The placenta synthesizes glycogen, cholesterol, and fatty acids.

PLACENTAL TRANSFER

Gases. Oxygen, carbon dioxide, and carbon monoxide cross the placental membrane by *simple diffusion.* Interruption of oxy-

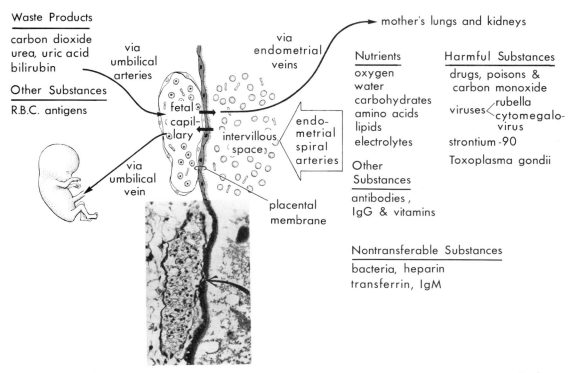

Figure 8–7 Diagrammatic illustration of placental transfer (Inset photomicrograph from Javert, C. T.: *Spontaneous and Habitual Abortion.* Copyright © 1957 by McGraw-Hill, Inc. Used by permission of McGraw-Hill Book Company.)

gen transport for even a few minutes will endanger embryonic/fetal survival.

Nutrients. Water is rapidly and freely exchanged between mother and fetus, and in increasing amounts as pregnancy advances. There is little or no transfer of maternal cholesterol, triglycerides, or phospholipids. There is transport of free fatty acids, but the amount transferred is probably relatively small. Vitamins cross the placenta and are essential for normal development. Water-soluble vitamins cross the placental membrane more quickly than fat-soluble ones. Glucose is quickly transferred.

Hormones. Protein hormones do not reach the fetus in significant amounts, except for a slow transfer of thyroxine and triiodothyronine. Unconjugated steroid hormones pass the placental membrane rather freely, unless they are firmly bound to proteins. Testosterone and certain synthetic progestins cross the placenta and may cause external masculinization of female fetuses (see Chapter 9).

Electrolytes. These are freely exchanged across the placenta in significant quantities, each at its own rate. *When a mother receives intravenous fluids, they also pass to the fetus and affect its water and electrolyte status.*

Antibodies. Some passive immunity is conferred upon the fetus by transplacental transfer of maternal antibodies. The alpha and beta globulins reach the fetus in very small quantities, but many of the gamma globulins, notably the IgG (7S) class, are readily transported to the fetus. Maternal antibodies confer immunity on the fetus to such diseases as diphtheria, smallpox, and measles, but no immunity is acquired to pertussis (whooping cough) or chickenpox.

Although the placental membrane separates the maternal and fetal circulations, small amounts of blood may pass from the fetus to the mother. If the fetus is Rh-positive and the mother Rh-negative, the fetal cells may stimulate the formation of anti-Rh antibody by the mother. This passes to the fetal blood stream and causes hemolysis of fetal Rh-positive blood cells and anemia in the fetus. Some fetuses with this condition, known as *hemolytic disease of the newborn*

(HDN), or erythroblastosis fetalis, fail to make a satisfactory intrauterine adjustment and may die unless delivered early or given intrauterine blood transfusions (discussed in Chapter 7).

Exchange transfusions are also performed after birth, using the umbilical vein. Most of the infant's blood is replaced with Rh-negative donor blood. This technique prevents death of erythroblastotic babies who are very anemic. It also avoids brain damage by preventing or controlling hyperbilirubinemia.

When the placenta separates at birth (see Fig. 8–9*F*), the mother often receives a small transfusion of fetal blood into her circulation from ruptured fetal chorionic vessels. If she is Rh-negative and the infant Rh-positive, the fetal red cells can stimulate a permanent antibody response in the mother. These fetal red blood cells can be destroyed rapidly by giving the mother high-titer anti-Rh antibody. In this way, she does not become sensitized. For more information on hemolytic disease of the newborn, see Thompson and Thompson (1980).

Wastes. The major waste product, carbon dioxide, diffuses across the placenta even more rapidly than oxygen. Urea and uric acid pass the placental membrane by simple diffusion.

Drugs. Almost all drugs cross the placenta freely; some cause congenital malformations (see Chapter 9). Fetal drug addiction may occur following maternal use of drugs such as heroin, resulting in withdrawal symptoms. Except for the muscle relaxants, such as succinylcholine and curare, most agents used for the management of labor readily cross the placenta. These drugs may cause respiratory depression of the newborn infant. All sedatives and analgesics affect the fetus to some degree.

Infectious Agents. Rubella, cytomegalovirus, and coxsackie viruses and those associated with variola, varicella, measles, encephalitis, and poliomyelitis may pass through the placental membrane and cause fetal infection. In some cases (e.g., *rubella virus*), congenital malformations may be produced (see Chapter 9).

ENDOCRINE SECRETION

The *syncytiotrophoblast* synthesizes the following hormones:

Protein Hormones. The two well-documented protein products of the placenta are: (1) *human chorionic gonadotropin* (hCG) and (2) human chorionic somatomammotropin (hCS) or human placental lactogen (hPL).

Steroid Hormones. Estrogens and progesterones are the only steroid hormones known to be secreted by the placenta.

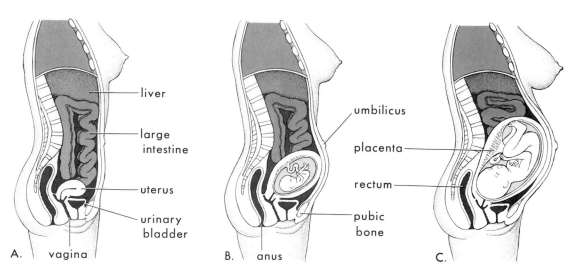

Figure 8–8 Drawings of sagittal sections of a female. *A*, Not pregnant. *B*, 20 weeks pregnant. *C*, 30 weeks pregnant. Note that as the fetus enlarges, the uterus increases in size and its superior part rises out of the pelvic cavity to accommodate the rapidly growing fetus. The mother's intestines are displaced by the growth of the fetus and uterus and her abdominal skin and muscles are greatly stretched.

UTERINE GROWTH DURING PREGNANCY

The uterus normally lies entirely in the pelvis (Fig. 8–8A). During pregnancy the uterus expands as the fetus grows, and rises out of the pelvic cavity to the level of the mother's umbilicus (navel) by about 20 weeks (Fig. 8–8B). By 28 to 30 weeks, the uterus in the pregnant female occupies a large part of the abdominopelvic cavity and reaches the epigastric region (Fig. 8–8C).

PARTURITION OR LABOR

The *birth process* by which the fetus, placenta, and fetal membranes are expelled from the mother's reproductive tract (Figs. 8–9 and 8–10) is called *parturition* (labor, or childbirth).

The onset of labor is caused mainly by hormonal influences (e.g., oxytocin). Although occurring in a continuous sequence, labor is divided into three stages for convenience of description.

The *first stage of labor* is the dilatation stage. The amnion and chorion are forced into the cervical canal by contractions of the uterus (Fig. 8–9A). The cervix dilates slowly, and when it is fully dilated, or even before, the amniotic and chorionic sacs rupture, allowing the fluid to escape. During the *second stage of labor*, the expulsion stage, the contractions of the uterus become stronger and are aided by voluntary contractions of the maternal abdominal muscles. The baby is forced through the cervical canal and the vagina (Fig. 8–9B to E). The *third stage of labor* is the interval from birth to the expulsion of the placenta and membranes, which are now referred to as the "afterbirth."

The placenta separates through the spongy layer of the decidua basalis. After delivery of the baby, the uterus continues to contract. As a result, a hematoma forms behind the placenta (Fig. 8–9F) and separates it from the

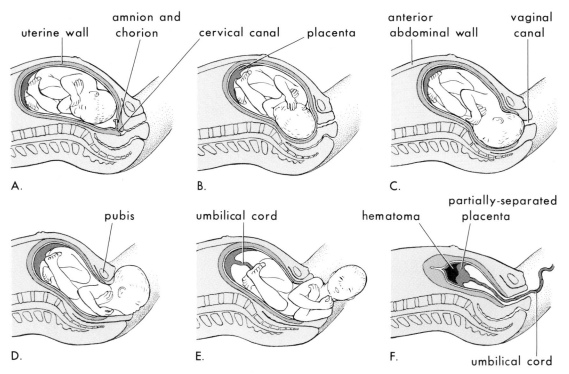

Figure 8–9   Drawings illustrating the processes of birth. *A* and *B*, The cervix is dilating during the first stage of labor as the result of the amnion and chorion being forced into the cervical canal. *C* to *E*, The fetus passes through the cervix and vagina during the second stage of labor. *F*, As the uterus contracts during the third stage of labor, the placenta folds up and pulls away from the uterine wall. Separation of the placenta results in bleeding, forming a large hematoma. Later the placenta and its associated membranes are expelled from the uterus (not shown) by further uterine contractions.

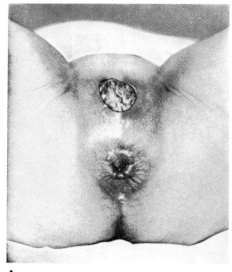

Figure 8–10 Photographs illustrating delivery of the baby's head during the second stage of labor. *A*, The head distends the mother's perineum, and part of the scalp becomes visible; this is called "crowning." *B*, The perineum slips back over the face. *C*, The head is delivered; subsequently the body of the fetus is expelled. (From Greenhill, J. B., and Friedman, E. A.: *Biological Principles and Modern Practice of Obstetrics*. Philadelphia, W. B. Saunders Company, 1974.)

A

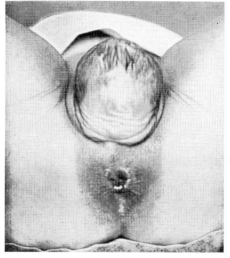

B

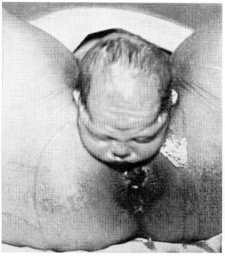

C

decidua basalis. After delivery of the placenta, the uterine contractions constrict the spiral arteries that formerly supplied the intervillous spaces. These persistent contractions, which are almost "tonic" in nature, prevent excessive bleeding from the placental site.

THE FULL-TERM PLACENTA

The placenta (Gr. *plakous*, "a flat cake") commonly has the form of a flat circular or oval disc (Fig. 8–11) with a diameter of 15 to 20 cm and a thickness of 2 to 3 cm. The placenta weighs 500 to 600 gm, usually about one-sixth the weight of the fetus. The margins of the placenta are continuous with the ruptured amniotic and chorionic sacs (Figs. 8–5 and 8–11*A* and *C*). Several variations in placental shape occur, e.g., accessory placenta (Fig. 8–12), bidiscoid placenta, and diffuse placenta.

Maternal Surface (Fig. 8–11*A*). The characteristic cobblestone appearance of this surface is caused by the 10 to 38 cotyledons. The surface of the cotyledons is usually cov-

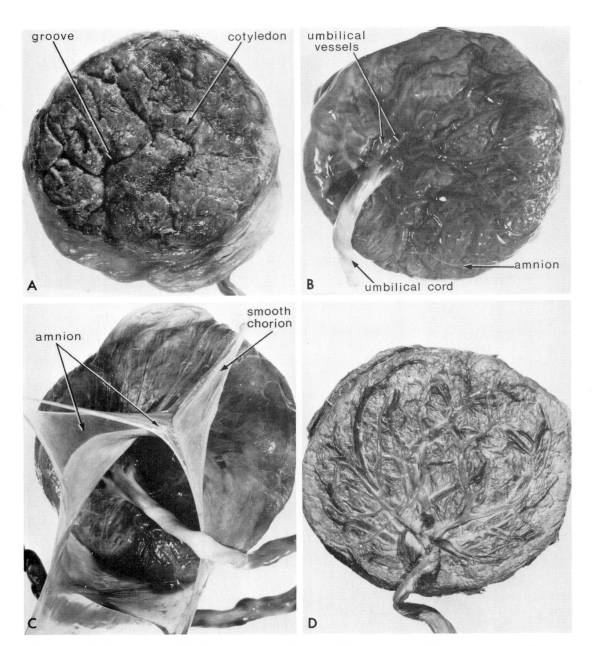

Figure 8–11   Photographs of full-term placentas. *About one-third actual size. A,* Maternal (or uterine) surface, showing cotyledons and grooves. *B,* Fetal (or amniotic) surface, showing the blood vessels running under the amnion and converging to form the umbilical vessels at the attachment of the umbilical cord. *C,* The amnion and smooth chorion are arranged to show that they are (1) fused and (2) continuous with the margins of the placenta. *D,* Placenta with a marginal attachment of the cord, often called a battledore placenta because of its resemblance to the bat used in the medieval game of battledore and shuttlecock.

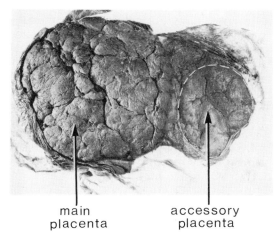

main placenta   accessory placenta

Figure 8–12 Photograph of the maternal surface of a full-term placenta with an associated accessory placenta. *About one-quarter actual size.*

ered by thin grayish shreds of decidua basalis. Most of the decidua, however, is temporarily retained in the uterus and shed with subsequent uterine bleeding.

Fetal Surface (Fig. 8–11*B*). The umbilical cord attaches to this surface, and its amniotic covering is continuous with the amnion adherent to this surface of the placenta. The vessels radiating from the umbilical cord are clearly visible through the smooth transparent amnion.

THE UMBILICAL CORD

The attachment of the umbilical cord is usually near the center of the placenta (Fig. 8–11*B*), but it may be located anywhere (e.g., at the edge, Fig. 8–11*D*). The cord is usually 1 to 2 cm in diameter and 30 to 90 cm in length.

The umbilical cord usually contains two arteries and one vein. These vessels are surrounded by mucoid connective tissue, often called Wharton's jelly (Fig. 8–13*A*). Because the umbilical vein is longer than the arteries and the vessels are longer than the cord, twisting and bending of the vessels is common. The vessels frequently form loops, producing so-called *false knots* which are of no significance. True knots in the cord may be hazardous to the fetus (Fig. 8–14). Simple looping of the cord around the fetus occasionally occurs (Fig. 8–15). In about one-fifth of all deliveries, the cord is looped once around the neck. In up to 1 per cent of newborns, only one umbilical artery is present (Fig. 8–13*B*), a condition often associated with fetal abnormalities, particularly of the cardiovascular system.

THE AMNION AND AMNIOTIC FLUID

The amnion is a *membranous sac* that surrounds the embryo and later the fetus (Figs.

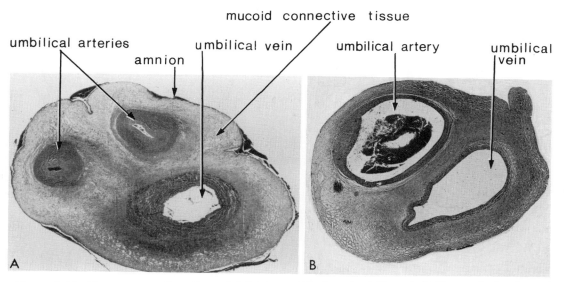

mucoid connective tissue

umbilical arteries   amnion   umbilical vein   umbilical artery   umbilical vein

A   B

Figure 8–13 Transverse sections through full-term umbilical cords. *A*, Normal. *B*, Abnormal, showing only one artery. (×3.) (From Javert, C. T.: *Spontaneous and Habitual Abortion.* Copyright © 1957 by McGraw-Hill, Inc. Used by permission of McGraw-Hill Book Company.)

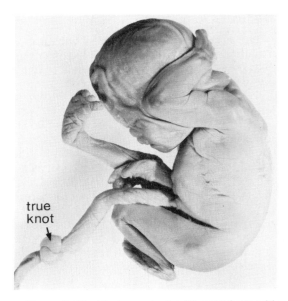

Figure 8–14 Photograph of a 20-week fetus with a true knot (arrow) in the umbilical cord. *Half actual size.* The diameter of the cord is greater in the portion closest to the fetus, indicating that there was an obstruction of blood flow in the umbilical arteries.

8–15 and 8–16). Formation of the amniotic cavity and early development of the amnion are described in Chapter 4. Because the amnion is attached to the margins of the embryonic disc (Fig. 8–16A), its junction with the embryo becomes located on the ventral surface as a result of folding of the embryo (see Chapter 6). As the amniotic sac enlarges, it gradually sheaths the umbilical cord, forming its epithelial covering (Fig. 8–16C and D).

Origin of Amniotic Fluid. Most fluid is derived from the maternal blood. Later, the fetus also makes a contribution by excreting urine into the amniotic fluid.

Amniotic fluid is normally swallowed by the fetus and absorbed by the gastrointestinal tract. In fetal conditions such as renal agenesis (absence of kidneys) or urethral obstruction, the volume of amniotic fluid may be abnormally small (oligohydramnios). An excess of amniotic fluid (polyhydramnios) may occur when the fetus does not drink the usual amount of fluid. This condition is often associated with malformations of the central nervous system, e.g., anencephaly and hy-

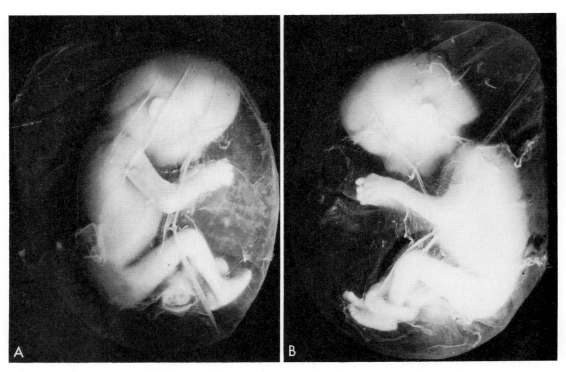

Figure 8–15 Photographs of a 12-week fetus within the amniotic sac. *Actual size.* Note the umbilical cord looped around the left foot of the fetus. Coiling of the cord around parts of the fetus affects development of them only when the coils are so tight that the circulation to them is affected.

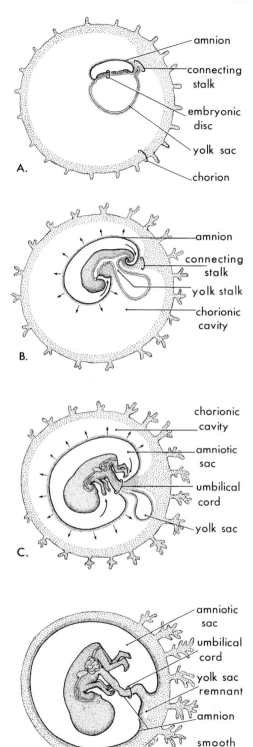

A.

amnion

connecting
stalk

embryonic
disc

yolk sac

chorion

B.

amnion

connecting
stalk

yolk stalk

chorionic
cavity

C.

chorionic
cavity

amniotic
sac

umbilical
cord

yolk sac

D.

amniotic
sac

umbilical
cord

yolk sac
remnant

amnion

smooth
chorion

Figure 8–16 Drawings illustrating how the amnion becomes the outer covering of the umbilical cord and how the yolk sac is partially incorporated into the embryo as the primitive gut. *A*, Three weeks. *B*, Four weeks. *C*, 10 weeks. *D*, 20 weeks.

drocephalus (see Chapter 17). In other malformations, such as esophageal or duodenal atresia (see Chapter 13), amniotic fluid accumulates because it is unable to pass to the intestine for absorption.

Significance of Amniotic Fluid. The embryo, suspended by the umbilical cord, floats freely in amniotic fluid. This buoyant medium (1) permits symmetrical growth and development of the embryo; (2) prevents adherence of the amnion to the embryo; (3) *cushions the embryo against jolts* by distributing impacts the mother may receive; (4) *helps to control the embryo's body temperature* by maintaining a relatively constant temperature; and (5) enables the fetus to move freely, thus aiding musculoskeletal development.

THE YOLK SAC

Early development of the yolk sac is described in Chapters 4 and 5. By nine weeks, the yolk sac has shrunk to a pear-shaped remnant, about 5 mm in diameter, which is connected to the midgut by the narrow yolk stalk (Fig. 8–16*C*). Although the human yolk sac is nonfunctional as far as yolk storage is concerned, its development is essential for several reasons. (1) It appears to have a role in the transfer of nutrients to the embryo during the second and third weeks while the uteroplacental circulation is being established. (2) Blood develops on the walls of the yolk sac beginning in the third week and continues to form here until hemopoietic activity begins in the liver during the sixth week. (3) During the fourth week, the dorsal part of the yolk sac is incorporated into the embryo as the primitive gut (see Fig. 6–1); this gives rise to the epithelium of the trachea, bronchi, and lungs, and of the digestive tract. (4) Primordial germ cells appear in the wall of the yolk sac early in the third week and subsequently migrate to the developing sex glands or gonads, where they become the primitive germ cells (spermatogonia or oogonia—see Chapter 14).

Fate of the Yolk Sac (Fig. 8–16). The yolk sac shrinks as pregnancy advances and eventually becomes very small. The yolk stalk usually detaches from the gut by the end of the fifth week. In about 2 per cent of adults, the intra-abdominal part of the yolk stalk persists as a diverticulum of the ileum known as *Meckel's diverticulum* (see Chapter 13).

THE ALLANTOIS

The early development of the allantois is described in Chapter 5. Although the allantois does not function in human embryos, it is important for two reasons: (1) blood formation occurs in its walls during the first two months; and (2) its blood vessels become the umbilical vein and arteries (Fig. 8–17A and B).

Fate of the Allantois. During the second month, the extraembryonic portion of the allantois degenerates. The intraembryonic portion of the allantois runs from the umbilicus to the urinary bladder with which it is continuous (Fig. 8–17B). As the bladder enlarges, the allantois involutes to form a thick tube called the *urachus*. After birth, the urachus becomes a fibrous cord called the *median umbilical ligament* (Fig. 8–17D).

MULTIPLE PREGNANCY

Multiple births are more common nowadays, owing to overstimulation of ovulation that occurs when human gonadotropins are administered to women with *ovulatory failure* (failure of ovulation).

TWINS

Twins may originate from two zygotes (Fig. 8–18), in which case they are *dizygotic*, nonidentical or fraternal, or from one zygote (Fig. 8–19), i.e., *monozygotic* or identical. Twins occur about once in 80 to 90 pregnancies; about two-thirds of the total number are dizygotic twins. In addition, the rate of monozygotic twinning shows little variation with the mother's age, whereas dizygotic twinning increases with maternal age.

There is a tendency for dizygotic, but not monozygotic, twins to repeat in families. It has also been found that if the firstborn are twins, a repetition of twinning or some other form of multiple birth is about five times more likely to occur at the next pregnancy than it is in the general population.

Dizygotic Twins (Fig. 8–18). Because they result from the fertilization of two ova

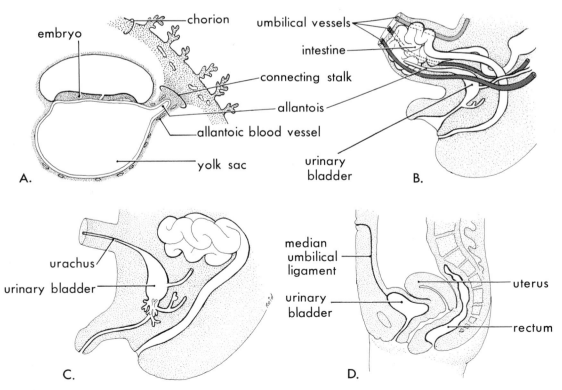

Figure 8–17 Drawings illustrating the development and usual fate of the allantois. *A*, Three weeks. *B*, Nine weeks. *C*, Three-month male. *D*, Adult female.

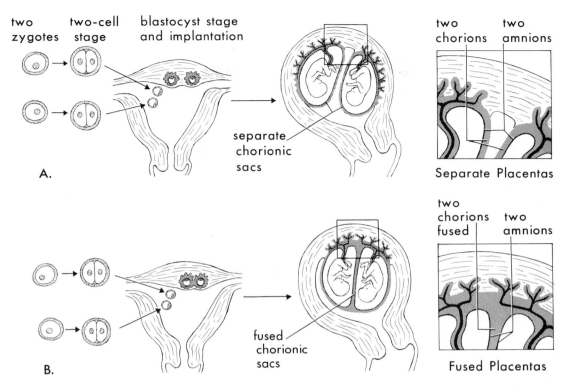

Figure 8–18 Diagrams illustrating *how dizygotic twins develop* from two zygotes. The relations of the fetal membranes and placentas are shown for instances in which, *A*, the blastocysts implant separately, and *B*, the blastocysts implant close together. In both cases there are two amnions and two chorions, and the placentas may be separate or fused.

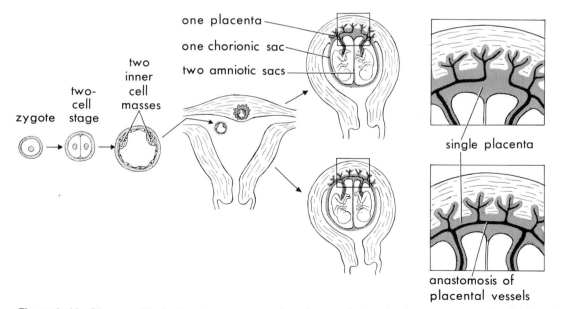

Figure 8–19 Diagrams illustrating *how monozygotic twins usually develop* from one zygote by division of the inner cell mass. Such twins always have separate amnions, a single chorion, and a common placenta.

by different sperms, the twins may be of the same sex or of different sexes. For the same reason, they are no more alike genetically than brothers or sisters born at different times. Dizygotic twins always have two amnions and two chorions, but the chorions and placentas may be fused.

Monozygotic Twins (Figs. 8–19 and 8–20). Because they result from the fertilization of one ovum, the twins are (1) of the same sex, (2) genetically identical, and (3) very similar in physical appearance. Physical differences between identical twins are caused by environmental factors, e.g., anastomosis of placental vessels resulting in differences in blood supply from the placenta.

Monozygotic twinning usually begins around the end of the first week and results from division of the inner cell mass into two embryonic primordia. Subsequently, two identical embryos, each in its own amniotic sac, develop within one chorionic sac. The

twins have a common placenta and often some placental vessels join.

Very rarely, later division of embryonic cells results in monozygotic twins which are in one amniotic and one chorionic sac (Fig. 8–20A). Such twins are rarely delivered alive because the umbilical cords are frequently entangled so that circulation ceases and one or both fetuses die.

Conjoined Twins (Figs. 8–20B and C and 8–21). If the embryonic disc does not divide completely, various types of conjoined twins may form. These are named according to the regions that are attached, e.g., "thoracopagus," which indicates that there is anterior union of the thoracic regions.

OTHER MULTIPLE BIRTHS

Triplets occur once in about 8100 pregnancies and may be derived from (1) one zygote and be identical, (2) two zygotes and consist

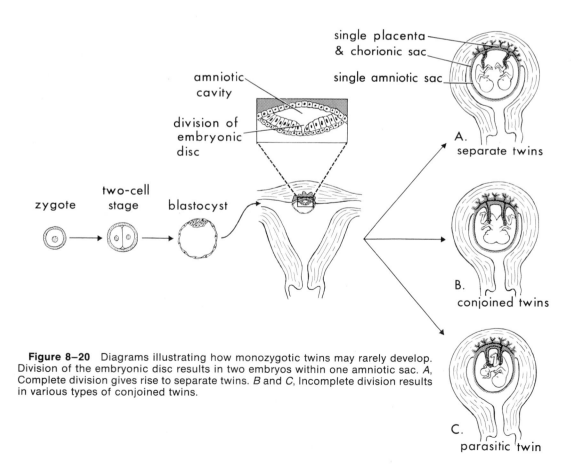

Figure 8–20 Diagrams illustrating how monozygotic twins may rarely develop. Division of the embryonic disc results in two embryos within one amniotic sac. *A,* Complete division gives rise to separate twins. *B* and *C,* Incomplete division results in various types of conjoined twins.

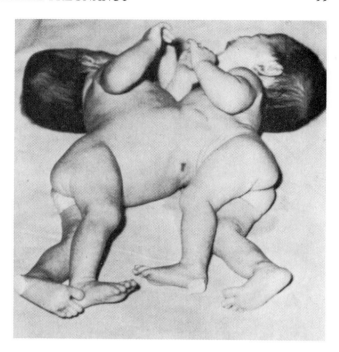

Figure 8–21 *A*, Photograph of newborn conjoined twins showing ventral union (thoracopagus). *B*, The twins about four years after separation. (From de Vries, P. A.: Case history—the San Francisco twins; *in* Bergsma, D. [Ed.]: *Conjoined Twins. Birth Defects. Original Article Series*, Vol. III, No. 1, April, 1967. © The National Foundation, New York.)

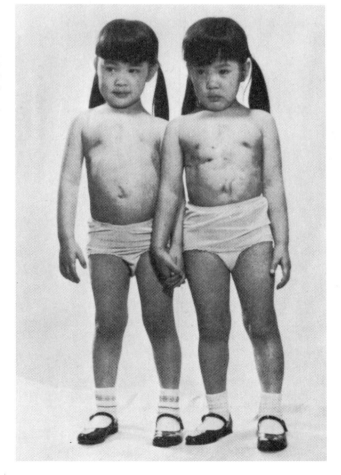

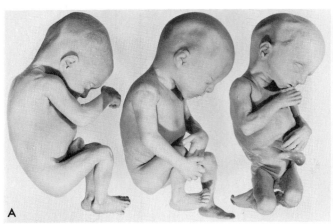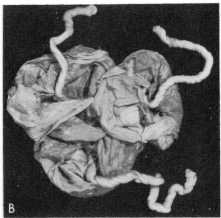

Figure 8–22   *A*, Photograph of 20-week triplets: monozygotic male twins (left) and a single female (right). *B*, Photograph of their fused placentas shows the twin placenta with two amnions (left) and the single placenta (upper right).

of identical twins and a single infant (Fig. 8–22), or (3) three zygotes and be of the same sex or of different sexes. In the last case, the infants are no more similar than those from three separate pregnancies.

Similar possible combinations occur in *quadruplets, quintuplets, sextuplets, septuplets,* and so forth. Types of multiple births higher than triplets are normally very rare, but they have occurred more often in recent years following the administration of gonadotropins to women with ovulatory failure.

SUMMARY

In addition to the embryo, the zygote gives rise to the fetal membranes and most of the placenta. The placenta consists of two parts: (1) a fetal portion derived from the *villous chorion,* and (2) a maternal portion formed by the *decidua basalis.* The two parts work together in placental transfer.

The fetal circulation is separated from the maternal circulation by a thin layer of fetal tissues known as the *placental membrane.* It is a permeable membrane that allows water, oxygen, other nutrient substances, hormones, and noxious agents to pass from the mother to the embryo (fetus). Some products of excretion pass from the embryo (fetus) to the mother through the placental membrane.

The principal activities of the placenta are (1) metabolism, (2) transfer, and (3) endocrine secretion.

The fetal membranes and placenta(s) in multiple pregnancy vary considerably depending on the derivation of the embryos and when division of the embryonic cells occurs. *The common type of twins is dizygotic*, with two amnions, two chorions, and two placentas which may or may not be fused. About a third of all twins are derived from one zygote; these *monozygotic twins* commonly have two amnions, one chorion, and one placenta. Other types of multiple birth (triplets and so forth) may be derived from one or more zygotes.

Although the yolk sac and allantois are vestigial structures, their formation is essential for normal embryonic development. Both are important early sites of blood formation, and part of the yolk sac is incorporated into the embryo as the primitive gut.

The amnion forms a sac for amniotic fluid and provides a covering for the umbilical cord. The amniotic fluid provides a protective buffer for the embryo, room for fetal movements, and assistance in the regulation of fetal body temperature.

SUGGESTED SUPPLEMENTARY READING

Boyd, J. D., and Hamilton, W. J.: *The Human Placenta.*
   Cambridge, W. Heffer and Sons Ltd., 1970.
*An excellent reference text on the placenta. The electron
micrographs and color illustrations are superb.*

Thompson, J. S., and Thompson, M. W.: *Genetics In
   Medicine*, 3rd ed. Philadelphia, W. B. Saunders Company, 1980, pp. 214–216.
*A very good account of hemolytic disease of the newborn
and the Rh blood group system.*

9

CONGENITAL MALFORMATIONS AND THEIR CAUSES

Congenital malformations are anatomical or structural abnormalities present at birth. They may be macroscopic (visible with the unaided eye) or microscopic (visible with a microscope), on the surface or within the body.

About 20 per cent of deaths in the neonatal period (the period just before and just after birth) are attributed to congenital malformations. Congenital malformations are the largest single cause of severe illness and death during infancy and childhood.

The branch of embryology dealing with abnormal development and congenital malformations is called *teratology*. It is estimated that nearly 10 per cent of human developmental abnormalities result from the actions of drugs, viruses, and other environmental factors. About three per cent of liveborn infants have one or more congenital malformations, and this figure is doubled by the end of the first year owing to the discovery of malformations that were indiscernible at birth.

Although it is customary to divide the causes of congenital malformations into (1) *genetic factors* (chromosomal abnormalities or mutant genes) and (2) *environmental factors*, it is not usually possible to separate clearly the factors which cause the abnormalities. Most common malformations result from an interaction of genetic and environmental factors (*multifactorial inheritance*).

MALFORMATIONS CAUSED BY GENETIC FACTORS

Numerically, genetic factors are probably most important as causes of congenital malformations. Genetic factors initiate mechanisms of malformation by biochemical or other means at the subcellular, cellular, or tissue level. The mechanism initiated by the genetic factor may be identical with or similar to the causal mechanism initiated by a *teratogen* (e.g., a drug or a virus).

Chromosomal abnormalities are present in about 1 of 200 newborn infants. Chromosome complements are subject to two kinds of changes: (1) numerical and (2) structural.

NUMERICAL CHROMOSOMAL ABNORMALITIES

Numerical abnormalities of chromosomes usually arise as the result of nondisjunction. This is an error in cell division in which there is failure of the paired chromosomes or sister chromatids to separate or disjoin at anaphase. This error may occur during a mitotic division or during the first or second meiotic division (Fig. 9–1).

Normally, the chromosomes exist in pairs; human females have 22 pairs of autosomes plus two X chromosomes, and males have 22 pairs of autosomes plus one X and one Y chromosome (Fig. 9–2).

Changes in chromosome number usually represent *aneuploidy*, which is any deviation from the diploid number of 46 chromosomes. The cells may be hypodiploid (usually 45) or hyperdiploid (usually 47 to 49).

Monosomy. Most embryos lacking a sex chromosome die, but some survive and develop characteristics of *Turner syndrome* (Fig. 9–3).

Embryos missing an autosome or ordinary chromosome usually die; hence monosomy of an autosome is extremely rare in living persons.

Trisomy. If three chromosomes are present instead of the usual pair, the disorder is called trisomy. The usual cause of trisomy is nondisjunction or nonseparation of chromosomes, resulting in a germ cell with 24 instead of 23 chromosomes (see Fig. 9–1). If this cell

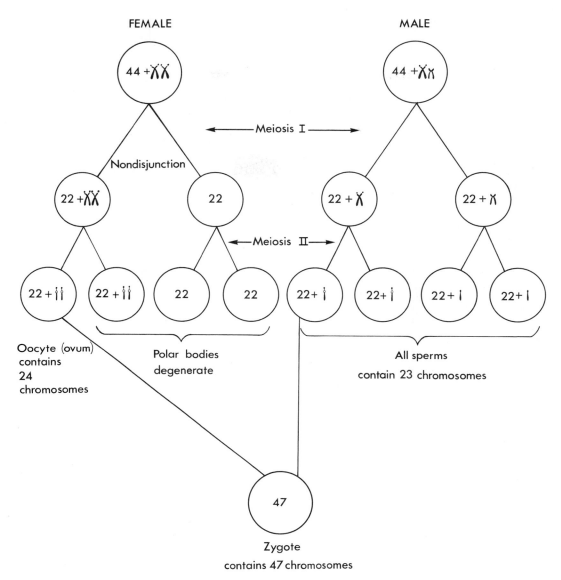

Figure 9–1 Diagram showing the first meiotic nondisjunction in a female resulting in an abnormal oocyte (ovum) with 24 chromosomes and how subsequent fertilization by a normal sperm produce a zygote with 47 chromosomes.

is subsequently involved in fertilization, a zygote with 47 chromosomes forms.

Trisomy of the autosomes is primarily associated with three syndromes (Table 9–1). The most common condition is trisomy 21 or Down syndrome (Fig. 9–4), in which three number 21 chromosomes are present. Trisomy 18 (Fig. 9–5) and trisomy 13 (Fig. 9–6) are less common.

Autosomal trisomies occur with increasing frequency as maternal age increases, particularly trisomy 21, which is present once in about 2000 births in mothers under 25, but one in about 100 mothers over the age of 40.

Trisomy of the sex chromosomes is a relatively common condition (Table 9–2); however, because there are no characteristic physical findings in infants or children, it is rarely detected until adolescence (Fig. 9–7). *Sex chromatin patterns* are useful in detect-

Text continued on page 108

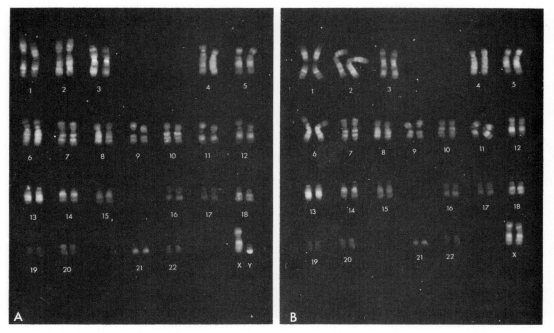

Figure 9–2 *A,* Normal male karyotype with Giemsa banding (G banding). *B,* Similar bands in a normal female karyotype. Caspersson et al. (1970) observed that when chromosomes are stained with quinacrine mustard or related compounds and examined by fluorescent microscopy, each pair of chromosomes stains in a distinctive pattern of bright and dim bands, called Q bands. They form the basis of the classification of chromosomes. (Courtesy of Dr. M. Ray, Department of Pediatrics, Division of Genetics, and Department of Anatomy, University of Manitoba and the Health Sciences Centre, Winnipeg, Canada.)

TABLE 9–1   TRISOMY OF THE AUTOSOMES

Disorder	Incidence	Usual Characteristics
Trisomy 21 or Down syndrome*	1:800	Mental deficiency; hypotonia; flat nasal bridge; upward slant to palpebral fissures; protruding tongue; simian crease; congenital heart defects.
Trisomy 18†	1:8000	Mental deficiency; growth retardation; prominent occiput; short sternum; ventricular septal defect; micrognathia; low-set malformed ears; flexed fingers.
Trisomy 13†	1:7000	Mental deficiency; sloping forehead; malformed ears; microphthalmos; bilateral cleft lip and/or palate; polydactyly; posterior prominence of the heels.

* The importance of this disorder in the overall problem of mental retardation is indicated by the fact that persons with Down syndrome represent 10 to 15 per cent of institutionalized mental defectives. Down syndrome is by far the most common and best known of the chromosomal disorders. The old name "mongolism," now rarely used, refers to the somewhat oriental appearance of the face caused by the slanting appearance of the eyes.

† Infants with this syndrome rarely survive beyond a few months.

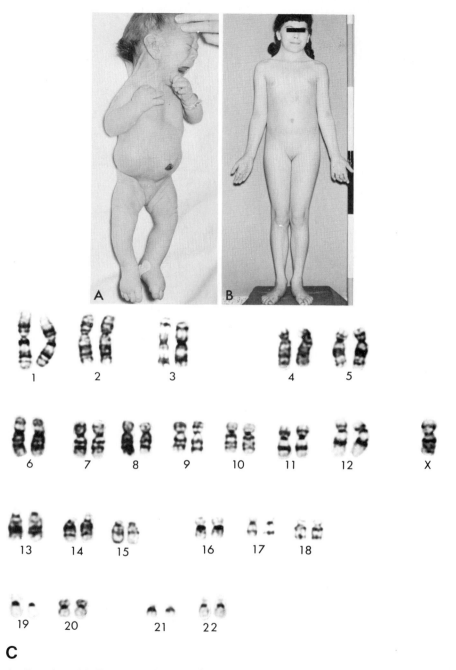

Figure 9–3 Females with Turner syndrome (XO sex chromosome complement). *A*, Newborn infant. Note the webbed neck. *B*, 13-year-old girl showing the classic features of the syndrome: short stature, webbed neck, absence of sexual maturation, and broad, shield-like chest with widely spaced nipples. (From Moore, K. L.: *The Sex Chromatin*. Philadelphia, W. B. Saunders Company, 1966.) *C*, G-banding karyotype. Note the presence of only one X chromosome. (Courtesy of Dr. M. Ray, Department of Pediatrics, Division of Genetics, and Department of Anatomy, University of Manitoba and the Health Sciences Centre, Winnipeg, Canada.)

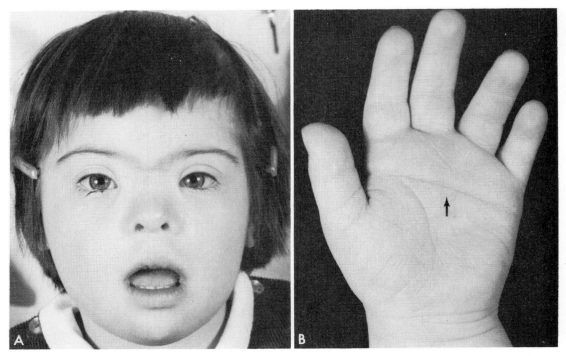

Figure 9–4 *A,* Photograph of a 3½-year-old girl, showing the typical facial appearance associated with Down syndrome. Note the flat, broad face, oblique palpebral fissures, epicanthus, speckling of the iris, and furrowed lower lip. *B,* The typical short, broad hand of this child shows the characteristic single transverse palmar or simian crease (arrow). About half the palms of patients with Down syndrome have a single crease, and *about 1 per cent of normal persons have this unusual palm pattern.*
(From Bartalos, M., and Baramki, T. A.: *Medical Cytogenetics.* Baltimore, Williams & Wilkins Co., 1967.)

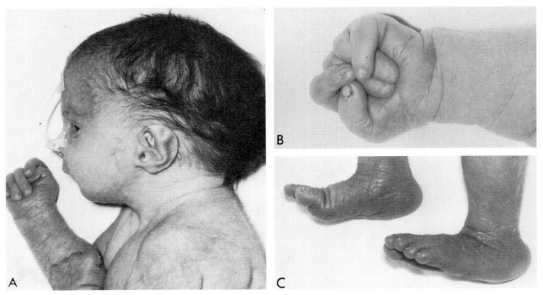

Figure 9–5 Photographs of an infant with trisomy 18 syndrome. *A,* Prominent occiput and malformed ears. *B,* Typical flexed fingers. *C,* So-called rocker-bottom feet, showing posterior prominences of the heels. Probably 95 per cent of trisomy 18 fetuses abort spontaneously. The mean survival time of those who live after birth is two months. (Courtesy of Dr. Harry Medovy, Children's Centre, Winnipeg.)

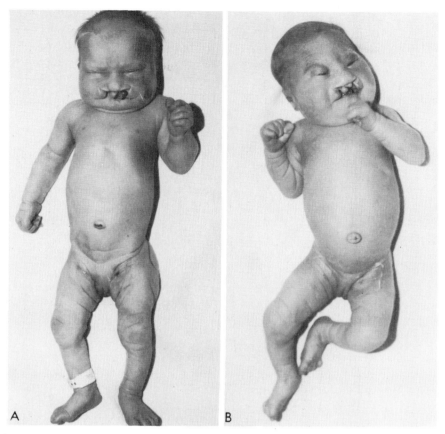

Figure 9–6   Female infants with trisomy 13 syndrome. Note bilateral cleft lip, sloping forehead, and rocker-bottom feet. Trisomy 13 is a severe disorder and is fatal within the first month in about half of the liveborn infants. (From Smith, D. W.: *Amer. J. Obstet. Gynec. 90*:1055, 1964.)

TABLE 9–2   TRISOMY OF THE SEX CHROMOSOMES

Chromosome Complement*	Phenotype†	Incidence	Usual Characteristics
47,XXX	Female	1:1000	Normal in appearance; fertile; may be mentally retarded.
47,XXY	Male	1:1000	Klinefelter syndrome: small testes, hyalinization of seminiferous tubules. aspermatogenesis; may be mentally retarded.
47,XYY	Male	1:1000	Normal in appearance, often tall; may have personality disorder.

* The number designates the total number of chromosomes, including the sex chromosomes shown after the comma.
† A person's outward appearance resulting from his or her genetic constitution or genotype.

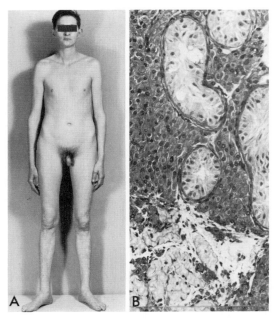

Figure 9–7 *A,* Adult male with XXY Klinefelter syndrome. Note the relatively long lower limbs and normal trunk length. *B,* Section of a testicular biopsy showing some seminiferous tubules without germ cells and others that are hyalinized. (From Ferguson-Smith, M. A.: *in* Moore, K. L. [Ed.]: *The Sex Chromatin.* Philadelphia, W. B. Saunders Company, 1966.)

ing trisomy of the sex chromosomes because two masses of sex chromatin are present in XXX females (Fig. 9–8*C*), and cells of XXY males are chromatin-positive.

Tetrasomy and Pentasomy. Some persons, usually mentally retarded, have four or five sex chromosomes. Usually the greater the number of X chromosomes present, the greater the severity of the mental retardation and physical impairment. The extra sex chromosomes do not accentuate male or female characteristics.

STRUCTURAL CHROMOSOMAL ABNORMALITIES

Most structural abnormalities result from chromosome breaks induced by environmental factors, e.g., radiation, drugs, and viruses. The type of abnormality which results depends upon what happens to the broken pieces of chromosomes (Figs. 9–9 and 9–10). For details about these chromosome abnormalities, see Moore (1982) and Thompson and Thompson (1980).

MALFORMATIONS CAUSED BY MUTANT GENES

About 10 to 15 per cent of congenital malformations are caused by mutant genes. Because these malformations are inherited according to mendelian laws, predictions can be made about the probability of their occurrence in the affected person's children and other relatives. Although a great many genes mutate (undergo changes), most mutant genes do not cause congenital malformations. Examples of *dominantly inherited* congenital malformations are achondroplasia (Fig. 9–11) and polydactyly or extra digits (see Chapter 16). Other malformations are attributed to *autosomal recessive inheritance,* e.g., microcephaly (see Chapter 17).

A mutation usually involves a loss or a change of the function of a gene (Thompson and Thompson, 1980). Because a random change is unlikely to lead to an improvement in development, most mutations are deleterious and some are lethal.

The mutation rate can be increased by a number of environmental agents, e.g., large doses of radiation and many chemicals, especially carcinogenic (cancer-inducing) ones.

MALFORMATIONS CAUSED BY ENVIRONMENTAL FACTORS

The human embryo is well protected in the uterus, but certain agents, called *teratogens,* may induce congenital malformations when the tissues and organs are developing. The embryonic organs are most sensitive to noxious agents during periods of rapid differentiation.

Six mechanisms can cause congenital malformations: (1) too little growth, (2) too little resorption, (3) too much resorption, (4) re-

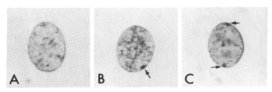

Figure 9–8 Oral epithelial nuclei stained with cresylecht violet (×2000). *A,* From normal male. No sex chromatin is visible (chromatin-negative). *B,* From normal female. The arrow indicates a typical mass of sex chromatin (chromatin-positive). *C,* From female with XXX trisomy. The arrows indicate two masses of sex chromatin. (*A* and *B* from Moore, K. L., and Barr, M. L.: *Lancet* 2:57, 1955.)

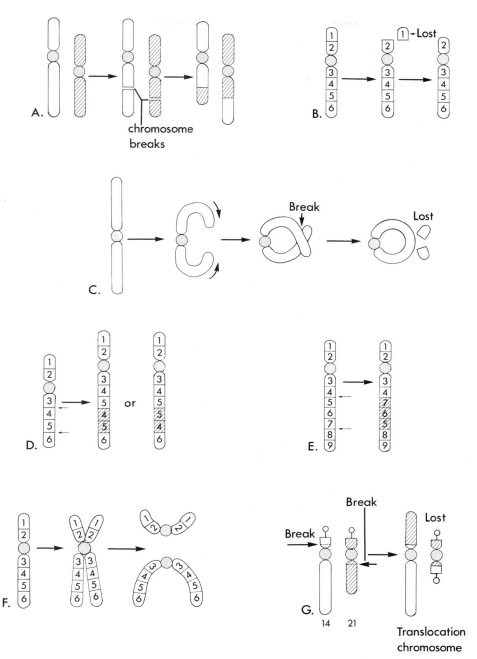

Figure 9–9 Diagrams illustrating structural abnormalities of chromosomes. *A*, Reciprocal translocation. *B*, Terminal deletion. *C*, Ring. *D*, Duplication. *E*, Paracentric inversion. *F*, Isochromosome. *G*, Robertsonian translocation.

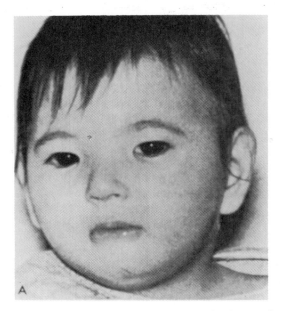
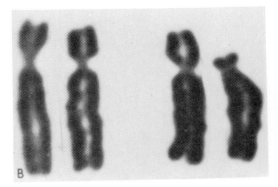

Figure 9–10   *A*, Male infant with cri du chat syndrome, showing the typical moon-faced appearance. *B*, The infant's chromosomes show a deletion of chromosome number 5 (*arrow*) on the right. This syndrome received its name because of the resemblance of the cry of an affected child to the mewing of a cat. These children are severely retarded mentally. (Courtesy of Dr. J. de Grouchy, Paris.)

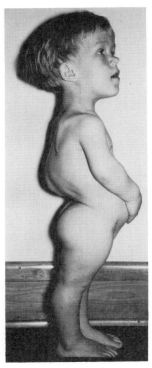

Figure 9–11   A child with achondroplasia, showing short limbs, relatively large head, thoracic kyphosis, and protrusion of the abdomen. (Courtesy of Dr. Harry Medovy, Children's Centre, Winnipeg.)

sorption in the wrong location, (5) normal growth in an abnormal position, and (6) overgrowth of a tissue or structure.

Sensitive or Critical Periods. Environmental disturbances during the first two weeks after fertilization may interfere with implantation of the blastocyst or cause early death and/or abortion of the embryo. Development of the embryo is most easily disturbed during the *organogenetic period*, particularly from days 15 to 60. During this period, teratogenic agents are most likely to produce congenital malformations. Each organ has a critical period during which its development may be deranged (Fig. 9–12). Physiological defects, minor morphological abnormalities, and functional disturbances, particularly of the central nervous system, are likely to result from disturbances during the fetal period.

The most critical period in the development of an embryo or in the growth of a particular tissue or organ is during the *time of most rapid cell division*. The critical period varies in accordance with the timing and duration of the period of increasing cell numbers for the tissue or organ concerned.

The critical period for brain growth and development extends into infancy. The brain is

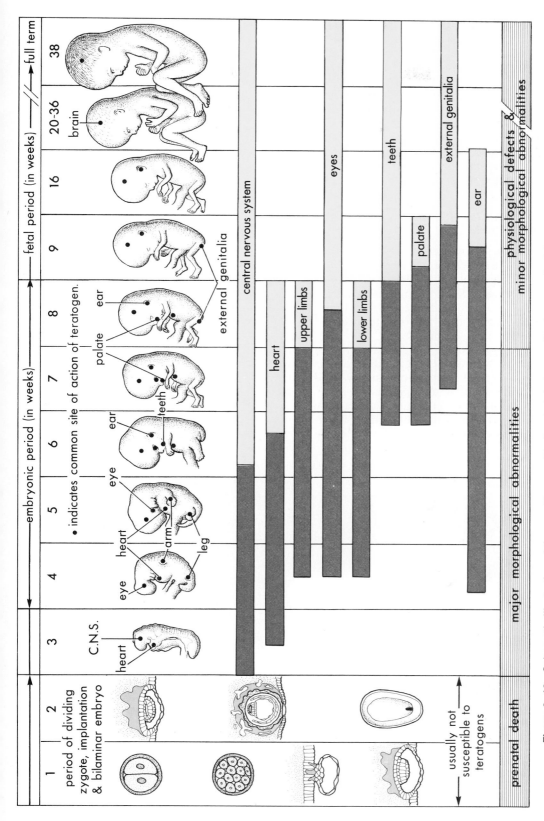

Figure 9–12 Schematic illustration of the sensitive or critical periods in human development. Red denotes highly sensitive periods; yellow indicates stages that are less sensitive to teratogens. Note that each organ or structure has a critical period during which its development may be deranged, and that physiological defects, functional disturbances, and minor morphological changes are likely to result from disturbances during the fetal period. Severe mental retardation may result from exposure of the developing human to high levels of radiation during the 8- to 16-week period.

growing rapidly at birth and continues to do so throughout the first two years after birth.

Tooth development also continues long after birth (see Chapter 19); hence, development of the permanent teeth may be affected by *tetracyclines* from 18 weeks (prenatal) to 16 years.

The skeletal system has a prolonged critical period of development, extending into adolescence and early adulthood. Hence, growth of skeletal tissues provides a very good gauge of general growth.

TERATOGENS AND HUMAN MALFORMATIONS

A teratogen is any agent that can induce or increase the incidence of a congenital malformation. The general objective of teratogenicity testing of such chemicals as drugs, food additives, and pesticides is to attempt to identify agents that may be teratogenic during human development.

Drugs vary considerably in their teratogenicity. Some cause severe malformations (e.g., thalidomide); other commonly-used drugs may produce mental and growth retardation (e.g., alcohol). Pregnant women take an average of four drugs, excluding nutritional supplements, and 40 per cent of these women take the drugs during the critical period of human development. *Only 2 to 3 per cent of congenital malformations are caused by drugs and chemicals.* Few drugs have been positively implicated as teratogenic agents during human development (Table 9–3). Their use should be avoided by pregnant women and by those likely to conceive.

Alcohol (Fig. 9–13). Alcoholism is the most common drug abuse problem and affects 1 to 2 per cent of women of childbearing age. Infants born to chronic alcoholic mothers exhibit prenatal and postnatal growth deficiency, mental retardation, and congenital malformations. Short palpebral fissures, maxillary hypoplasia, abnormal palmar creases, joint anomalies, and congenital heart disease are present in most infants. This set of symptoms is known as the *fetal alcohol syndrome*. Even moderate maternal alcohol consumption (e.g., 2 to 3 ounces per day) may produce some symptoms of the syndrome, especially if the drinking is associated with malnutrition. "*Binge drinking*" (heavy consumption of alcohol for one to three days) during pregnancy is very likely to harm the embryo.

Androgenic Agents (Fig. 9–14). The administration of synthetic progestins to prevent abortion has produced masculinization

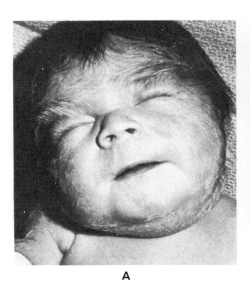 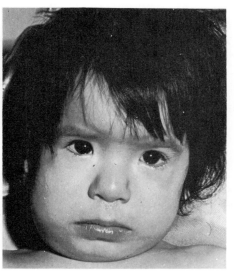

A   B

Figure 9–13 Photographs showing the facial appearance of an infant with the *fetal alcohol syndrome.* The characteristic triad of abnormalities includes growth deficiency, mental retardation, and abnormal facial features. *A*, At birth. *B*, At one year. (*A* is from Jones, K. L., and Smith, D. W.: *Lancet 2*:999, 1973; *B* is from Jones, K. L., et al.: *Lancet 1*:1267, 1973.)

TABLE 9–3   TERATOGENS KNOWN TO CAUSE HUMAN MALFORMATIONS

Teratogens	Congenital Malformations
Androgenic Agents	
Ethisterone	Varying degrees of masculinization of female fetuses: ambiguous
Norethisterone	external genitalia caused by labial fusion and clitoral
Testosterone	hypertrophy.
Drugs and Chemicals	
Alcohol	*Fetal alcohol syndrome:* intrauterine growth retardation (IUGR); mental retardation; microcephaly; ocular anomalies; joint abnormalities; short palpebral fissures.
Aminopterin	Wide range of skeletal defects; IUGR; malformations of central nervous system, notably anencephaly.
Busulfan	Stunted growth; skeletal abnormalities; corneal opacities; cleft palate; hypoplasia of various organs.
Phenytoin (diphenylhydantoin)	*Fetal hydantoin syndrome:* IUGR; microcephaly; mental retardation; ridged metopic suture; inner epicanthal folds; eyelid ptosis; broad depressed nasal bridge; phalangeal hypoplasia.
Lithium carbonate	Various malformations, usually involving the heart and great vessels.
Methotrexate	Multiple malformations, especially skeletal, involving the face, skull, limbs, and vertebral column.
Thalidomide	Amelia, meromelia, and other limb deformities; external ear, cardiac, and gastrointestinal malformations.
Warfarin	Nasal hypoplasia; chondroplasia punctata; mental retardation; optic atrophy; microcephaly.
Infectious Agents	
Cytomegalovirus	Microcephaly; hydrocephaly; microphthalmia; microgyria; mental retardation; cerebral calcifications.
Herpes simplex virus	Microcephaly; microphthalmia; retinal dysplasia.
Rubella virus	Cataracts; glaucoma; chorioretinitis; deafness; microphthalmia; congenital heart defects.
Toxoplasma gondii	Microcephaly; microphthalmia; hydrocephaly; chorioretinitis; cerebral calcifications.
Treponema pallidum	Hydrocephalus; congenital deafness; mental retardation.
High-level Radiation	Microcephaly; mental retardation; skeletal malformations.

of female fetuses (Table 9–3). Any hormone that has masculinizing activities may affect development of the external genitalia of female fetuses.

Antibiotics.   *Tetracyclines pass the placental membrane and are deposited in the embryo's bones and teeth* at sites of active calcification. Tetracycline therapy during the

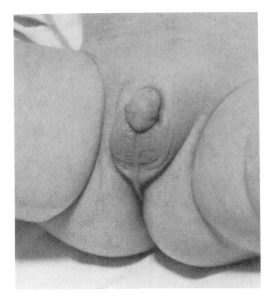
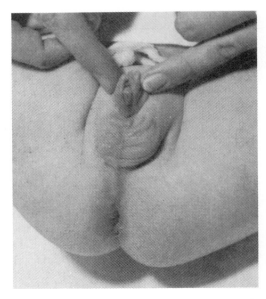

Figure 9–14   The external genitalia of a newborn female infant showing labial fusion and enlargement of the clitoris caused by an androgenic agent given to the infant's mother during the first trimester. (From Jones, H. W., and Scott, W. W.: *Hermaphroditism, Genital Anomalies and Related Endocrine Disorders.* Baltimore, Williams & Wilkins Co., 1958.)

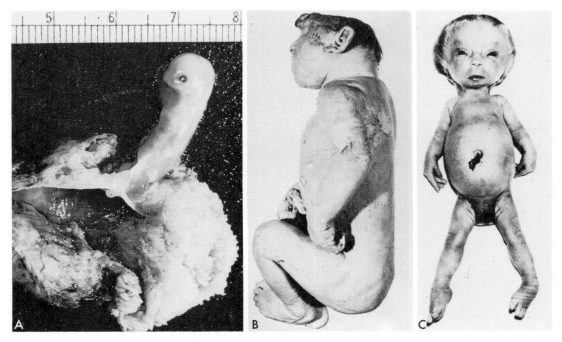

Figure 9–15   Aminopterin-induced congenital malformations. *A,* Grossly malformed embryo and its membranes. (Courtesy of Dr. J. B. Thiersch, Seattle, Washington.) *B,* Newborn infant with anencephaly or partial absence of the brain. (From Thiersch, J. B.: *in* Wolstenholme, G. E. W., and O'Connor, C. M. [Eds.]: *Ciba Foundation Symposium on Congenital Malformations.* London, J. & A. Churchill, Ltd., 1960, pp. 152–154.) *C,* Newborn infant showing marked intrauterine growth retardation (2380 gm), a large head, a small mandible, deformed ears, clubhands, and clubfeet. (From Warkany, J., Beaudry, P. H., and Hornstein, S.: *Amer. J. Dis. Child. 97*:274, 1960.)

second and third trimesters of pregnancy may cause minor tooth defects and yellow to brown discoloration of the deciduous or primary teeth. *Penicillin appears to be harmless to the human embryo.*

Anticoagulants. All anticoagulants except heparin cross the placental membrane (see Fig. 8–7) and may cause hemorrhage in the fetus. *Warfarin is now considered to be a teratogen.* Warfarin derivatives are vitamin K antagonists and therefore are anticoagulants. There are several reports of infants born with hypoplasia of the nasal bones and other abnormalities whose mothers took this anticoagulant during the critical period of their embryo's development. Second- and third-trimester exposure may result in mental retardation, optic atrophy, and microcephaly.

As heparin does not cross the placental membrane, it is not a teratogen and does not affect the embryo or fetus.

Anticonvulsants. There is now strong suggestive evidence that *trimethadione* (Tridione) and *paramethadione* (Paradione) may cause fetal facial dysmorphia, cardiac defects, cleft palate, and intrauterine growth retardation (IUGR) when given to pregnant women. Seven cases of hypoplasia of the terminal phalanges in infants of epileptics have been reported. All mothers had taken phenytoin and a barbiturate.

Phenytoin (diphenylhydantoin) is definitely a teratogen. A *fetal hydantoin syndrome* is now recognized, consisting of the following abnormalities: IUGR, microcephaly, mental retardation, a ridged metopic suture, inner epicanthal folds, eyelid ptosis, a broad depressed nasal bridge, nail and/or distal phalangeal hypoplasia, and hernias.

Phenobarbital appears to be a safe antiepileptic drug for use during pregnancy.

Antitumor Agents. Most tumor-inhibiting chemicals are highly teratogenic. *Aminopterin* is a potent teratogen which can induce major congenital malformations (Fig. 9–15), especially of the central nervous system. *Methotrexate*, a derivative of aminopterin, is also teratogenic.

Thyroid Drugs. *Potassium iodide* and *radioactive iodine* may cause congenital goiter. Propylthiouracil interferes with thyroxine formation in the fetus and may cause goiter.

Thalidomide. A mass of evidence has shown that this drug is a potent teratogen. It has been estimated that 7000 infants were

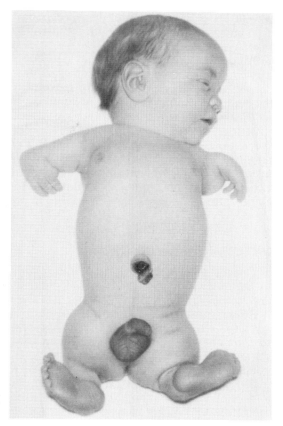

Figure 9–16 Newborn male infant showing typically malformed limbs (meromelia) caused by thalidomide. (From Moore, K. L.: *Manitoba Med. Rev.* 43:306, 1963.)

malformed by thalidomide (Fig. 9–16). The malformations ranged from amelia (absence of limbs) through intermediate stages of development (rudimentary limbs) to micromelia (short limbs). Thalidomide also causes malformations of other structures.

Lysergic Acid Diethylamide (LSD). This socially used drug may be teratogenic. Of 161 infants born to women who ingested LSD before conception and/or during the pregnancy, five infants had limb deficiency anomalies. These observations *suggest* that LSD may be teratogenic and that ingestion of it should be avoided during pregnancy.

Marijuana. There is no evidence that this drug is teratogenic in humans, but there is no assurance that heavy usage of it does not affect the embryo in some way.

Phencyclidine (PCP, "Angel Dust"). An infant with several malformations and behavioral abnormalities was born to a mother who used PCP throughout her pregnancy. This suggests, but does not prove, a causal association.

Salicylates. There is some evidence that *aspirin*, the most commonly ingested drug during pregnancy, is potentially harmful to the embryo or fetus when administered to the mother in *large doses*.

Drug Testing in Animals. Although the testing of drugs in pregnant animals is important, it should be emphasized that the results are of limited value for predicting drug effects on human embryos. Animal experiments can only suggest similar effects in humans.

INFECTIOUS AGENTS

Three viruses are known to be teratogenic in humans: rubella virus, cytomegalovirus, and herpes simplex virus.

Rubella Virus (German Measles). About 15 to 20 per cent of infants born to women who have had German measles during the first trimester of pregnancy are congenitally malformed. The usual triad of malformations is *cataract* (Fig. 9–17A), *cardiac malformations*, and *deafness*, but other malformations occur occasionally, e.g., glaucoma (Fig. 9–17B). The earlier in pregnancy the maternal rubella infection occurs, the greater is the danger of the embryo being malformed. Most infants have congenital malformations if the disease occurs during the first five weeks after fertilization. This is understandable because this period includes the most susceptible organogenetic periods of the eye, ear, heart and brain (Fig. 9–12). Malformations may result from infections during the second and third trimesters, but usually functional defects of the central nervous system and ear result.

Cytomegalovirus. Infection with cytomegalovirus (CMV) is probably the most common viral infection of the human fetus. Because the disease seems to be fatal when it affects the embryo or young fetus, it is believed that most pregnancies end in abortion when the infection occurs during the first trimester. Infection with this virus during the second and third trimesters causes abnormalities of the brain (microcephaly) and of the eyes (microphthalmia).

Herpes Simplex Virus. Infection of the fetus with this virus usually occurs late in pregnancy, probably most often during delivery. The congenital abnormalities that have been observed in fetuses infected several weeks before birth are microcephaly, microphthalmia, retinal dysplasia, and mental retardation.

Two other microorganisms are known to be teratogens in humans, *Toxoplasma gondii* and *Treponema pallidum*.

Toxoplasma Gondii. This intracellular parasite can be contracted from eating raw or poorly cooked meat (usually pork or mutton), by contact with infected animals (usually cats), or from the soil. This organism may cross the placental membrane and infect the fetus, causing destructive changes in the brain and eye, resulting in microcephaly, microphthalmia, and hydrocephaly (see Chapters 17 and 18).

Syphilis. *Treponema pallidum*, the small spiral-shaped microorganism that causes sy-

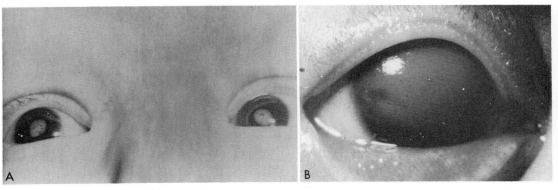

Figure 9–17   Congenital malformations of the eye caused by the rubella virus. *A*, Cataracts. (From Cooper, L. Z., et al.: *Amer. J. Dis. Child.* 110:416, 1965. Courtesy of Dr. Richard Baragry, Department of Ophthalmology, Cornell-New York Hospital.) *B*, Glaucoma. (From Cooper, L. Z., et al.: *Amer. J. Dis. Child.* 110:416, 1965. Courtesy of Dr. Daniel I. Weiss, Department of Ophthalmology, New York University School of Medicine.)

philis, rapidly penetrates the placental membrane after the twentieth week of gestation, when the cytotrophoblast disappears (see Chapter 8). Untreated primary maternal infections (acquired during pregnancy) nearly always cause serious fetal infection, but adequate treatment of the mother before the sixteenth week kills the organism, thereby preventing it from crossing the placental membrane and infecting the fetus. Secondary maternal infections (acquired before pregnancy) seldom result in fetal disease and malformations. If the mother is untreated, stillbirths result in one fourth of cases. The tissues most often extensively involved in the dead fetuses are bone, bone marrow, lungs, liver, and spleen, but any organ system may be involved.

RADIATION

Ionizing radiations are potent teratogens. Exposure to radiation may injure embryonic cells, resulting in cell death, chromosome injury, and retardation of growth. The severity of embryonic damage is related to the absorbed dose, the dose rate, and the stage of embryonic or fetal development during which the exposure occurs.

Large amounts of ionizing radiation produce congenital malformations and mental retardation. Large doses of radiation (over 25,000 millirads) are harmful to the *developing* central nervous system. For this reason, therapeutic abortion may be recommended when radiation exposure to the embryo or young fetus exceeds 25,000 millirads.

There is no proof that human congenital malformations have been caused by diagnostic levels of radiation. Scattered radiation from an x-ray examination of a part of the body that is not near the uterus (e.g., chest, sinuses, teeth) produces only a dose of a few millirads, which is not teratogenic to the embryo.

It is prudent to be cautious during diagnostic examinations of the pelvic region in pregnant women (x-ray examinations and medical diagnostic tests using radioisotopes) because they result in exposure of the embryo to 0.3 to 2 rads.

SUMMARY

A congenital malformation is an anatomical abnormality present at birth. Much progress has been made in recent years in the search for causes of congenital malformations, but satisfactory explanations are still lacking for most of them. Developmental abnormalities may be macroscopic or microscopic, on the surface or within the body. Some congenital malformations are caused by *genetic factors* (chromosomal abnormalities and mutant genes) and a few are caused by *environmental factors* (infectious agents and teratogenic drugs), but most common malformations result from a complex interaction of genetic and environmental factors (multifactorial inheritance).

During the first two weeks of development, teratogenic agents may kill the embryo or cause chromosomal abnormalities which give rise to congenital malformations. During the *organogenetic period*, particularly from days 15 to 60, teratogenic agents may cause major congenital malformations. During the fetal period, teratogens may produce minor morphological and functional abnormalities, particularly of the brain and the eyes. However, it must be stressed that some drugs and infections may adversely affect the fetus without causing congenital malformations.

SUGGESTED SUPPLEMENTARY READING

Moore, K. L.: *The Developing Human. Clinically Oriented Embryology*, 3rd ed. Philadelphia, W. B. Saunders Company, 1982, Chapter 8.
More information is given and other illustrations of congenital malformations are shown. The discussions of causes of human malformations are also more extensive.
Persaud, T. V. N.: *Prenatal Pathology: Fetal Medicine.* Springfield, IL, Charles C Thomas, 1979.
This book covers the main aspects of teratology and provides essential information on the causes, mechanisms, and prenatal detection of birth defects.
Thompson, J. S., and Thompson, M. W.: *Genetics in Medicine*, 3rd ed. Philadelphia, W. B. Saunders Company, 1980, Chapters 6 and 7.
These chapters provide clear descriptions and illustrations of chromosomal aberrations, including the clinical aspects of autosomal and sex chromosomal disorders.

10

BODY CAVITIES, PRIMITIVE MESENTERIES, AND THE DIAPHRAGM

THE INTRAEMBRYONIC COELOM

Early development of the intraembryonic coelom or embryonic body cavity is described in Chapter 5. By the fourth week it appears as a horseshoe-shaped cavity in the cardiogenic and lateral mesoderm (Fig. 10–1A). The curve or bend of the "horseshoe" represents the future *pericardial cavity*, and its limbs or lateral extensions indicate the future *pleural and peritoneal cavities*.

The intraembryonic coelom provides room for organ development and movement. For a while the intraembryonic coelom communicates with the extraembryonic coelom at the lateral edges of the embryonic disc (Fig. 10–1A and B). This communication is largely occluded during folding of the embryonic disc into a cylindrical embryo, but persists for

awhile around the stalk of the yolk sac (Fig. 10–2E). This communication is important, for, as described in Chapter 13, most of the midgut herniates through this communication into the umbilical cord (see Figs. 7–3 and 13–6), where it develops into most of the small intestine and part of the large intestine.

During transverse folding of the embryo, the lateral limbs or extensions of the intraembryonic coelom come together and fuse on the ventral aspect of the embryo (Fig. 10–2C and F). In the region of the future peritoneal cavity, the ventral mesentery degenerates, forming a large peritoneal cavity extending from inferior to the heart to the pelvic region.

Three body cavities are now recognizable: (1) a large *pericardial cavity* around the heart (Fig. 10–2B and E); (2) two relatively small *pericardioperitoneal canals* (or pleural can-

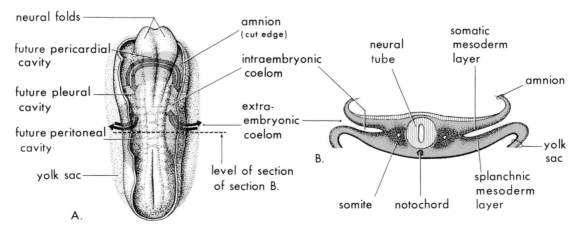

Figure 10–1 *A*, Embryo of about 22 days showing the outline of the horsehoe-shaped intraembryonic coelom. The amnion has been removed and the coelom is shown as if the embryo were translucent. The continuity of the coelom and the communication of its right and left extremities with the extraembryonic coelom is indicated by arrows. *B*, Transverse section through the embryo at the level shown in *A*.

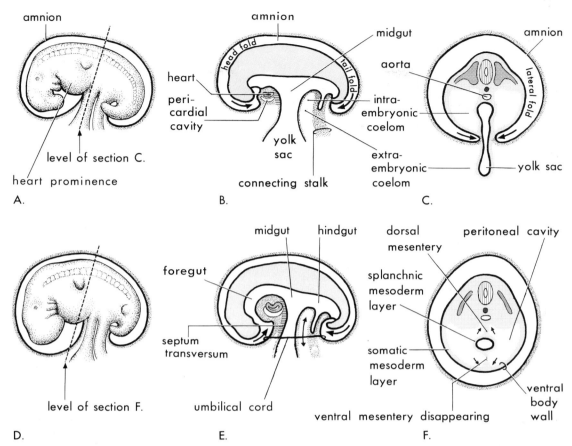

Figure 10-2 Drawings illustrating folding of the embryo and its effects on the intraembryonic coelom and other structures. *A,* Lateral view of an embryo of about 26 days. *B,* Schematic longitudinal section of this embryo showing the head and tail folds. *C,* Transverse section at the level shown in *A* indicating how the lateral folds give the embryo a cylindrical form. *D,* Lateral view of a 28-day embryo. *E,* Schematic longitudinal section of this embryo showing the reduced communication between the intraembryonic and extraembryonic coeloms or cavities (double-headed arrow). *F,* Transverse section as indicated in *D,* illustrating formation of the ventral body wall and disappearance of the ventral mesentery. The arrows indicate the junction of the somatic and splanchnic mesoderm layers. The somatic mesoderm layer will become the parietal peritoneum, which lines the abdominal wall, and the splanchnic mesoderm layer will become the visceral peritoneum covering an organ (e.g., the stomach).

als) connecting the pericardial and peritoneal cavities (Fig. 10–3); and (3) a large *peritoneal cavity* containing the abdominal and pelvic viscera (see Figs. 10–2F and 13–6).

With formation of the head fold, the heart and pericardial cavity move or "swing" ventrally beneath the foregut (see Fig. 10–2B and E). The pericardial cavity then opens dorsally into the pericardioperitoneal canals, which pass dorsal to the septum transversum on each side of the foregut (Fig. 10–3). The *septum transversum* is a transverse sheet of

mesoderm which separates the pericardial cavity from the peritoneal cavity, forming a partial diaphragm or partition between them.

DIVISION OF THE COELOM

Partitions form at both ends of the pericardioperitoneal canals and separate the pericardial cavity from the pleural cavities, and the pleural cavities from the peritoneal cavity.

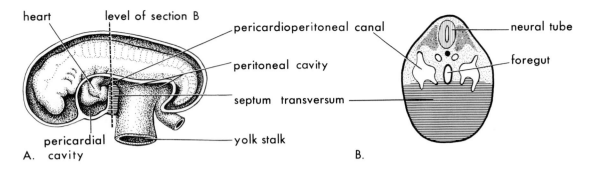

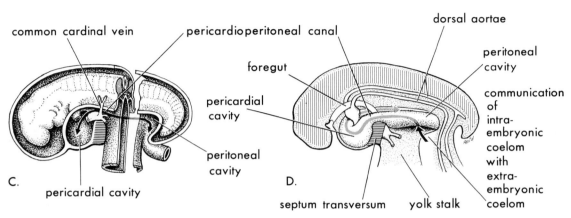

Figure 10–3 Schematic drawings of a four-week embryo (about 24 days). *A*, The lateral wall of the pericardial cavity has been removed to show the heart. *B*, Transverse section illustrating the relationship of the pericardioperitoneal canals to the septum transversum (partial diaphragm) and the foregut. *C*, Lateral view with the heart removed. The embryo has been sectioned transversely to show the continuity of the intraembryonic and extraembryonic coeloms. *D*, Sketch showing the pericardioperitoneal canals arising from the dorsal wall of the pericardial cavity and passing on each side of the foregut to join the peritoneal cavity. The arrows show the communication of the extraembryonic coelom with the intraembryonic coelom and the continuity of the intraembryonic coelom at this stage.

The *pleuropericardial membranes* (Fig. 10–4) separate the pericardial cavity from the pleural cavities. Initially, this pair of membranes appears as ridges or bulges containing the *common cardinal veins* which pass to the heart (Fig. 10–4A). These veins drain the primitive venous system into the sinus venosus of the primitive heart (see Chapter 15). At first the pleuropericardial membranes are free dorsally and project into the cranial ends of the pericardioperitoneal canals; however, after expansion of the pleural cavities, the pleuropericardial membranes fuse with one another and with the mesoderm ventral to the esophagus (Fig. 10–4C).

The *pleuroperitoneal membranes* separate the pleural cavities from the peritoneal cavity (Fig. 10–5). This pair of membranes is mainly produced as the developing lungs and pleural cavities expand by invading the body wall.

They are attached dorsolaterally to the body wall, and their crescentic free edges initially project into the caudal ends of the pericardioperitoneal canals (Fig. 10–5B), and later fuse with other diaphragmatic components to form the diaphragm (Fig. 10–5C to E).

DEVELOPMENT OF THE DIAPHRAGM

The diaphragm is a dome-shaped musculotendinous partition separating the thoracic and abdominopelvic cavities. It mainly *develops from four structures* (Fig. 10–5).

The Septum Transversum (Figs. 10–2E, 10–3, and 10–5). The *transverse septum* initially forms a thick incomplete partition or partial diaphragm between the pericardial and peritoneal cavities. Later it fuses dorsally with the mesoderm ventral to the esophagus and with the pleuroperitoneal mem-

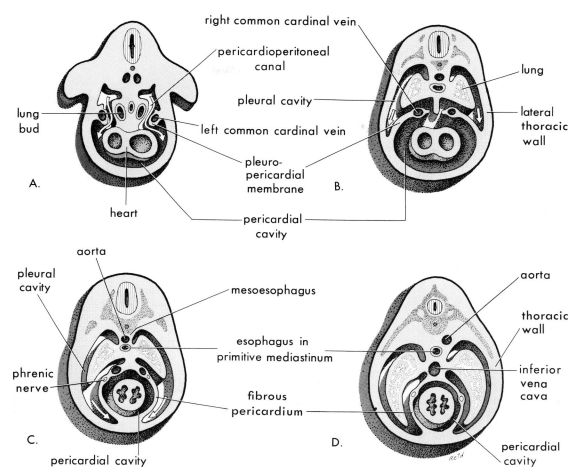

Figure 10–4 Schematic drawings of transverse sections through an embryo cranial to the septum transversum, illustrating successive stages in the separation of the pleural cavities from the pericardial cavity. Growth and development of the lungs, expansion of the pleural cavities, and formation of the fibrous pericardium are also shown. *A,* Five weeks. The arrows indicate the communications between the pericardioperitoneal canals and the pericardial cavity. *B,* Six weeks. The arrows indicate development of the pleural cavities as extensions of the pericardioperitoneal canals and as expansion of the pleural cavities into the body wall. *C,* Seven weeks. Expansion of the pleural cavities ventrally around the heart is shown. The pleuropericardial membranes are now fused in the midline with each other and with the mesoderm ventral to the esophagus. *D,* Eight weeks. Continued expansion of the lungs and pleural cavities and formation of the fibrous pericardium and chest wall are illustrated.

branes. Eventually, it forms the *central tendon* of the adult diaphragm (Fig. 10–5*E*).

The Pleuroperitoneal Membranes (Fig. 10–5).   These membranes fuse with the dorsal mesentery of the esophagus and with the dorsal portion of the septum transversum, thereby completing the partition between the thoracic and abdominopelvic cavities. Although the pleuroperitoneal membranes form large portions of the primitive diaphragm, they represent relatively small intermediate portions of the fully-developed diaphragm (Fig. 10–5*E*).

Dorsal Mesentery of the Esophagus (Figs. 10–4 and 10–5).   This mesentery constitutes the median portion of the diaphragm. The *crura of the diaphragm* develop from muscle fibers that grow into the dorsal mesentery of the esophagus (mesoesophagus).

The Body Wall (Fig. 10–5).   As the lungs grow, the pleural cavities enlarge and burrow into the lateral body walls (Fig. 10–4). During this "excavation" process, body-wall tissue is split into two layers: (1) an outer layer that will form part of the definite body wall, and (2) an inner layer that contributes to periph-

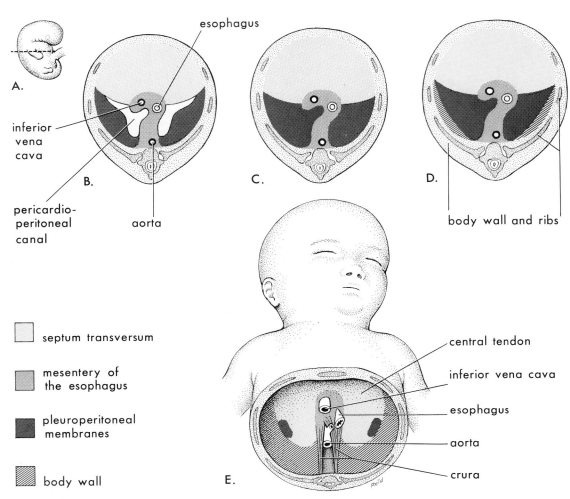

septum transversum

mesentery of the esophagus

pleuroperitoneal membranes

body wall

Figure 10–5 Drawings illustrating development of the diaphragm as viewed from below. *A*, Sketch of a lateral view of an embryo at the end of the fifth week (*actual size*) indicating the level of section. *B*, Transverse section showing the unfused pleuroperitoneal membranes. *C*, Similar section at the end of the sixth week after fusion of the pleuroperitoneal membranes with the other two diaphragmatic components. *D*, Transverse section through a 12-week embryo after ingrowth of the fourth diaphragmatic component from the body wall. *E*, View of the diaphragm of a newborn infant, indicating the probable embryological origin of its components.

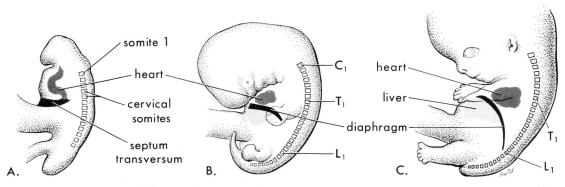

Figure 10–6 Diagrams illustrating positional changes of the developing diaphragm. *A*, About 24 days. The septum transversum (primordium of the diaphragm, in part) is at the level of the third, fourth, and fifth cervical segments. *B*, About 41 days. *C*, About 52 days.

eral portions of the diaphragm, external to the portions derived from the pleuroperitoneal membranes.

POSITIONAL CHANGES AND INNERVATION OF THE DIAPHRAGM

During the fourth week, the septum transversum lies opposite the third, fourth, and fifth *cervical somites* (Fig. 10–6*A*). During the fifth week, myoblasts (primitive muscle cells) from the *myotomes* of these somites migrate into the developing diaphragm and bring their nerves with them. Thus, the nerve supply of the diaphragm is from the *third, fourth, and fifth cervical nerves*, which are contained in the *phrenic nerves*. These nerves pass to the septum transversum via the pleuropericardial membranes. This explains why the phrenic nerves subsequently come to lie on the fibrous pericardium (Fig. 10–4*C* and *D*).

Rapid growth of the dorsal part of the embryo's body compared with the ventral part results in an apparent migration or descent of the diaphragm. By the sixth week, the developing diaphragm is at the level of the thoracic somites (Fig. 10–6*B*). The phrenic nerves now take a descending course, and, as the diaphragm "moves" relatively farther caudally in the body, these nerves are correspondingly lengthened. By the beginning of the eighth week, the dorsal part of the diaphragm lies at the level of the first lumbar vertebra (Fig. 10–6*C*).

As the parts of the diaphragm fuse (Fig. 10–5), mesenchyme of the septum transversum extends into the other parts and forms myoblasts that differentiate into the muscle of the diaphragm. Hence, *the motor nerve supply to the diaphragm is via the phrenic nerves (ventral rami of C3, 4, and 5)*.

The phrenic nerve is also sensory to the central region of the diaphragm, but its peripheral region, which develops from the body wall (Fig. 10–5*E*), receives sensory

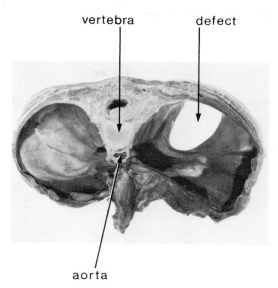

vertebra   defect

aorta

Figure 10–7 Photograph of a transverse section through the thoracic region of a newborn infant, viewed from above. Note the large left posterolateral defect of the diaphragm. *Half actual size.*

nerves from the lower six or seven intercostal nerves.

CONGENITAL DIAPHRAGMATIC HERNIA

A posterolateral defect of the diaphragm is a relatively common developmental abnormality (Fig. 10–7). It occurs about once in 2000 births and results from failure of the pleuroperitoneal membrane on the affected side to fuse with other diaphragmatic components. The defect, usually on the left side, consists of a large opening in the posterolateral region of the diaphragm, usually in the region of the kidney. There is free communication between the abdominal and pleural cavities. As a result, the intestines and other abdominal organs pass into the thorax. Because of the presence of the abdominal viscera in the chest, the heart is pushed anteriorly and the lungs are compressed.

SUMMARY

The *intraembryonic coelom* or embryonic body cavity begins to develop near the end of the third week. By the beginning of the fourth week, it appears as a continuous horseshoe-shaped cavity in the cardiogenic and lateral mesoderm. During folding of the embryonic disc in the fourth week, the lateral limbs or extensions of the coelom are brought together on the ventral aspect of the embryo, where they merge in the region of the future peritoneal cavity.

As the peritoneal portions of the intraembryonic coelom come together, the splanchnic mesoderm encloses the primitive gut and suspends it from the dorsal body wall by a double-layered membrane known as the *dorsal mesentery*.

Until the seventh week, the *pericardial cavity* communicates with the peritoneal cavity through paired *pericardioperitoneal canals*. During the fifth and sixth weeks, partitions or membranes form at the cranial and caudal ends of these canals. The cranial *pleuropericardial membranes* separate the pericardial cavity from the pleural cavities, and the caudal *pleuroperitoneal membranes* separate the pleural cavities from the peritoneal cavity.

The diaphragm develops from four main structures: (1) the septum transversum, (2) the pleuroperitoneal membranes, (3) the dorsal mesentery of the esophagus, and (4) the body wall.

Posterolateral defect of the diaphragm is the common type of congenital diaphragmatic defect and is associated with herniation of abdominal viscera into the thoracic cavity. *Congenital diaphragmatic hernia* occurs five times more often on the left side than on the right and results from failure of the pleuroperitoneal membrane on the affected side to fuse with the other diaphragmatic components and separate the pleural and peritoneal cavities.

SUGGESTED SUPPLEMENTARY READING

Avery, M. E.: Disorders of the diaphragm; *in* Avery, M. E., and Taeusch, H. W. (Eds.): *Diseases of the Newborn*, 5th ed. Philadelphia, W. B. Saunders Company, 1983.
This book contains short descriptions of congenital diaphragmatic hernias and their treatment.
Behrman, R. E., and Vaughan, V. C. (Eds.): *Nelson Textbook of Pediatrics*, 12th ed. Philadelphia, W. B. Saunders Company, 1983.
This large book contains a good discussion of congenital defects of the diaphragm.

11

THE BRANCHIAL APPARATUS AND ITS DERIVATIVES

The branchial apparatus consists of (1) *branchial arches*, (2) *pharyngeal pouches*, (3) *branchial grooves*, and (4) *branchial membranes* (Fig. 11–1). The derivatives of the branchial apparatus contribute greatly to the formation of the head and neck of the fetus.

The cranial region of an early human embryo somewhat resembles a fish embryo of a comparable stage, but these ancestral structures become rearranged and adapted to new functions or disappear.

Most congenital malformations of the head and neck originate during transformation of the branchial apparatus into adult derivatives.

In fish and larval amphibians, the branchial apparatus forms a system of gills for exchanging oxygen and carbon dioxide between the blood and the water. (The adjective "branchial" is from the Greek *branchia*, meaning "gill.") The branchial arches support the gills. A branchial apparatus develops in human embryos, but no gills form.

THE BRANCHIAL ARCHES

Branchial arches develop during the fourth week and appear as ridges on the future head and neck region (Figs. 11–1 and 11–2). The arches are separated from each other by *branchial grooves* (Fig. 11–1D), and are numbered in a craniocaudal sequence.

The mouth initially appears as a slight depression of the surface ectoderm, called the *stomodeum* or *primitive mouth* (Fig. 11–1D to G). At first this cavity is separated from the foregut or primitive pharynx by a bilaminar membrane, the *oropharyngeal (buccopharyngeal) membrane*. This membrane ruptures at about 24 days, bringing the digestive tract into communication with the amniotic cavity (Fig. 11–1J).

Fate of the Branchial Arches. The first branchial arch or *mandibular arch* is involved with development of the face. It develops two prominences (elevations) called the *mandibular prominence* (process) and the *maxillary prominence* (process). The mandibular prominence forms the lower jaw or mandible (Fig. 11–3G), and the maxillary prominence forms the upper jaw or maxilla, the zygomatic bone, and the squamous part of the temporal bone (see Fig. 16–6).

During the fifth week, the second branchial arch (hyoid arch) overgrows the third and fourth arches, forming an ectodermal depression known as the *cervical sinus* (Fig. 11–3A to D). During the sixth and seventh weeks, the second and sixth arches enlarge and merge with each other. Gradually, the second to fourth branchial grooves and the cervical sinus are obliterated, giving the neck a smooth contour (Fig. 11–3F and G). The branchial arches caudal to the second one make little contribution to the skin of the neck (Fig. 11–3G).

Derivatives of the Branchial Arch Arteries. The transformation of the aortic arches into the adult arterial pattern is described with the circulatory system in Chapter 15.

Derivatives of the Branchial Arch Cartilages (Fig. 11–4). The dorsal end of the *first arch cartilage* (Meckel's cartilage) becomes ossified to form two middle ear bones, the *malleus* and the *incus*. The intermediate portion of the cartilage regresses, and its perichondrium forms the *anterior ligament of the malleus* and the *sphenomandibular ligament*. The ventral portion of the first arch cartilage largely disappears; the mandible develops around it by intramembranous ossification.

The dorsal end of the *second arch cartilage*

Text continued on page 130

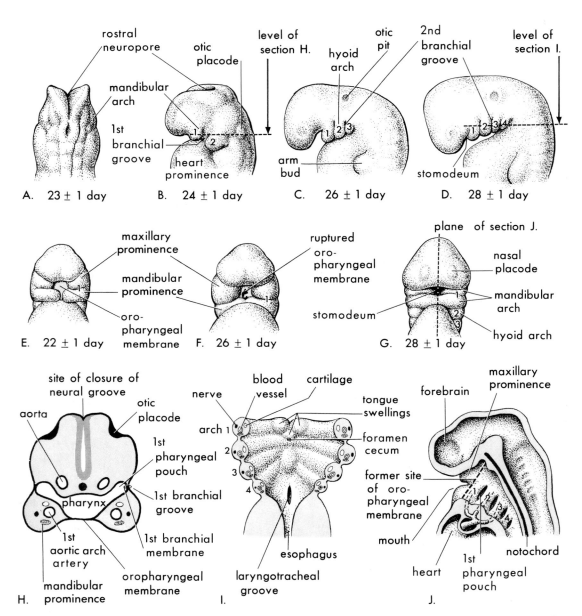

Figure 11–1 Drawings illustrating the human branchial apparatus. *A*, Dorsal view of the cranial part of an early embryo. *B* to *D*, Lateral views, showing later development of the branchial arches. *E* to *G*, Facial views illustrating the relationship of the first arch to the stomodeum or primitive mouth. *H*, Transverse section through the cranial region of an embryo. *I*, Horizontal section through the cranial region of an embryo, illustrating the branchial arch components and the floor of the primitive pharynx. *J*, Sagittal section of the cranial region of an embryo, illustrating the openings of the pharyngeal pouches in the lateral wall of the primitive pharynx.

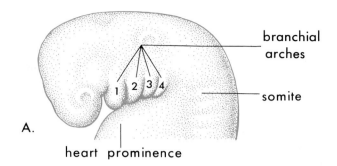

A.

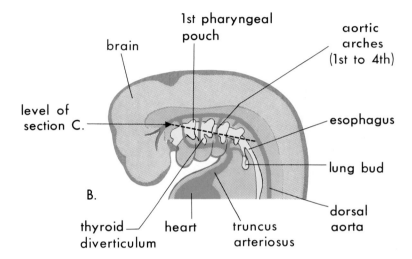

B.

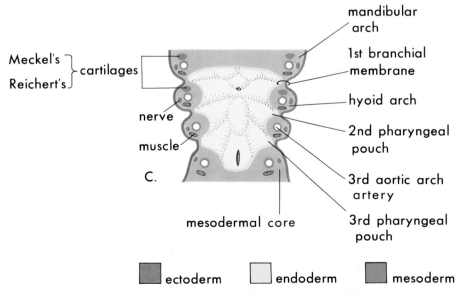

C.

ectoderm   endoderm   mesoderm

Figure 11–2   *A*, Drawing of the head and neck region of a 28-day embryo, illustrating the human branchial apparatus. *B*, Schematic drawing showing the pharyngeal pouches and aortic or branchial arch arteries, exposed by removal of the ectoderm and mesoderm. *C*, Horizontal section through the embryo, illustrating the germ layer of origin of the branchial arch components.

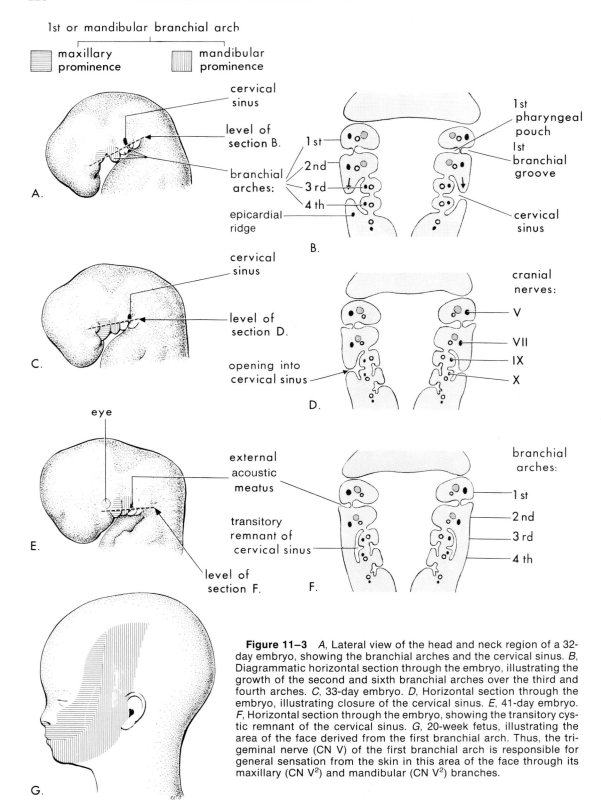

Figure 11–3 *A*, Lateral view of the head and neck region of a 32-day embryo, showing the branchial arches and the cervical sinus. *B*, Diagrammatic horizontal section through the embryo, illustrating the growth of the second and sixth branchial arches over the third and fourth arches. *C*, 33-day embryo. *D*, Horizontal section through the embryo, illustrating closure of the cervical sinus. *E*, 41-day embryo. *F*, Horizontal section through the embryo, showing the transitory cystic remnant of the cervical sinus. *G*, 20-week fetus, illustrating the area of the face derived from the first branchial arch. Thus, the trigeminal nerve (CN V) of the first branchial arch is responsible for general sensation from the skin in this area of the face through its maxillary (CN V^2) and mandibular (CN V^2) branches.

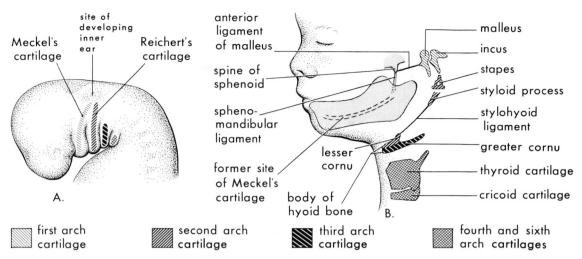

| ▨ first arch cartilage | ▨ second arch cartilage | ▨ third arch cartilage | ▨ fourth and sixth arch cartilages |

Figure 11–4 *A,* Schematic lateral view of the head and neck region of a four-week embryo, illustrating the location of the branchial arch cartilages. *B,* Similar view of a 24-week fetus, illustrating the adult derivatives of the branchial arch cartilages. Note that the mandible is formed by membranous ossification of the mesenchymal tissue surrounding Meckel's cartilage. This cartilage acts as a template, or guide, but does not contribute directly to the formation of the mandible.

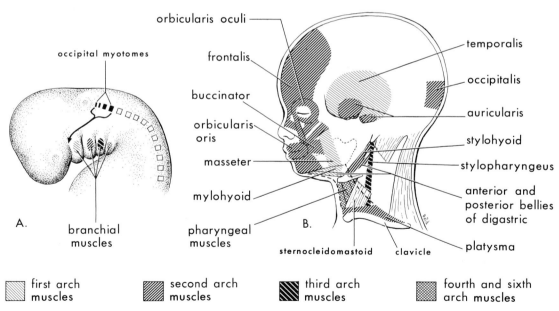

| ▨ first arch muscles | ▨ second arch muscles | ▨ third arch muscles | ▨ fourth and sixth arch muscles |

Figure 11–5 *A,* Sketch of lateral view of the head and neck region of a four-week embryo, showing the branchial muscles. The arrow shows the pathway taken by myoblasts from the occipital myotomes to form the tongue musculature. *B,* Sketch of the head and neck of a 20-week fetus dissected to show the muscles derived from the branchial arches. Parts of the platysma and sternocleidomastoid muscles have been removed to show the deeper muscles. Note that myoblasts from the second branchial arch migrate from the neck region to the head and give rise to the muscles of facial expression. Thus, these muscles are supplied by the facial nerve, the nerve of the second branchial arch.

(Reichert's cartilage) also ossifies and forms the *stapes* of the middle ear and the *styloid process* of the temporal bone. The portion of cartilage between the styloid process and the hyoid bone regresses, and its perichondrium forms the *stylohyoid ligament*. The ventral end of the second arch cartilage ossifies to form the lesser cornu and superior part of the body of the *hyoid bone*.

The *third arch cartilage* is located in the ventral portion of the arch and ossifies to from the greater cornu and inferior part of the body of the hyoid bone.

The *fourth and sixth arch cartilages* are in the ventral regions of the arches. They fuse to form the *laryngeal cartilages*. The rudimentary fifth branchial arch, if present, has no recognizable cartilage.

Derivatives of the Branchial Arch Muscles (Fig. 11–5).   The muscle elements in the branchial arches form various striated muscles in the head and neck.

THE PHARYNGEAL POUCHES

The primitive pharynx is wide cranially and narrow caudally. The endoderm of the pharynx lines the inner aspects of the branchial arches and passes into balloon-like outgrowths called *pharyngeal pouches* (see Figs. 11–1*H* to *J* and 11–2*B* and *C*). The pouches develop in a craniocaudal sequence between the branchial arches, e.g., the first pouch lies between the first and second branchial arches. There are four well-defined pairs of pharyngeal pouches. The fifth pharyngeal pouch is rudimentary or absent.

DERIVATIVES OF THE PHARYNGEAL POUCHES

The First Pharyngeal Pouch (Fig. 11–6).   This pouch expands into an elongate *tubotympanic recess* which forms the *tympanic cavity* and *mastoid antrum*. Its connection with the pharynx gradually elongates to form the *auditory tube* (pharyngotympanic tube).

The Second Pharyngeal Pouch (Fig. 11–6).   The endoderm of this pouch proliferates and forms buds that grow into the underlying mesenchyme. The central parts of these buds break down, forming the *tonsillar crypts*. The pouch endoderm forms the surface epithelium and the *lining of the crypts of the palatine tonsil*. The mesenchyme surrounding the crypts differentiates into lymphoid tissue and soon becomes organized into *lymphatic nodules*. Although it is largely ob-

literated as the palatine tonsil develops, part of the cavity of this pouch remains as the *intratonsillar cleft* (Fig. 11–6*C*).

The Third Pharyngeal Pouch (Fig. 11–6).   This pouch expands into a solid dorsal bulbar portion and a hollow ventral elongate portion. Each dorsal bulbar portion differentiates into an *inferior parathyroid gland*. The elongate ventral portions form two masses that eventually meet and fuse to form the *thymus*. The *thymus* and parathyroid glands migrate caudally. Later the parathyroid glands separate from the thymus and come to lie on the dorsal surface of the thyroid gland which has descended from the foramen cecum of the tongue.

The Fourth Pharyngeal Pouch (Fig. 11–6).   This pouch also expands into a dorsal bulbar portion and a ventral elongate portion. Each dorsal portion develops into a *superior parathyroid gland*. The ventral elongate portion of each fourth pouch develops into an *ultimobranchial body* which becomes incorporated into the thyroid gland and gives rise to its *parafollicular* or *C cells*. These cells produce *calcitonin*, a hormone involved in the regulation of the normal calcium level in body fluids.

The Fifth Pharyngeal Pouch.   This is a rudimentary structure which, if present, is partially incorporated into the fourth pouch.

THE BRANCHIAL GROOVES

The future neck region of the human embryo exhibits four branchial grooves on each side during the fourth and fifth weeks (see Figs. 11–1 and 11–3). These dorsoventral grooves *separate the branchial arches externally*. Only one pair of branchial grooves contributes to adult structures. The first branchial groove persists as the epithelium of the *external acoustic meatus* (Fig. 11–6*C*). The other branchial grooves come to lie in a depression called the *cervical sinus* and are normally obliterated with it as the neck develops.

THE BRANCHIAL MEMBRANES

Four branchial membranes appear on each side of the future neck region of the human embryo during the fourth week (see Figs. 11–1*H* and 11–2*C*). *They form where the epithelia of a branchial groove and a pharyngeal pouch approach each other*, but they are temporary structures in the human embryo. The endoderm of the pharyngeal pouches and

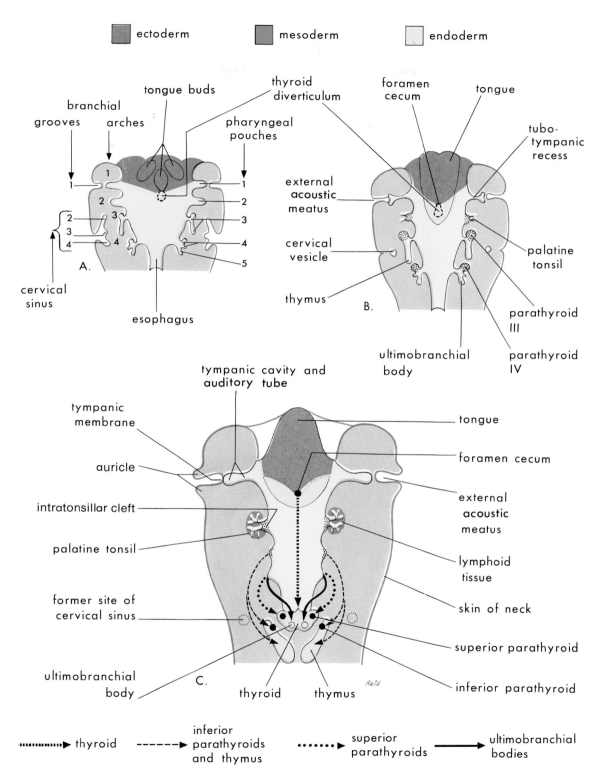

Figure 11–6 Schematic horizontal sections at the level shown in Figure 11–3A, illustrating the adult derivatives of the pharyngeal pouches. A, Five weeks. B, Six weeks. C, Seven weeks.

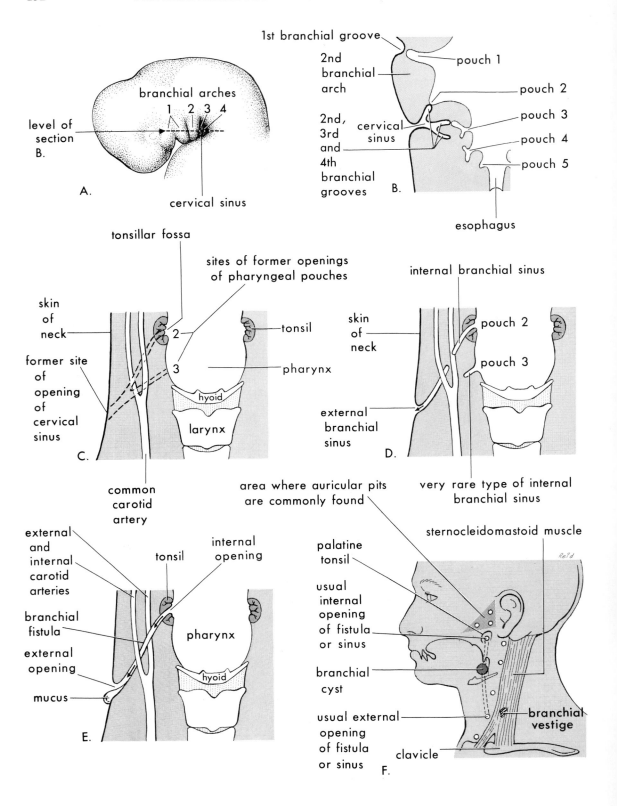

the ectoderm of the branchial grooves are soon separated by mesoderm. Only one pair of branchial membranes contributes to the formation of adult structures. The first branchial membrane, along with the intervening layer of mesoderm, gives rise to the *tympanic membrane*, or eardrum (Fig. 11–6C).

BRANCHIAL ANOMALIES

Congenital malformations of the head and of the neck originate mainly during transformation of the branchial apparatus into adult structures (Fig. 11–7). Most of these abnormalities represent *remnants of the branchial apparatus* that normally disappear as these structures develop. Most of *these malformations are uncommon.*

Congenital Auricular Sinuses and Cysts (Fig. 11–7F). Small blind pits, or cysts, in the skin are commonly found in a triangular area anterior to the ear, but may occur in other sites around the auricle or in the lobule. Most of these pits and cysts are remnants of the first branchial groove.

Branchial Sinus, or Lateral Cervical Sinus (Figs. 11–7D and 11–8). Branchial sinuses are uncommon, and almost all that

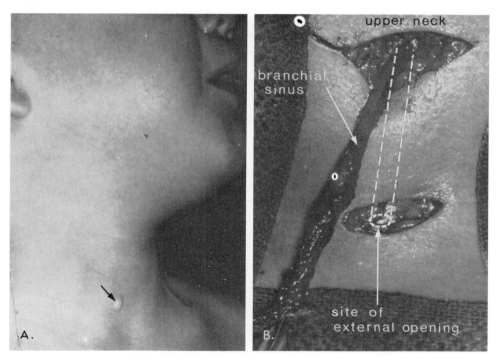

Figure 11–8   *A*, Photograph of a child's neck showing mucus dripping from an external branchial sinus (arrow). *B*, Photographs of a branchial sinus taken during excision. The external opening in the skin of the neck and the original course of the sinus in the subcutaneous tissue are indicated by broken lines. (From Swenson, O.: *Pediatric Surgery,* 1958. Courtesy of Appleton-Century-Crofts, Publishing Division of Prentice-Hall, Inc., Englewood Cliffs, New Jersey.)

Figure 11–7   *A*, Drawing of the head and neck region of a five-week embryo. *B*, Horizontal section through the embryo, illustrating the relationship of the cervical sinus to the branchial arches and pharyngeal pouches. *C*, Diagrammatic sketch of the adult neck region, indicating the former sites of openings of the cervical sinus and the pharyngeal pouches. The broken lines indicate possible courses of branchial fistulas. *D*, Similar sketch showing the embryological basis of various types of branchial sinus. *E*, Drawing of a branchial fistula resulting from persistence of parts of the second branchial groove and the second pharyngeal pouch. *F*, Sketch showing possible sites of branchial cysts and openings of branchial sinuses and fistulas. A branchial vestige is also illustrated.

open externally on the side of the neck result from failure of the second branchial groove and the cervical sinus to obliterate. A blind pit or channel then remains, which typically opens on the line of the anterior border of the sternocleidomastoid muscle in the inferior third of the neck. Often there is an intermittent discharge of mucus from the opening.

External branchial sinuses are commonly detected during infancy owing to the discharge of material from their orifices on the neck. Branchial sinuses are bilateral in about 10 per cent of cases and are commonly associated with auricular sinuses in the lobule of the auricle.

Internal branchial sinuses opening into the pharynx are very rare. Because they usually open into the intratonsillar cleft or near the palatopharyngeal arch, almost all these sinuses result from persistence of part of the second pharyngeal pouch (Fig. 11–7D).

Branchial Fistula (Fig. 11–7E). An abnormal tract (canal) opening both on the side of the neck and in the pharynx is called a *branchial fistula*. It is usually the result of persistence of parts of the second branchial groove and second pharyngeal pouch. The fistula ascends from its cervical opening through the subcutaneous tissue, the platysma muscle, and the deep fascia to reach the carotid sheath. It then passes between the internal and external carotid arteries and usually opens in the intratonsillar cleft. In older patients, there may occasionally be a disagreeable taste in the mouth, owing to the discharge of material into the pharynx from the fistula.

Branchial Cyst, or Lateral Cervical Cyst (Fig. 11–7F). The third and fourth branchial arches are normally buried in the *cervical sinus*. Remnants of parts of the cervical sinus and/or the second branchial groove may persist and form spherical or elongate cysts. Although they may be associated with branchial sinuses and drain through them, these cysts often lie free in the neck just inferior to the angle of the mandible. They may, however, develop anywhere along the anterior border of the sternocleidomastoid muscle.

These cysts often do not become apparent until late childhood or early adulthood, when they produce a slowly enlarging, painless swelling in the neck. The cysts enlarge owing to the accumulation of fluid and cellular debris derived from desquamation of their epithelial linings.

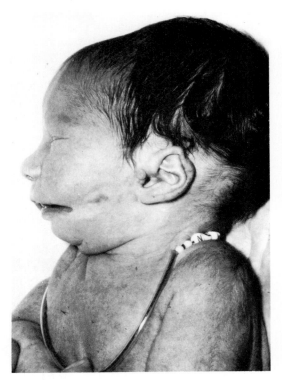

Figure 11–9   Photograph of an infant with the first arch syndrome, a pattern of malformations resulting from insufficient migration of neural crest cells into the first branchial arch. Note the following: deformed auricle of the external ear, preauricular appendage, defect in cheek between the ear and the mouth, hypoplasia of the mandible, and large mouth. (Courtesy of Dr. T. V. N. Persaud, Professor of Anatomy, University of Manitoba, Winnipeg, Canada.)

Branchial Vestiges (Fig. 11–7F). Normally, the branchial arch cartilages disappear, except for those parts that form ligaments or bones (Fig. 11–4B). Very rarely, cartilaginous or bony remnants of branchial arch cartilages may appear under the skin on the side of the neck. These are usually found anterior to the inferior third of the sternocleidomastoid muscle.

The First Arch Syndrome (Fig. 11–9). Maldevelopment of the components of the first branchial arch results in various congenital malformations of the eyes, the ears, the mandible, and the palate that together constitute the first arch syndrome. This set of symptoms is believed to be caused by *insufficient migration of cranial neural crest cells* into the first branchial arch during the fourth week. There are two main manifestations of the first arch syndrome.

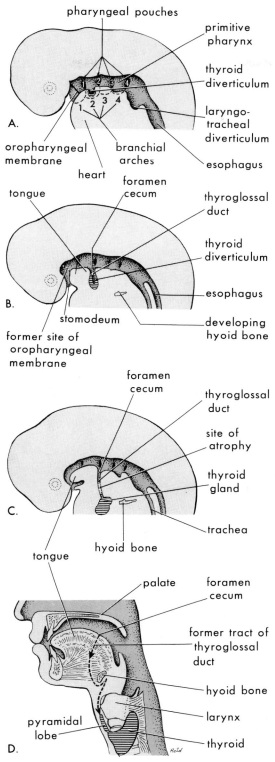

Figure 11–10   *A, B,* and *C,* Schematic sagittal sections of the head and neck region of embryos at four, five, and six weeks, respectively, illustrating successive stages of development of the thyroid gland. *D,* Similar section of an adult head, showing the path taken by the thyroid gland during its descent and the former tract of the thyroglossal duct.

In *Treacher Collins syndrome* (mandibulofacial dysostosis), which is caused by an autosomal dominant gene, there is malar hypoplasia with downslanting palpebral fissures, defects of the lower eyelid, deformed external ear, and, sometimes, abnormalities of the middle and internal ears.

In *Pierre Robin syndrome*, striking hypoplasia of the mandible, cleft palate, and defects of the eye and the ear are found. *In the Robin morphogenetic complex, the initiating defect was the small mandible (micrognathia),* which resulted in posterior displacement of the tongue and obstruction to the full closure of the palatine processes and a U-shaped bilateral cleft palate.

THE THYROID GLAND

The thyroid gland appears during the third week as a median endodermal thickening in the floor of the primitive pharynx (Figs. 11–6 and 11–10). This thickening soon becomes a downgrowth known as the *thyroid diverticulum*. The developing thyroid descends in the front of the neck, retaining its connection to the tongue by a narrow *thyroglossal duct*. This duct's opening in the tongue is called the *foramen cecum* (Fig. 11–10C).

By seven weeks the thyroid gland has usually reached its final site in the front of the neck, and the thyroglossal duct has normally disappeared. The original opening of the thyroglossal duct persists as a vestigial pit, the foramen cecum of the tongue (Figs. 11–10D and 11–12C).

CONGENITAL MALFORMATIONS OF THE THYROID GLAND

Thyroglossal Cysts and Sinuses (Fig. 11–11). Cysts may form anywhere along the course followed by the thyroglossal duct during descent of the thyroid gland from the tongue. Normally the thyroglossal duct atrophies and disappears, but remnants of it may persist and give rise to cysts in the tongue or in the midline of the neck, usually just inferior to the hyoid bone. The swelling usually develops as a painless, progressively enlarging, and movable mass. In some cases, an opening through the skin exists as a result of perforation following infection of the cyst. This forms a *thyroglossal duct sinus* that usually opens in the midline of the neck anterior to the laryngeal cartilages (Fig. 11–11A).

Ectopic Thyroid Gland and Accessory Thyroid Tissue. Very rarely, the thyroid fails to descend, resulting in a *lingual thyroid*. Incomplete descent may result in the thyroid gland appearing high in the neck at or just inferior to the hyoid bone. *Accessory thyroid tissue* may be functional, but it is often of insufficient size to maintain normal function if the thyroid gland is removed. Accessory thyroid tissue may result from pieces of the gland that become separated from the main gland, but it usually originates from remnants

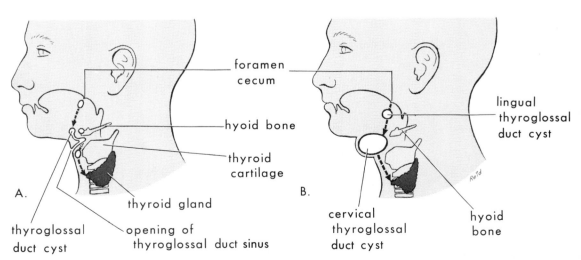

Figure 11–11 *A,* Diagrammatic sketch of the head, showing the possible locations of thyroglossal duct cysts. A thyroglossal duct sinus is also illustrated. The broken line indicates the course taken by the thyroglossal duct during descent of the thyroid gland from the foramen cecum to its final position in the front of the neck. *B,* A similar sketch illustrating lingual and cervical thyroglossal duct cysts. Most cysts are located near the hyoid bone.

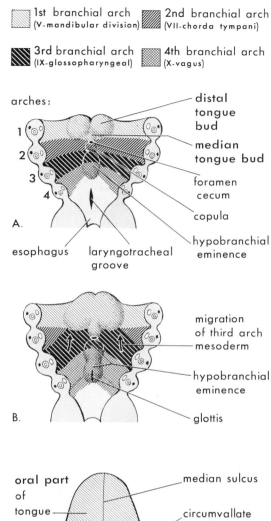

1st branchial arch (V-mandibular division)   2nd branchial arch (VII-chorda tympani)

3rd branchial arch (IX-glossopharyngeal)   4th branchial arch (X-vagus)

arches:

1
2
3
4

A.

distal tongue bud

median tongue bud

foramen cecum

copula

hypobranchial eminence

esophagus   laryngotracheal groove

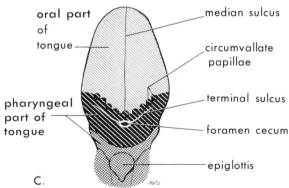

migration of third arch mesoderm

hypobranchial eminence

glottis

B.

Figure 11–12   *A* and *B*, Schematic horizontal sections through the pharynx at the level shown in Figure 11–3*A*, showing successive stages in the development of the tongue during the fourth and fifth weeks. *C*, Adult tongue showing the branchial arch derivation of the nerve supply of the mucosa.

oral part of tongue

pharyngeal part of tongue

C.

median sulcus

circumvallate papillae

terminal sulcus

foramen cecum

epiglottis

of the thyroglossal duct. It may be found anywhere from the tongue to the usual site of the thyroid gland.

THE TONGUE

The first indication of tongue development appears around the end of the fourth week

as a median elevation, the *median tongue bud* (tuberculum impar) in the floor of the pharynx just rostral to the foramen cecum (Fig. 11–12*A*). Two oval *distal tongue buds* (lateral lingual swellings) soon develop on each side of the median tongue bud. The distal tongue buds rapidly increase in size, merge with each other, and overgrow the median

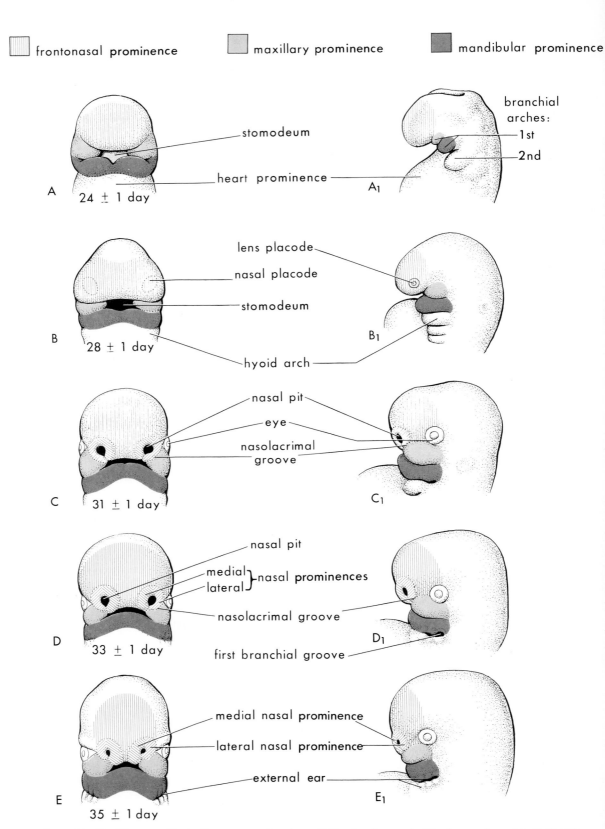

Figure 11–13 Diagrams illustrating progressive stages in the development of the human face. *A* to *E*, Fourth and fifth weeks.

Illustration continued on opposite page

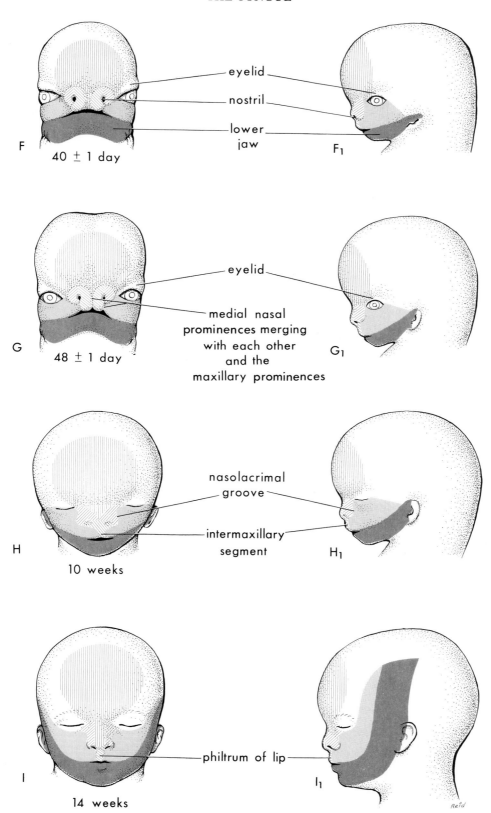

Figure 11–13 *Continued. F* to *I*, Sixth to fourteenth weeks.

tongue bud. The fused distal tongue buds form the *anterior two-thirds*, or oral part, of the tongue (Fig. 11–12C).

The *posterior third*, or pharyngeal part, of the tongue is initially indicated by two elevations that develop caudal to the foramen cecum (Fig. 11–12A). One, the *copula* (connector), is formed by fusion of the ventromedial parts of the second branchial arches; the other, the *hypobranchial eminence*, develops caudal to the copula from mesoderm in the ventromedial parts of the third and fourth branchial arches.

As the tongue develops, the copula is gradually overgrown by the hypobranchial eminence (Fig. 11–12B and C). As a result, the posterior third of the tongue develops from the cranial part of the hypobranchial eminence. The line of fusion of the anterior and posterior parts of the tongue is roughly indicated by the V-shaped groove called the *terminal sulcus* (Fig. 11–12C).

Branchial arch mesenchyme forms the connective tissue and the lymphatic and blood vessels of the tongue, and probably some of its muscle fibers. Most of the tongue musculature, however, is derived from myoblasts that migrate from the *myotomes of the occipital somites* (Fig. 11–5A). These myoblasts (primitive muscle cells) migrate into the tongue, where they differentiate into the muscles. The hypoglossal nerve (cranial nerve XII) accompanies the myoblasts during their migration and innervates the *tongue musculature* when it develops.

CONGENITAL MALFORMATIONS OF THE TONGUE

Congenital Cysts and Fistulas (Fig. 11–11). *Cysts within the tongue*, just superior to the hyoid bone, are usually derived from *remnants of the thyroglossal duct*. They may enlarge and produce symptoms of pharyngeal discomfort and/or *dysphagia* (difficulty in swallowing).

Fistulas in the tongue are also derived from persistence of the thyroglossal duct, and they open through the *foramen cecum* into the mouth.

Ankyloglossia (Tongue-Tie). The frenulum normally connects the inferior surface of the anterior part of the tongue to the floor of the mouth. In tongue-tie, the frenulum extends to near the tip of the tongue and interferes with its free protrusion. Usually, the

frenulum stretches with time so that surgical correction of the malformation is rarely necessary.

Macroglossia. An excessively large tongue is not common and results from generalized hypertrophy of the tongue. These cases usually result from lymphangioma or muscular hypertrophy.

Microglossia. An abnormally small tongue is rare and is usually associated with micrognathia (underdeveloped mandible with recession of the chin).

Cleft Tongue. Rarely, incomplete fusion of the distal tongue buds posteriorly may result in a median groove, or *cleft of the tongue*; usually, the cleft does not extend to the tip.

Bifid Tongue. Complete failure of fusion of the distal tongue buds results in a cleft in the oral part of the tongue.

DEVELOPMENT OF THE FACE

The *five facial primordia* appear around the stomodeum or primitive mouth early in the fourth week (Figs. 11–1E and 11–13A).

The large *frontonasal prominence* (elevation) constitutes the cranial boundary of the stomodeum. The paired *maxillary prominences* of the first branchial arch form the lateral boundaries of the stomodeum, and the paired *mandibular prominences* of this same arch constitute the caudal boundary of the stomodeum.

Bilateral oval-shaped thickenings of the surface ectoderm, called *nasal placodes*, develop on each side of the caudal part of frontonasal elevation (Fig. 11–13B). Horseshoe-shaped *medial and lateral nasal prominences* (elevations) develop at the margins of the nasal placodes (Fig. 11–13C and D). As a result, the nasal placodes lie in depressions called *nasal pits* (Fig. 11–13C). The maxillary prominences grow rapidly and soon approach each other and the medial nasal prominences (Fig. 11–13D and E).

During the sixth and seventh weeks, the medial nasal prominences merge with each other and the maxillary prominences (Fig. 11–13F and G). As the medial nasal prominences merge with each other, they form an *intermaxillary segment* of the maxilla (Fig. 11–13H). This segment gives rise to (1) the middle portion of the upper lip called the *philtrum*; (2) the premaxillary part of the maxilla

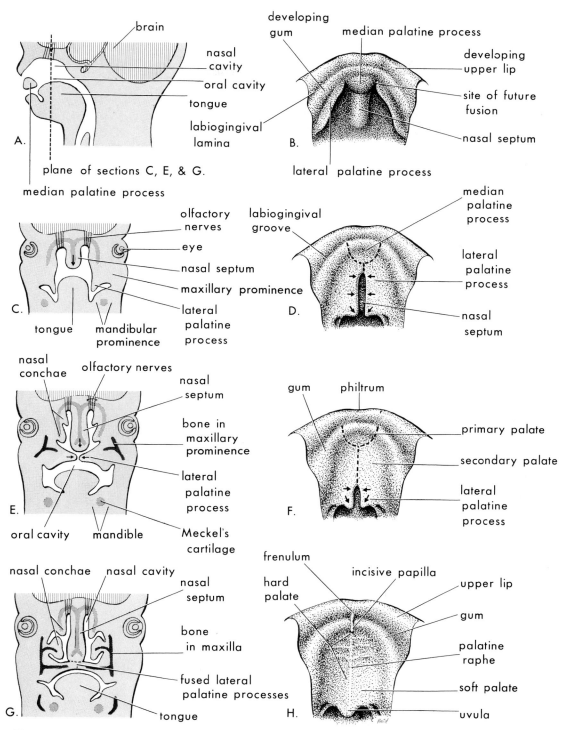

Figure 11–14 *A*, Sketch of a sagittal section of the embryonic head at the end of the sixth week showing the primary palate. *B, D, F*, and *H*, Drawings of the roof of the mouth from the sixth to twelfth weeks illustrating development of the palate. The broken lines in *D* and *F* indicate sites of fusion of the palatine processes; the arrows indicate medial and posterior growth of the lateral palatine processes. *C, E*, and *G*, Drawings of frontal sections of the head illustrating fusion of the lateral palatine processes with each other and the nasal septum, and separation of the nasal and oral cavities.

and its associated gingiva (gum); and (3) the *primary palate*.

The lateral parts of the upper lip, most of the maxilla, and the *secondary palate* form from the maxillary prominences (Figs. 11–13*H* and *I* and 11–14). These prominences merge laterally with the mandibular prominences.

The *frontonasal prominence* (Fig. 11–13) forms the forehead and the dorsum and apex of the nose. The sides (alae) of the nose are derived from the lateral nasal prominences (Fig. 11–13*H* and *I*).

The mandibular prominences merge with each other in the fourth week and the groove between them disappears before the end of the fifth week (Fig. 11–13*D*). The mandibular prominences give rise to the mandible (lower jaw), lower lip, and the inferior part of the face. Final development of the face occurs slowly and results mainly from changes in the proportion and relative position of the facial components.

The smallness of the face at birth results from (1) the rudimentary upper and lower jaws, (2) the unerupted teeth, and (3) the small size of the nasal cavities and maxillary air sinuses.

DEVELOPMENT OF THE PALATE

The palate develops from the *primary palate* and the *secondary palate*. Although palatogenesis begins toward the end of the fifth week, fusion of the palate's parts is not complete until about the twelfth week.

The Primary Palate (Fig. 11–14). The primary palate, or *median palatine process*, develops at the end of the fifth week from the innermost part of the *intermaxillary segment* of the maxilla. It forms a wedge-shaped mass of mesoderm between the maxillary prominences of the developing maxilla.

The Secondary Palate (Fig. 11–14). The secondary palate develops from

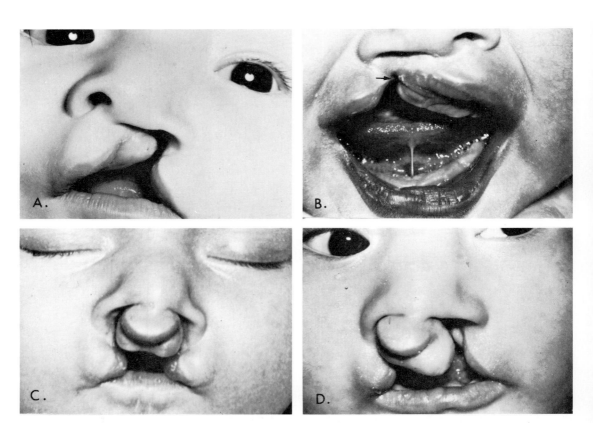

Figure 11–15   Photographs illustrating the various types of cleft lip. *A* and *B*, Unilateral cleft lip. The cleft in *B* is incomplete; the arrow indicates a band of tissue (Simonart's band) connecting the parts of the lip. *C* and *D*, Bilateral cleft lip. Note that the intermaxillary segment of the maxilla protrudes between the clefts in the lip. Deformed, supernumerary, or absent teeth are often associated abnormalities. (Courtesy of Dr. D. A. Kernahan, The Children's Memorial Hospital, Chicago.)

two horizontal projections from the maxillary prominences, called the *lateral palatine processes* (Fig. 11–14*B*). These shelflike structures initially project downward on each side of the tongue (Fig. 11–14*C*), but as the jaws develop, the tongue moves downward and the lateral palatine processes gradually grow toward each other and fuse (Fig. 11–14*E* and *G*). They also fuse with the primary palate and the *nasal septum* (Fig. 11–14*D* to *H*). The fusion begins anteriorly during the ninth week and is complete posteriorly in the region of the *uvula* by the twelfth week. The uvula (Latin, meaning "little grape") is the last part of the palate to form. The *palatine raphe* indicates the line of fusion of the lateral palatine processes (Fig. 11–14*H*).

Bone gradually develops in the primary palate, forming the *premaxillary part of the maxilla*, which carries the incisor teeth. Concurrently, bone extends from the maxillae and palatine bones into the lateral palatine processes to form the *hard palate* (Fig. 11–14). The posterior portions of the lateral palatine processes do not become ossified but extend beyond the nasal septum and fuse to form the *soft palate and uvula* (Fig. 11–14*D*, *F*, and *H*).

CLEFT LIP AND CLEFT PALATE

Cleft lip and cleft palate are common malformations of the face and palate. Although often associated, cleft lip and cleft palate are embryologically and etiologically distinct malformations. They originate at different times during development and involve different developmental processes.

Cleft Lip (Figs. 11–15 to 11–19). This malformation of the upper lip, without or with cleft palate, occurs about once in 1000 births. The defect may be unilateral or bilateral and is *more common in males*. The clefts vary from a small notch to a complete division of the lip and alveolar part of the maxilla.

Unilateral cleft lip results from failure of the maxillary prominence on the affected side to merge with the merged medial nasal prominences (Fig. 11–16).

Bilateral cleft lip results from failure of the maxillary prominences to meet and merge with the medial nasal prominences. In complete bilateral cleft of the upper lip and alveolar part of the maxilla, the intermaxillary segment hangs free and projects anteriorly (Fig. 11–15*C* and *D*). The defects may be similar or dissimilar, with varying degrees of defect on each side.

Cleft Palate (Figs. 11–17 and 11–18). Cleft palate, with or without cleft lip, occurs about once in 2500 births. The clefts may be unilateral or bilateral and are *more common in females*. A cleft may involve only the uvula, or it may extend through the soft and hard regions of the palate. In severe cases associated with cleft lip, the cleft in the anterior and posterior regions of the palate extends through the alveolar part of the maxilla and the lip on both sides. The embryological basis of cleft palate is failure of the mesenchymal masses of the lateral palatine processes to meet and fuse with each other, with the nasal septum, and/or with the median palatine process or primary palate.

The great majority of cases of cleft lip and cleft palate are determined by multiple factors, genetic and possibly also nongenetic, each causing only a minor developmental defect. This is called *multifactorial inheritance*. These factors seem to operate by influencing the amount of neural crest mesenchyme that migrates into the embryonic facial primordia. If this amount is insufficient, clefting of the lip and/or palate occurs.

Studies of twins indicate that genetic factors are of more importance in cleft lip, with or without cleft palate, than in cleft palate alone. A sibling of a child with a cleft palate has an elevated risk of having a cleft palate, but no increased risk of having a cleft lip.

FACIAL CLEFTS

Various types of facial cleft occur, but they are all *extremely rare*. Severe clefts are usually associated with gross malformations of the head. In *median cleft of the lower lip and mandible* (Fig. 11–19*B*), there is a deep cleft resulting from failure of the mandibular prominences of the first branchial arch to merge completely with each other.

Oblique facial clefts are often bilateral and extend from the upper lip to the medial margin of the orbit (Fig. 11–19*C*). They result from failure of the maxillary prominences to merge with the lateral and medial nasal prominences. *Lateral* or *transverse facial clefts* run from the mouth toward the ear. Bilateral clefts leave the mouth very large, a condition called *macrostomia* (Fig. 11–19*D*); this abnormality results from failure of the maxillary and mandibular prominences to merge.

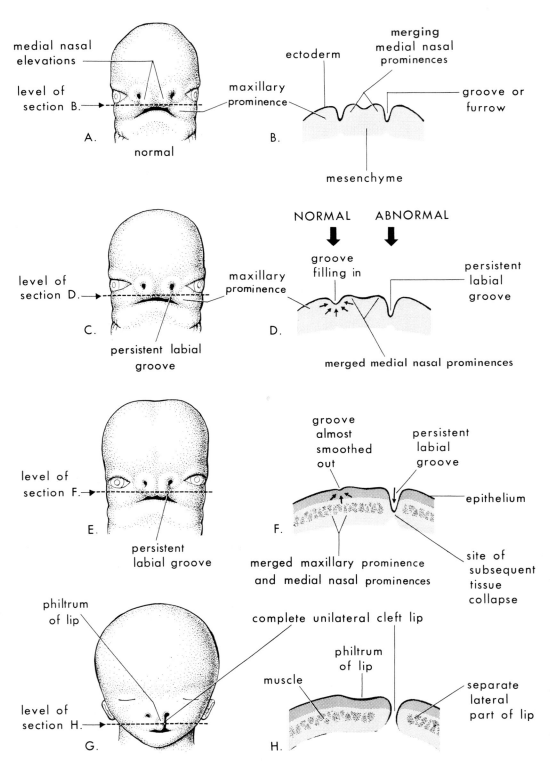

Figure 11–16 *See legend on opposite page*

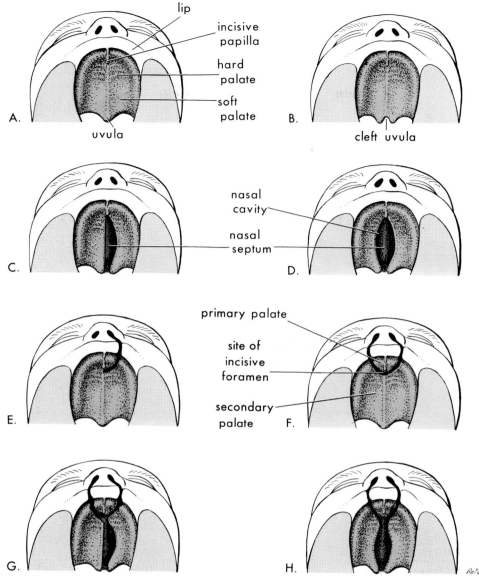

Figure 11–17 Drawings of various types of cleft lip and palate. *A,* Normal lip and palate. *B,* Cleft uvula. *C,* Unilateral cleft of the posterior or secondary palate. *D,* Bilateral cleft of the posterior palate. *E,* Complete unilateral cleft of the lip and alveolar process with a unilateral cleft of the anterior or primary palate. *F,* Complete bilateral cleft of the lip and alveolar process with bilateral cleft of the anterior palate. *G,* Complete bilateral cleft of the lip and alveolar process with bilateral cleft of the anterior palate and unilateral cleft of the posterior palate. *H,* Complete bilateral cleft of the lip and alveolar process with complete bilateral cleft of the anterior and posterior palate.

Figure 11–16 Drawings illustrating the embryological basis of complete unilateral cleft lip. *A,* Five-week embryo. *B,* Horizontal section through the head, illustrating the grooves between the maxillary prominences and the merging medial nasal prominences. *C,* Six-week embryo, showing a persistent labial groove on the left side. *D,* Horizontal section through the head, showing the groove gradually filling in on the right side because of proliferation of the mesenchyme (arrows). *E,* Seven-week embryo. *F,* Horizontal section through the head, showing that the epithelium on the right has almost been pushed out of the groove between the maxillary prominence and medial nasal prominence. *G,* 10-week fetus with a complete unilateral cleft lip. *H,* Horizontal section through the head after stretching of the epithelium and breakdown of the tissues in the floor of the persistent labial groove on the left side, forming a complete unilateral cleft lip. (From Moore, K. L.: *The Developing Human: Clinically Oriented Embryology,* 3rd ed. Philadelphia, W. B. Saunders Company, 1982.)

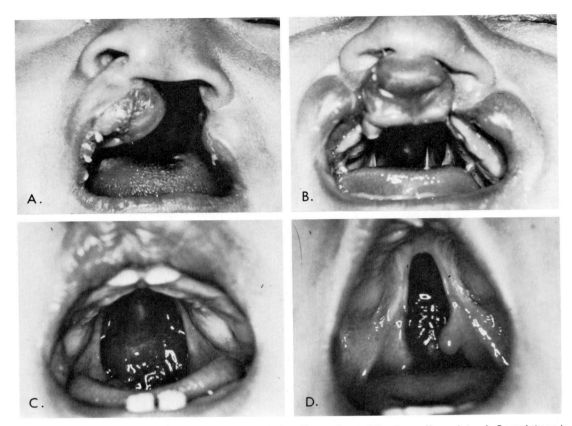

Figure 11–18 Photographs illustrating congenital malformations of the lip and/or palate. *A*, Complete unilateral cleft of the lip and alveolar process of the maxilla. *B*, Complete bilateral cleft of the lip and alveolar processes of the maxillae with bilateral cleft of the anterior palate. Note the protruding intermaxillary segment between the clefts in the lip. *C* and *D*, Bilateral cleft of the posterior or secondary palate. The lip is normal. (Courtesy of Dr. Harry Medovy, Children's Centre, Winnipeg.)

OTHER RARE FACIAL MALFORMATIONS

Congenital microstomia (small mouth) results from excessive merging of the maxillary and mandibular prominences of the first arch (Fig. 11–19*E*). A *single nostril* results when only one nasal placode forms (Fig. 11–19*E*). *Bifid nose* results from failure of the medial nasal prominences to merge completely (Fig. 11–19*F*).

SUMMARY

During the fourth and fifth weeks, the primitive pharynx is bounded laterally by barlike *branchial arches*. Each arch consists of a core of mesenchymal tissue covered externally by *surface ectoderm* and internally by *endoderm*. Each branchial arch also contains an artery, a cartilage bar, a nerve, and a muscle component.

Externally, between the arches, are *branchial grooves*. Internally, between the arches, are extensions of the pharynx called *pharyngeal pouches*. The ectoderm of each branchial groove contacts the endoderm of each pharyngeal pouch, thus forming *branchial membranes*. The pharyngeal pouches and the branchial arches, grooves, and membranes make up the *branchial apparatus*, which contributes greatly to the formation of the head and neck.

Development of the tongue, face, lips,

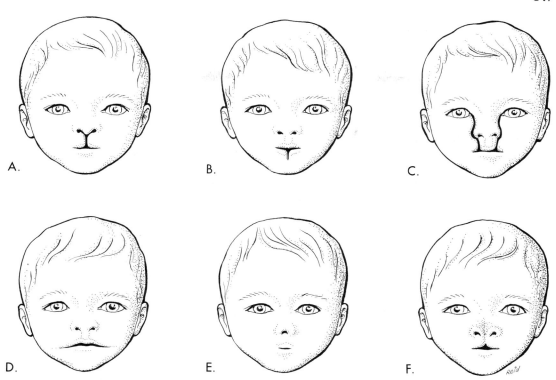

Figure 11–19 Drawings of very rare malformations of the face. *A*, Median cleft lip. *B*, Median cleft of the lower lip and jaw. *C*, Bilateral oblique facial clefts with complete bilateral cleft lip. *D*, Macrostomia or lateral facial cleft. *E*, Single nostril and microstomia; these malformations are not usually associated. *F*, Bifid nose and incomplete median cleft lip.

jaws, palate, pharynx, and neck largely involves transformation of the branchial apparatus into adult structures. The branchial grooves disappear except for the first, which persists as the *external acoustic meatus*. The branchial membranes also disappear, except for the first, which becomes the *tympanic membrane*. The pharyngeal pouches give rise to the *tympanic cavity* and *mastoid antrum*, the *auditory tube*, the palatine tonsil, the thymus, and the parathyroid glands. The thyroid gland develops from a downgrowth from the floor of the pharynx in the region where the tongue develops.

Most congenital malformations of the head and neck originate during transformation of the branchial apparatus into adult structures. *Branchial cysts*, *sinuses*, or *fistulas* may develop from parts of the second branchial groove, the *cervical sinus*, or the second pharyngeal pouch which fail to obliterate.

An *ectopic thyroid gland* results when the thyroid gland fails to descend, or only partially descends, from its site of origin in the tongue. The *thyroglossal duct* may persist or remnants of it may give rise to *thyroglossal duct cysts*; these cysts, if infected, may form thyroglossal duct sinuses which open anteriorly in the midline of the neck.

Cleft lip is the most common congenital abnormality of the face. Although frequently associated with cleft palate, cleft lip and cleft palate are etiologically distinct malformations which involve different developmental processes occurring at different times. *Cleft lip* results from failure of mesenchymal masses of the medial nasal prominences and maxillary prominences to merge, whereas *cleft palate* results from failure of the mesenchymal masses of the palatine processes to fuse.

The great majority of cases of cleft lip, with or without cleft palate, are caused by a combination of genetic and environmental factors (*multifactorial inheritance*). These factors appear to act by influencing the amount of *neural crest mesenchyme* that develops in the maxillary prominences of the first branchial arch. If this amount is insufficient, clefting of the lip and/or palate occurs.

SUGGESTED SUPPLEMENTARY READING

Jaffe, B. F.: The branchial arches—normal development and abnormalities; *in* Ferguson, C. F., and Kendig, E. L., Jr. (Eds.): *Disorders of the Respiratory Tract in Children. Vol. II, Pediatric Otolaryngology*, 2nd ed. Philadelphia, W. B. Saunders Company, 1972, pp. 1118–1125.
Clinical discussions of branchial sinuses, branchial cysts, and thyroglossal duct sinuses and cysts are given. Several good clinical photographs are included.
Ross, R., and Johnston, M. C.: *Cleft Lip and Palate.* Baltimore, Williams & Wilkins Co., 1972.
Presents a comprehensive analysis of basic cleft lip and cleft palate problems and describes how these defects are repaired.

12

THE RESPIRATORY SYSTEM

The respiratory system *begins to form during the fourth week*. A median *laryngotracheal groove* develops in the caudal end of the ventral wall of the primitive pharyngeal floor (Fig. 12–1). Soon this groove deepens to form a *laryngotracheal diverticulum* or outpouching ventral to the primitive pharynx (Fig. 12–2*A*). As this diverticulum grows caudally, it gradually separates from the pharynx. *Tracheoesophageal folds* grow toward each other and fuse to form the *tracheoesophageal septum* (Fig. 12–2*E*). This septum divides the cranial part of the foregut into the *laryngotracheal tube* and the *esophagus* (Fig. 12–2*F*). The laryngotracheal tube is the primordium of the larynx, the trachea, and the lungs. It retains its communication with the pharynx through the *laryngeal aditus* or inlet of the larynx (Fig. 12–2*C*).

DEVELOPMENT OF THE LARYNX

The endodermal lining of the cranial end of the laryngotracheal tube and the surrounding mesenchyme from the fourth and sixth pairs of branchial arches develop into the larynx. The *laryngeal cartilages* develop from the fourth and sixth pairs of branchial arch cartilages (see Fig. 11–4). The epiglottis develops from the caudal half of the *hypobranchial eminence* (see Fig. 11–12). Folds of mucous membrane of the larynx become the *vocal folds* (cords). The *laryngeal muscles* develop from muscle elements in the fourth and sixth pairs of branchial arches.

DEVELOPMENT OF THE TRACHEA

The endodermal lining of the laryngotracheal tube distal to the larynx gives rise to the epithelium and glands of the trachea. The cartilage, connective tissue, and muscle of the trachea are derived from the surrounding splanchnic mesenchyme (Fig. 12–3).

Tracheoesophageal Fistula (Fig. 12–4). A communication, or fistula, connecting the trachea and the esophagus occurs about once in every 2500 births; most infants af-

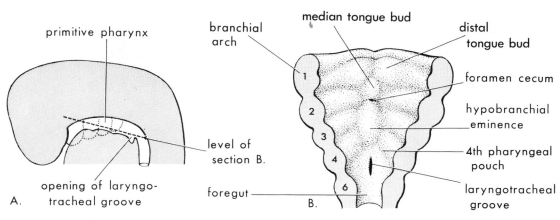

Figure 12–1 *A*, Diagrammatic sagittal section of the cranial half of a human embryo of about 26 days showing the laryngotracheal groove in the caudal end of the floor of the primitive pharynx (develops from the cranial part of the foregut). *B*, Horizontal section at the level shown in *A*, illustrating the floor of the primitive pharynx and the location of the laryngotracheal groove.

149

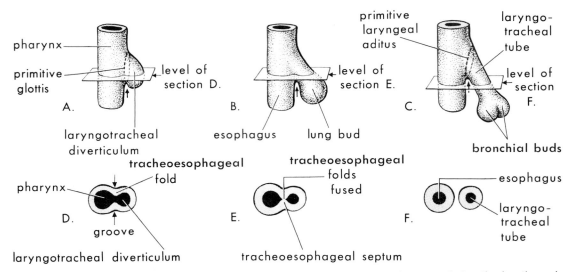

Figure 12–2   Successive stages of development of the tracheoesophageal septum during the fourth week. *A, B,* and *C,* Lateral views of the caudal part of the primitive pharynx illustrating partitioning of the foregut into the esophagus and laryngotracheal tube. *D, E,* and *F,* Transverse sections illustrating development of the tracheoesophageal septum and division of the cranial part of the foregut into the laryngotracheal tube and the esophagus.

fected are males. Tracheoesophageal fistula is usually associated with *esophageal atresia*; in all cases, there is an abnormal communication between the trachea and the esophagus.

Tracheoesophageal fistula results from incomplete division of the foregut into respiratory and digestive portions during the fourth and fifth weeks. Incomplete fusion of the tracheoesophageal folds results in *a defective tracheoesophageal septum*, leaving a communication between the trachea and the esophagus. There are four main varieties of tracheoesophageal fistula. The most common abnormality is for the cranial portion of the esophagus to end blindly (esophageal

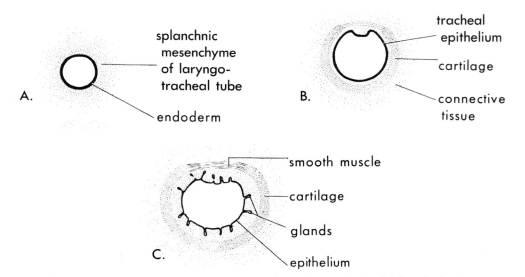

Figure 12–3   Drawings of transverse sections through the laryngotracheal tube illustrating progressive stages of development of the trachea. *A,* 4 weeks. *B,* 10 weeks. *C,* 11 weeks.

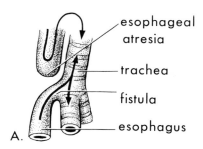

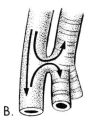

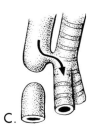

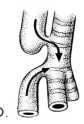

Figure 12–4 Sketches illustrating the four main varieties of tracheoesophageal fistula. Possible direction(s) of flow of contents is indicated by arrows. Esophageal atresia, as illustrated in *A*, occurs in about 90 per cent of cases. The abdomen rapidly becomes distended as the intestines fill with air. In *C*, air cannot enter the lower esophagus and the stomach.

atresia) and for the caudal portion to join the trachea near its bifurcation (Fig. 12–4*A*). Other varieties of this malformation are illustrated in Figure 12–4*B* to *D*.

Infants with the common type of esophageal atresia and tracheoesophageal fistula cough and choke on swallowing owing to ex-

cessive amounts of saliva accumulating in the mouth and the upper respiratory tract. When the infant swallows milk and saliva, they rapidly fill the esophageal pouch and are regurgitated. They then pass into the trachea, resulting in gagging, coughing, and *respiratory distress*. Gastric contents may also reflux through the fistula into the trachea and the lungs from the stomach. This may result in pneumonia or pneumonitis (inflammation of the lungs).

An excess of amniotic fluid (*polyhydramnios*) may be associated with esophageal atresia and tracheoesophageal fistula, because amniotic fluid may not pass to the stomach and intestines for absorption and subsequent placental transfer to the mother's blood for disposal. *Normal fetuses swallow amniotic fluid*, which is absorbed through the intestines into their blood. It then passes via the placenta into the maternal blood via the placenta (see Chapter 8), and is excreted by her kidneys.

DEVELOPMENT OF THE BRONCHI AND LUNGS

A *lung bud* develops at the caudal end of the laryngotracheal tube (Fig. 12–5*A*) and soon divides into two knoblike *bronchial buds* (Fig. 12–5*B*). These buds differentiate into the bronchi and lungs and grow laterally into the *pericardioperitoneal canals* or *primitive pleural cavities* (Fig. 12–6*A*).

Each bronchial bud enlarges to form a primary bronchus. Soon the primary bronchi subdivide into *secondary bronchi*. On the right, the superior secondary bronchus will supply the superior lobe of the lung, whereas the inferior secondary bronchus soon subdivides into two bronchi, one to the middle lobe of the right lung and the other to the inferior lobe. On the left, the two secondary bronchi supply the superior and inferior lobes of the lung.

Each secondary bronchus subsequently undergoes progressive dichotomous branching; that is, each branch bifurcates repeatedly into branches. Tertiary (segmental) bronchi, 10 in the right lung and 8 or 9 in the left, begin to form by the seventh week. As this occurs, the surrounding mesenchymal tissue divides. Each tertiary (segmental) bronchus with its surrounding mass of mesenchyme will form a *bronchopulmonary segment*. By 24 weeks,

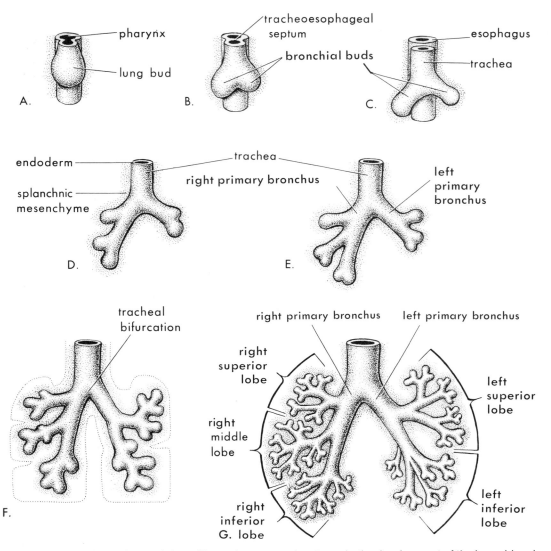

Figure 12–5 Drawings of ventral views illustrating successive stages in the development of the bronchi and lungs. *A* to *D*, 4 weeks. *E*, 5 weeks. *F*, 6 weeks. *G*, 8 weeks.

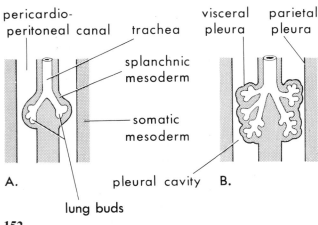

Figure 12–6 Diagrams illustrating the growth of the developing lungs into the splanchnic mesoderm of the medial walls of the pericardioperitoneal canals (primitive pleural cavities), and the development of the layers of the pleura. *A*, 5 weeks. *B*, 6 weeks.

about 17 orders of branches have formed and the respiratory bronchioles are present (Fig. 12–7*A*). An additional seven orders of airways develop after birth.

As the bronchi develop, cartilaginous rings, or plates, develop from the surrounding mesenchyme. This splanchnic mesenchyme also gives rise to the bronchial smooth musculature and connective tissue and to the pulmonary connective tissue and capillaries.

As the lungs develop, they acquire a layer of *visceral pleura* from the splanchnic mesenchyme (Fig. 12–6*B*). With expansion, the lungs and pleural cavities grow caudally into the mesenchyme of the body wall and soon come to lie close to the heart (see Fig. 10–4). The thoracic body wall becomes lined by a layer of *parietal pleura*, derived from the somatic mesoderm (see Fig. 12–6*B*).

Lung development may be divided into four stages.

The Pseudoglandular Period (5 to 17 Weeks). Microscopically, the developing lung somewhat resembles a gland. The air-conducting system develops during this period, but respiration is not possible.

The Canalicular Period (16 to 25 Weeks). The lumina of the bronchi and bronchioles enlarge, and the lung tissue becomes highly vascular. Each terminal bronchiole gives rise to two or more *respiratory bronchioles* (Fig. 12–7*A*). Each of these then divides into three to six sacculations called *alveolar ducts*. Toward the end of this period, the lining cells of these ducts become attenuated, permitting the blood capillaries to project as capillary loops into the future air spaces. Respiration is possible toward the end of this period because some thin-walled saccules, called *terminal sacs* (primitive alveoli), have developed at the ends of the respiratory branchioles, and these regions are well vascularized (Fig. 12–7*A*).

The Terminal Sac Period (24 Weeks to Birth). The alveolar ducts give rise to clusters of thin-walled terminal air sacs or primitive *pulmonary alveoli* (Fig. 12–7*A* and *B*). The capillary network proliferates rapidly in the mesenchyme around the developing alveoli, and *some capillaries bulge into these thin air sacs*. There is concurrent active development of lymphatic capillaries. By 26 weeks, sufficient terminal air sacs are usually

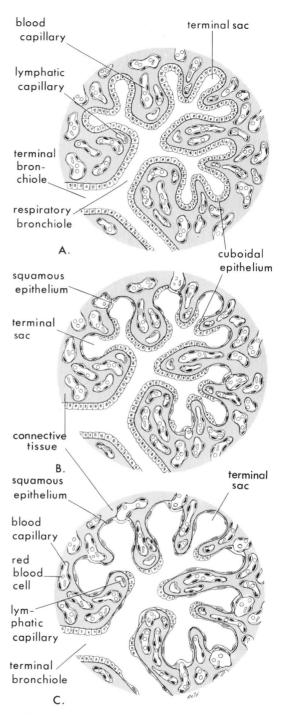

Figure 12–7 Diagrammatic sketches of sections illustrating progressive stages of lung development. *A*, 24 weeks. *B*, 26 weeks. *C*, Newborn infant.

present to permit survival of a prematurely born infant. The development of an adequate pulmonary vasculature is critical to the survival of premature infants.

During this period the type II alveolar cells produce *surfactant*, a substance that covers the internal surface of the alveoli before birth. It is capable of lowering the surface tension at the air-alveolar interface, thereby maintaining patency of the alveoli and facilitating expansion of the lungs at birth. Absence or deficiency of surfactant appears to be a major cause of *hyaline membrane disease*, principally a disease of premature infants.

The Alveolar Period (Late Fetal Period to About Eight Years). The lining of the terminal air sacs becomes extremely thin, thus forming *characteristic pulmonary alveoli* (Fig. 12–7C). One-eighth to one-sixth of the adult number of alveoli are present at birth; their number increases until about the eighth year.

The lungs at birth are about half inflated with liquid derived from the lungs, the amniotic cavity, and the tracheal glands. Consequently, aeration of the lungs at birth involves rapid replacement of intra-alveolar fluid by air.

Respiratory Distress Syndrome. Infants born prematurely are most susceptible to the *respiratory distress syndrome*. Shortly after birth, the infant develops rapid and labored breathing.

A deficiency of pulmonary surfactant appears to be a major cause of *hyaline membrane disease*, a common cause of death in the perinatal period. The lungs are underinflated and the alveoli contain a fluid of high protein content that resembles a hyaline (glassy) membrane.

SUMMARY

The lower respiratory system begins to develop around the middle of the fourth week from a median longitudinal *laryngotracheal groove* in the floor of the primitive pharynx. This groove deepens to produce a *laryngotracheal diverticulum* which is soon separated from the foregut by a *tracheoesophageal septum* to form the esophagus and the *laryngotracheal tube*. The lining of the laryngotracheal tube gives rise to the epithelium of the lower respiratory organs and the tracheobronchial glands. The splanchnic mesenchyme surrounding this tube forms the connective tissue, cartilage, muscle, and blood and lymphatic vessels of these organs.

The laryngotracheal tube divides at its termination into two *bronchial buds* (lung buds). Each bud soon enlarges to form a *primary bronchus* and then each of these gives rise to two new bronchial buds, which develop into *secondary bronchi*. The right inferior secondary bronchus soon divides into two bronchi. The *secondary bronchi* supply the lobes of the developing lungs. Branching continues until about 17 orders of branches have formed. Additional airways are formed after birth, until about 24 orders of branches are formed.

Lung development may be divided into four stages: (1) the *pseudoglandular period*, 5 to 17 weeks, when the bronchi and terminal bronchioles form; (2) the *canalicular period*, 16 to 25 weeks, when the lumina of the bronchi and terminal bronchioles enlarge, the respiratory bronchioles and alveolar ducts develop, and the lung tissue becomes highly vascular; (3) the *terminal sac period*, 24 weeks to birth, when the alveolar ducts give rise to terminal air sacs (primitive alveoli); and (4) the final stage of lung development, the *alveolar period*, from the late fetal period to about eight years of age, when the characteristic pulmonary alveoli develop.

The respiratory system develops so that it is capable of immediate function at birth. To be capable of respiration, the lungs must acquire an *alveolocapillary membrane* that is sufficiently thin, and an adequate amount of *surfactant* must be present.

Major congenital malformations of the lower respiratory system are rare, except for *tracheoesophageal fistula*, which is usually associated with *esophageal atresia*. These common malformations result from faulty partitioning of the foregut into the esophagus and trachea during the fourth and fifth weeks.

SUGGESTED SUPPLEMENTARY READING

Avery, M. E., Fletcher, B. D., and Williams, R.: *The Lung and Its Disorders in the Newborn Infant*, 4th ed. Philadelphia, W. B. Saunders Company, 1981.
A good discussion of the development of the lungs is presented, including descriptions of disorders of respiration in the neonatal period.
Behrman, R. E., and Vaughan, V. C. (Eds.): *Nelson Textbook of Pediatrics*, 12th ed. Philadelphia, W. B. Saunders Company, 1983.
Contains a discussion of the medical-surgical emergency that often occurs in the neonatal period owing to congenital herniation of abdominal contents into the thoracic cavity.
Villee, C. A., Villee, D. B., and Zuckerman, J.: *Respiratory Distress Syndrome*. New York, Academic Press, Inc., 1973.
This book resulted from a conference on lung development and function in relation to respiratory problems of newborn infants.

13

THE DIGESTIVE SYSTEM

The primitive gut forms during the fourth week, as the dorsal part of the yolk sac is enclosed in the embryo (Chapter 6). The endoderm of the primitive gut gives rise to most of the epithelium and glands of the digestive tract. The epithelium at the cranial and caudal extremities of the tract is derived from ectoderm of the *stomodeum* (primitive mouth) and the *proctodeum*, respectively (Fig. 13–1). The muscular and fibrous elements of the digestive tract, and the visceral peritoneum, are derived from the splanchnic mesenchyme surrounding the endodermal lining of the primitive gut.

For descriptive purposes, the primitive gut is divided into three parts: the *foregut*, the *midgut*, and the *hindgut* (Fig. 13–1).

THE FOREGUT

The Esophagus. The partitioning of the trachea from the esophagus by the *tracheoesophageal septum* is described in Chapter 12. Initially the esophagus is very short (Fig. 13–1), but it soon reaches its final relative length. The smooth muscle of the esophagus develops from the surrounding splanchnic mesenchyme.

The epithelium of the esophagus and the esophageal mucous glands are derived from endoderm. The epithelium of the esophagus proliferates and almost obliterates the lumen, but recanalization of the esophagus normally occurs by the end of the embryonic period.

Esophageal Atresia (see Fig. 12–4A). Esophageal atresia is usually associated with *tracheoesophageal fistula*. It may occur as a separate malformation, but this is exceedingly rare. Atresia probably results from deviation of the *tracheoesophageal septum* (see Fig. 12–2) in a posterior direction, but atresia could also result from failure of esophageal recanalization during the embryonic period.

When there is esophageal atresia, amniotic fluid cannot pass to the intestines for absorption and subsequent transfer to the placenta for disposal. This results in *polyhydramnios*, the accumulation of an excessive amount of amniotic fluid.

Newborn infants with esophageal atresia usually appear healthy, and their first one or two swallows are normal. Suddenly, fluid returns through the nose and mouth, and *respiratory distress* occurs. Confirmation of the presence of esophageal atresia can be made by demonstrating radiographically that a radiopaque catheter cannot pass into the stomach.

Esophageal Stenosis. Congenital stenosis, or narrowing of the esophagus is usually present in the distal third as either a web or a long segment of esophagus with only a threadlike lumen. Esophageal stenosis results from incomplete recanalization of the esophagus during the eighth week of development.

The Stomach. The stomach first appears as a fusiform dilatation of the caudal part of the foregut (Figs. 13–1 and 13–2A). This primordium soon enlarges and broadens ventrodorsally (Fig. 13–2B). The dorsal border grows faster than the ventral border, producing the *greater curvature* (Fig. 13–2C). As the stomach acquires its adult shape, it rotates in a clockwise direction around its longitudinal axis.

The stomach is suspended from the dorsal wall of the abdominal cavity by the *dorsal mesentery* or *dorsal mesogastrium* (Fig. 13–2A). The dorsal mesogastrium is carried to the left during rotation of the stomach and formation of a cavity known as the *omental bursa* or *lesser sac* of peritoneum (Fig. 13–2A to C). The lesser sac communicates with the main peritoneal cavity or *greater peritoneal sac* through a small opening, the *epiploic foramen* (Fig. 13–2D).

A *ventral mesentery* or *ventral mesogastrium* (Fig. 13–2B) exists only in the region

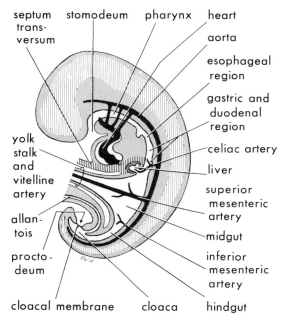

septum trans-versum   stomodeum   pharynx   heart
aorta
esophageal region
gastric and duodenal region
yolk stalk and vitelline artery
celiac artery
liver
superior mesenteric artery
allan-tois
midgut
procto-deum
inferior mesenteric artery
cloacal membrane   cloaca   hindgut

Figure 13–1 Drawing of a median section of a four-week embryo showing the primitive gut or early digestive system and its blood supply. At this stage the primitive gut is a long tube that extends the length of the embryo. It was formed by incorporation of the dorsal part of the yolk sac (see Fig. 6–1.)

of the inferior end of the esophagus, the stomach, and the superior part of the duodenum. It attaches the stomach and duodenum to the developing liver and the ventral abdominal wall (Fig. 13–2D).

Congenital Hypertrophic Pyloric Stenosis. Malformations of the stomach are very rare, except for pyloric stenosis. It affects 1 in every 150 male and 1 in every 750 female infants. In infants with this abnormality, there is a *marked thickening of the pylorus*, the distal sphincteric region of the stomach. The circular and, to a lesser degree, the longitudinal muscle in the pyloric region are hypertrophied. This results in *severe narrowing (stenosis)* of the pyloric canal and obstruction to the passage of food. Although the cause of congenital pyloric stenosis is unknown, the high incidence of the condition in both infants of monozygotic twins suggests the involvement of genetic factors.

The Duodenum. The duodenum develops from the caudal part of the foregut and the cranial part of the midgut. These parts grow rapidly and form a C-shaped loop that projects ventrally (Fig. 13–3B to D).

During the fifth and sixth weeks, the lumen

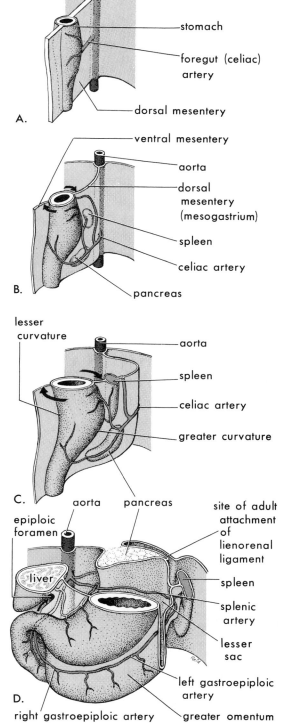

A.
aorta
stomach
foregut (celiac) artery
dorsal mesentery

B.
ventral mesentery
aorta
dorsal mesentery (mesogastrium)
spleen
celiac artery
pancreas

C.
lesser curvature
aorta
spleen
celiac artery
greater curvature

D.
aorta   pancreas
site of adult attachment of lienorenal ligament
epiploic foramen
liver
spleen
splenic artery
lesser sac
left gastroepiploic artery
right gastroepiploic artery
greater omentum

Figure 13–2 Drawings illustrating development and rotation of the stomach and formation of the greater omentum. *A*, About 30 days. *B*, About 35 days. *C*, About 40 days. *D*, About 48 days.

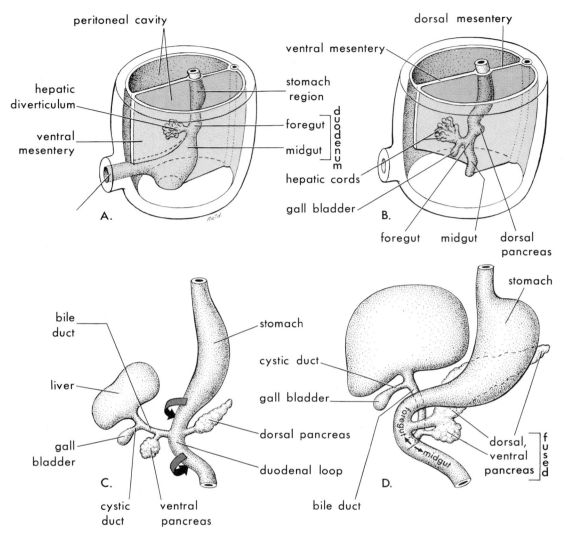

Figure 13–3 Drawings illustrating progressive stages in the development of the duodenum, liver, pancreas and extrahepatic biliary apparatus. *A,* Four weeks. *B* and *C,* Five weeks. *D,* Six weeks. The pancreas develops from dorsal and ventral buds that fuse to form the definitive pancreas. Note that, as the result of the positional changes of the duodenum, the entrance of the bile duct into the duodenum gradually shifts from its initial position to a posterior one. This explains why the bile duct in the adult passes posterior to the duodenum and the head of the pancreas.

of the duodenum becomes reduced and may be temporarily obliterated by epithelial cells, but it normally recanalizes by the end of the embryonic period.

Duodenal Stenosis (Fig. 13–4*A* and *E₃*). Narrowing of the duodenal lumen usually results from incomplete recanalization of the duodenum. Most stenoses involve the horizontal (third) and/or ascending (fourth) parts of the duodenum. Hence the vomitus usually contains bile.

Duodenal Atresia (Fig. 13–4*B*). Blockage of the lumen of the duodenum is not common,

except in premature infants and in those with Down syndrome (see Fig. 9–4). During the solid stage of duodenal development, the lumen is completely filled with epithelial cells. If reformation of the lumen fails to occur by a process of vacuolization (Fig. 13–4*D*), a short segment of the duodenum is occluded.

The Liver and Biliary Apparatus. The liver, the gallbladder, and the biliary duct system arise as a bud from the most caudal part of the foregut (see Fig. 13–3*A*). This *hepatic diverticulum* grows between the layers

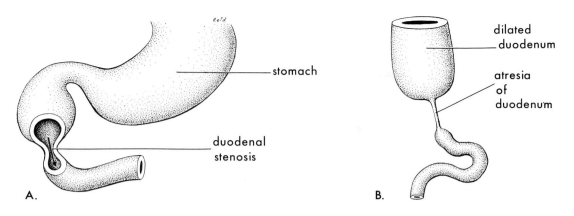

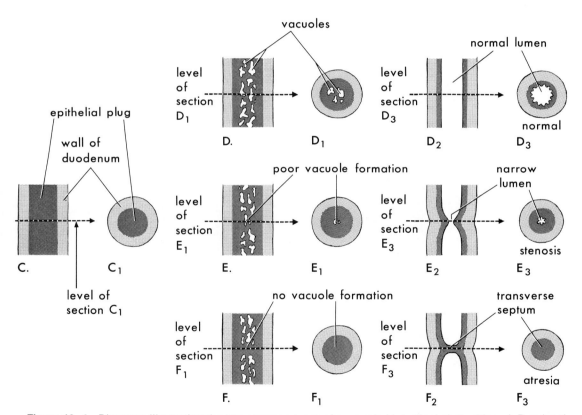

Figure 13–4 Diagrams illustrating the two common types of congenital intestinal obstruction. *A*, Duodenal stenosis. *B*, Duodenal atresia. *C* to *F*, Diagrammatic longitudinal and transverse sections of the duodenum showing: (1) normal recanalization (*D* to D_3), (2) stenosis (*E* to E_3), and (3) atresia (*F* to F_3).

of the ventral mesentery, where it rapidly enlarges and divides into two parts.

The large cranial part is the primordium of the liver. The endodermal cells of the hepatic diverticulum give rise to the parenchymal or *hepatic cells*, which soon become arranged in a series of branching and anastomosing plates. The fibrous and *hemopoietic*

tissue and *Kupffer cells* of the liver are derived from the splanchnic mesenchyme of the septum transversum.

The liver grows rapidly and soon fills most of the abdominal cavity (see Fig. 6–10*C* and *D*). *Hemopoiesis* (formation and development of blood cells) begins during the sixth week; this activity is mainly responsible for the relatively large size of the liver during the second month. By nine weeks, the liver represents about 10 per cent of the total weight of the fetus.

The small caudal portion of the hepatic diverticulum expands to form the *gallbladder* (see Fig. 13–3C). The stalk connecting the hepatic and cystic ducts to the duodenum becomes the *bile duct*.

The Pancreas. The pancreas develops from *dorsal and ventral pancreatic buds* of endodermal cells that arise from the caudal part of the foregut (Fig. 13–5A). When the duodenum grows and rotates to the right

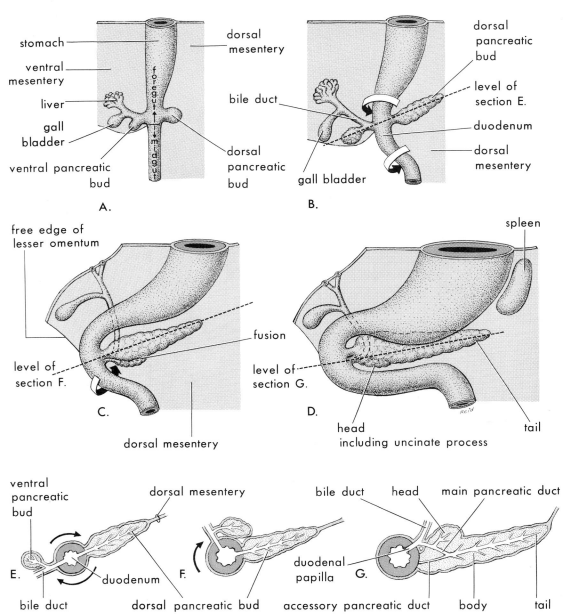

Figure 13–5 *A* to *D*, Schematic drawings showing the successive stages in the development of the pancreas from the fifth to the seventh weeks. *E* to *G*, Diagrammatic transverse sections through the duodenum and the developing pancreas. Growth and rotation (arrows) of the duodenum bring the ventral pancreatic bud toward the dorsal bud, and they subsequently fuse. Note that the common bile duct initially attaches to the ventral aspect of the duodenum, and is carried around to the dorsal aspect as the duodenum rotates.

(clockwise), the ventral bud is carried dorsally and fuses with the dorsal bud (Fig. 13–5D and G).

The Spleen. Development of the spleen is described here because this organ is derived from a mass of mesenchymal cells between the layers of the dorsal mesogastrium. The spleen, a large, vascular, lymphatic organ, acquires its characteristic shape early in the fetal period (see Figs. 13–2 and 13–5D).

THE MIDGUT

Rotation and Fixation of the Midgut. At first the midgut communicates widely with the yolk sac (see Fig. 13–1), but this connection soon becomes reduced to the narrow *yolk stalk* (see Figs. 6–10A and 13–6A).

Herniation of the Midgut. As the midgut elongates, it forms a ventral U-shaped *midgut loop* which projects into the umbilical cord (Fig. 13–6A). This "herniation" is a normal migration of the midgut into the extraembryonic coelom which occurs because there is not enough room in the abdomen. The space shortage is caused mainly by the relatively massive liver and kidneys.

Within the umbilical cord, the *midgut loop rotates counterclockwise*, as viewed from the ventral aspect of the embryo (Fig. 13–6B), around the axis of the *superior mesenteric artery*. This brings the cranial limb of the midgut loop to the right and the caudal limb to the left (Fig. 13–6B and B_1).

Return of the Midgut. During the tenth week, the intestines return rapidly to the abdomen, the so-called "reduction of the midgut hernia." As the intestines return, they undergo further rotation (Fig. 13–6C_1 and D_1). The decrease in the relative size of the liver and kidneys and enlargement of the abdominal cavity are likely important factors related to the return of the intestines to the abdomen. When the colon returns to the abdominal cavity, its cecal end rotates to the right side and then downward into the lower right quadrant of the abdomen (Fig. 13–6D and E).

Fixation of the Intestines. Lengthening of the proximal part of the colon gives rise to the hepatic flexure and ascending colon (Fig. 13–6D and E). As the ascending colon assumes its final position, its mesentery is pressed against the posterior abdominal wall. The mesentery of the ascending colon gradually disappears. The other derivatives of the midgut loop retain their mesenteries.

The Cecum and Appendix. The primordium of the cecum and appendix is the *cecal diverticulum*, which appears during the fifth week. This conical pouch appears on the caudal limb of the midgut loop (Fig. 13–6B). The distal end or apex of this blind sac does not grow so rapidly, and thus the appendix forms (Fig. 13–6E). By birth it is a long blind tube, relatively longer than in the adult.

Omphalocele (Fig. 13–7). This condition occurs once in about 6000 births and results from failure of the intestines to return to the abdomen during the second stage of rotation of the midgut loop. The hernia may consist of a single loop of bowel, or it may contain most of the intestines. The covering of the hernial sac is the amniotic epithelium of the umbilical cord.

Faulty closure of the lateral body folds during the fourth week (see Chapter 6) produces a large defect in the anterior abdominal wall and results in most of the abdominal viscera developing outside the embryo in a transparent sac of amnion. This severe type of omphalocele, sometimes called *eventration of the abdominal viscera*, is often associated with exstrophy of the urinary bladder (see Chapter 14).

Umbilical Hernia. When the intestines return normally to the abdominal cavity and then herniate either prenatally or postnatally through an inadequately closed umbilicus, an umbilical hernia forms. An umbilical hernia differs from an omphalocele in that *the protruding mass (omentum, or loop of bowel) is covered by subcutaneous tissue and skin.* The hernia usually does not reach its maximum size until the end of the first month after birth. It ranges in size from a marble to a grapefruit.

Nonrotation (Fig. 13–8A). This relatively common condition, often called "left-sided colon," is generally asymptomatic, but volvulus (twisting) of the intestines may occur. In nonrotation, the midgut loop does not rotate as it enters the abdomen; as a result, the caudal limb of the loop returns to the abdomen first and the small intestine lies on the right side of the abdomen and the entire large intestine on the left. When volvulus occurs, the superior mesenteric artery may be obstructed by the twisting. This results in *infarction* and gangrene of the bowel supplied by it.

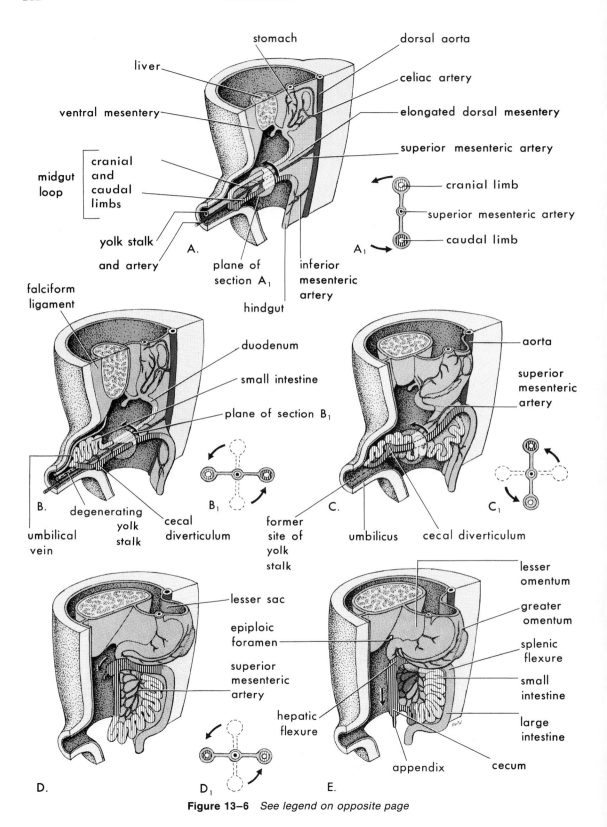

Figure 13–6   *See legend on opposite page*

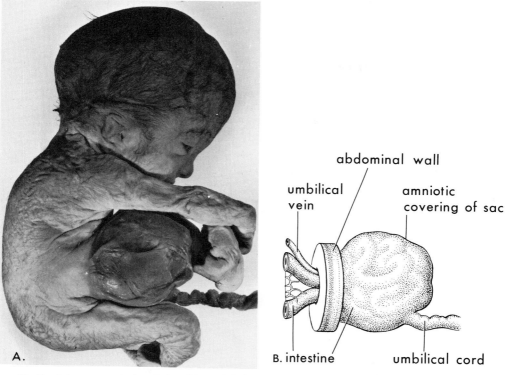

Figure 13–7   *A,* Large omphalocele in a 28-week fetus. *Half actual size. B,* Drawing illustrating the structure and contents of the hernial sac. This condition results when the intestines do not return to the abdominal cavity from the umbilical cord during the tenth week.

Mixed Rotation and Volvulus (Fig. 13–8*B*).   In this condition, the cecum lies inferior to the pylorus and is fixed to the posterior abdominal wall by peritoneal bands that pass over the duodenum. These bands and the frequent presence of volvulus of the intestines usually cause *duodenal obstruction.* This type of malrotation results from failure of the midgut loop to complete the final 90 degrees of rotation; consequently, the terminal part of the ileum returns to the abdomen first.

Subhepatic Cecum and Appendix (Fig. 13–8*D*).   Failure of the proximal part of the colon to elongate during the third stage of rotation results in the cecum remaining near the liver as the abdomen enlarges. More common in males, this condition occurs in about 6 per cent of fetuses and results in the cecum and the appendix being located in the subcostal region, near the inferior surface of the liver. Some elongation of the colon occurs during childhood; hence, a subhepatic cecum is not so common in adults.

Mobile Cecum.   In about 10 per cent of people the cecum has an unusual amount of freedom, so it may even become herniated

Figure 13–6   Drawings showing rotation of the midgut, as seen from the left. *A,* Around the end of the fifth week, showing the midgut loop partially within the umbilical cord. Note the elongated, double-layered dorsal mesentery containing the superior mesenteric artery. A_1, Transverse section through the midgut loop illustrates the initial relationship of the limbs of the midgut to the artery. *B,* Later stage showing the beginning of the midgut rotation. B_1 illustrates the 90-degree counterclockwise rotation which carries the cranial limb to the right. *C,* About 10 weeks, showing the intestines returning to the abdomen. C_1 illustrates a further rotation of 90 degrees. *D,* Slightly later, following return of intestines to the abdomen. D_1 shows there has been a further 90-degree rotation of the gut, making a total of 270 degrees. *E,* Late fetal period, after descent of the cecum to its normal position and fixation of the gut.

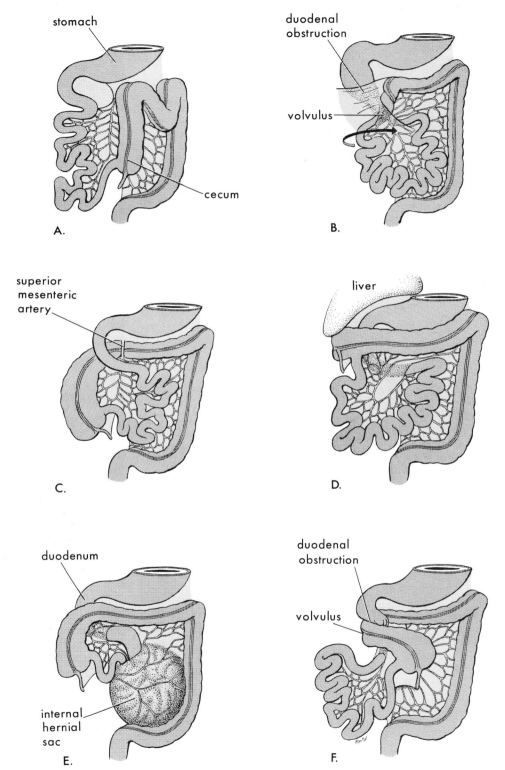

Figure 13–8 Drawings illustrating various abnormalities of midgut rotation. *A*, Nonrotation. *B*, Mixed rotation and volvulus (twisting of the intestines). *C*, Reversed rotation. *D*, Subhepatic cecum. *E*, Paraduodenal hernia. *F*, Midgut volvulus.

through the right inguinal canal. This condition results from incomplete fixation of the ascending colon. It is also significant because of the possible variations in position of the appendix and because volvulus of the cecum may occur.

Midgut Volvulus (Fig. 13–8F).   In this condition, the small bowel fails to enter the abdominal cavity normally and the mesenteries fail to undergo normal fixation. As a result, twisting of the intestine commonly occurs with incomplete rotation of the midgut loops. Because of the twisting of the intestines, *intestinal obstruction* and occlusion of the superior mesenteric artery frequently occur.

Intestinal Stenosis and Atresia (see Fig. 13–4).   Narrowing, or stenosis, and complete obstruction, or atresia, of the intestinal lumen occur most often in the duodenum and the ileum. The length of the area affected varies. Failure of an adequate number of vacuoles to form during recanalization leaves a transverse diaphragm, producing a so-called diaphragmatic atresia.

Most jejunoileal atresias are probably caused by infarction of the fetal bowel as the result of impairment of its blood supply. This probably occurs during the tenth week, when the intestines are returning to the abdomen. Malfixation of the gut predisposes it to strangulation and impairment of its blood supply, owing to *volvulus* (twisting of the gut).

Meckel's Diverticulum (Fig. 13–9). This ileal diverticulum is one of the most common malformations of the digestive tract; it occurs in 2 to 4 per cent of people. This malformation is three to five times more prevalent in males than in females. A Meckel's diverticulum is of clinical significance because it sometimes becomes inflamed and causes symptoms mimicking appendicitis.

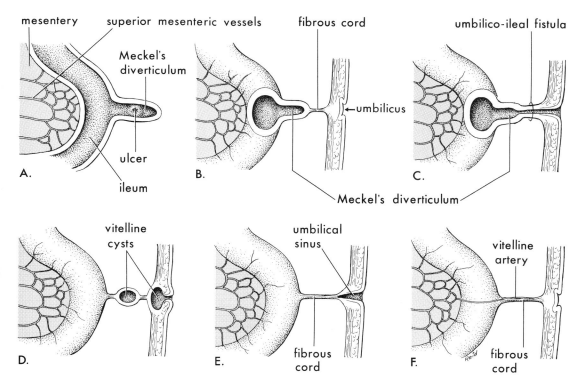

Figure 13–9 Drawings illustrating Meckel's diverticulum and other remnants of the yolk stalk. *A*, Section of the ileum and a Meckel's diverticulum with an ulcer. *B*, Meckel's diverticulum connected to the umbilicus by a fibrous cord. *C*, Umbilico-ileal fistula resulting from persistence of the entire intra-abdominal portion of the yolk stalk. *D*, Vitelline cysts at the umbilicus and in a fibrous remnant of the yolk stalk. *E*, Umbilical sinus resulting from the persistence of the yolk stalk near the umbilicus. The sinus is not always connected to the ileum by a fibrous cord as illustrated. *F*, The yolk stalk has persisted as a fibrous cord connecting the ileum with the umbilicus. A persistent vitelline artery extends along the fibrous cord to the umbilicus.

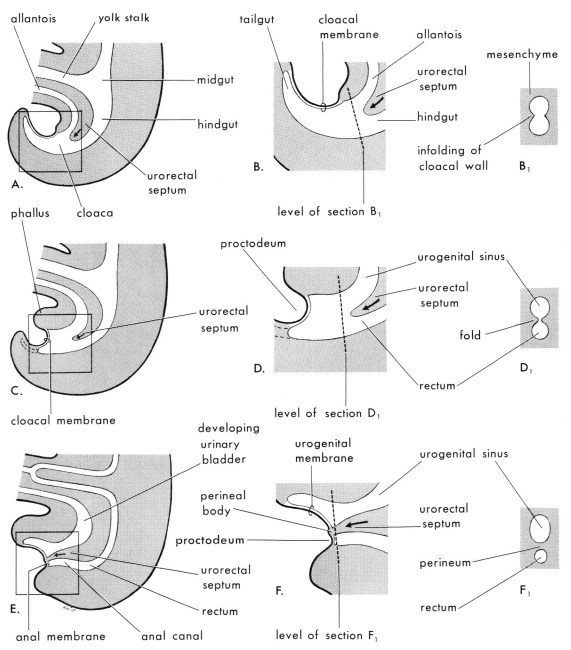

Figure 13–10 Drawings illustrating successive stages in the partitioning of the cloaca into the rectum and urogenital sinus by the urorectal septum. *A, C,* and *E,* Views from the left side at 4, 6, and 7 weeks, respectively. *B, D,* and *F* are enlargements of the cloacal region. $B_1, D_1,$ and F_1 are transverse sections through the cloaca at the levels shown in *B, D,* and *F.*

The wall of the diverticulum contains all layers of the ileum and *may contain gastric and pancreatic tissues*. The gastric mucosa often secretes acid, producing ulceration.

A Meckel's diverticulum represents the remnant of the proximal portion of the *yolk stalk*. Typically, it appears as a finger-like pouch, about 3 to 6 cm long, arising from the antimesenteric border of the ileum 40 to 50 cm from the ileocecal junction. A Meckel's diverticulum may be connected to the umbilicus by a fibrous cord or a fistula.

THE HINDGUT

The hindgut extends from the midgut to the cloacal membrane. This membrane is composed of endoderm of the cloaca and ectoderm of the *proctodeum* or *anal pit* (Fig. 13–10). The expanded terminal part of the hindgut, the *cloaca*, receives the allantois ventrally.

The cloaca is divided by a coronal sheet of mesenchyme, the *urorectal septum*, which develops in the angle between the allantois

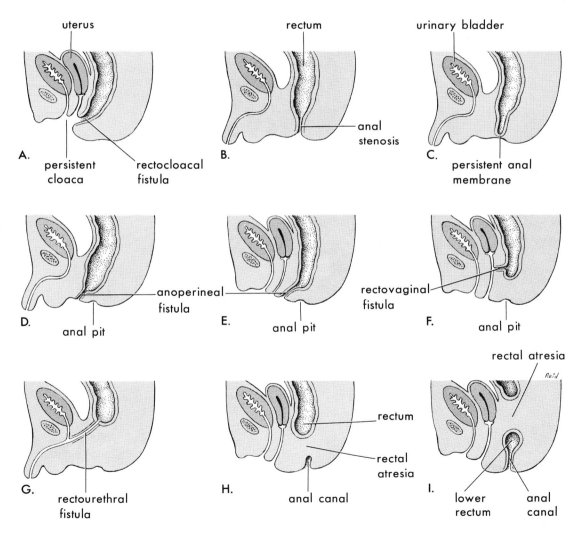

Figure 13–11   Drawings illustrating various anorectal malformations. *A,* Persistent cloaca. Note the common outlet for the intestinal, urinary, and reproductive tracts. This very rare condition usually occurs in females. *B,* Anal stenosis. *C,* Membranous atresia (covered anus). *D* and *E,* Anal agenesis with fistula. *F,* Anorectal agenesis with rectovaginal fistula. *G,* Anorectal agenesis with rectourethral fistula. *F* and *G* are sometimes called persistent cloaca. *H* and *I,* Rectal atresia. Sometimes the two segments of bowel are connected by a fibrous cord.

and the hindgut (Fig. 13–10*B*). As this septum grows toward the cloacal membrane, infoldings of the lateral walls of the cloaca form (Fig. 13–10*B₁*). These folds grow toward each other and fuse, dividing the cloaca into two parts: (1) the *rectum and upper anal canal* dorsally, and (2) the *urogenital sinus* ventrally (Fig. 13–10*D* and *F*).

By the end of the sixth week, the urorectal septum has fused with the cloacal membrane, dividing it into a dorsal *anal membrane* and a larger ventral *urogenital membrane* (Fig. 13–10*E* and *F*). The anal membranes rupture at the end of the seventh week, thus establishing the *anal canal*.

Imperforate Anus and Related Malformations.   Some form of imperforate anus occurs once in about 5000 births. Most anorectal malformations result from abnormal development of the urorectal septum, resulting in incomplete separation of the cloaca into urogenital and anorectal portions (Fig. 13–10). If the urorectal septum fails to develop, a *persistent cloaca* results (Fig. 13–11*A*).

Anal Agenesis With or Without Fistula (Fig. 13–11*D* and *E*).   The anal canal may end blindly, but more often there is an abnormal opening (ectopic anus) or fistula which opens into the perineum. The fistula may, however, open into the vulva in females or into the urethra in males. Anal agenesis with fistula results from incomplete separation of the cloaca by the urorectal septum.

Anal Stenosis (Fig. 13–11*B*).   The anus is in the normal position, but the anal canal is narrow. This malformation probably results from a slight dorsal deviation of the urorectal septum as it grows caudally to fuse with the cloacal membrane.

Membranous Atresia of the Anus (Fig. 13–11*C*).   The anus is in the normal position, but a thin layer of tissue separates the anal canal from the exterior. This rare condition results from failure of the anal membrane to perforate at the end of the seventh week.

Anorectal Agenesis With or Without Fistula (Fig. 13–11*F* and *G*).   The rectum ends well above the anal canal; *this is the most common type of anorectal malformation*. Although the rectum may end blindly, there is usually a fistula to the urethra in males or to the vagina in females. Anorectal agenesis has an embryological basis similar to that of anal agenesis, described previously.

Rectal Atresia (Fig. 13–11*H* and *I*). Both the anal canal and rectum are present, but they are separated by an atretic segment of rectum. The cause of rectal atresia is abnormal recanalization or defective blood supply, as discussed with malformations of the small intestines.

SUMMARY

The *primitive gut* forms during the fourth week by incorporation of the roof of the yolk sac into the embryo. It consists of three parts. The *foregut* gives rise to the pharynx and lower respiratory system, the esophagus, the stomach, the duodenum (as far as the bile duct), the pancreas, the liver, and the biliary apparatus.

The *midgut* gives rise to the duodenum (distal to the bile duct), the jejunum, the ileum, the cecum, the appendix, the ascending colon, and the right or proximal half to two-thirds of the transverse colon. The midgut herniates into the umbilical cord during the fifth week because of inadequate room in the abdomen. During the tenth week, the intestines rapidly return to the abdomen. *Omphalocele*, malrotation, and abnormalities of fixation result from failure of or abnormal return of the intestines to the abdomen. Because the gut is normally occluded at one stage, stenosis (narrowing), atresia (obstruction), and duplications may result if recanalization fails to occur or occurs abnormally. Various remnants of the yolk stalk may persist; *Meckel's diverticulum* is common and is clinically significant.

The *hindgut* gives rise to the left or distal one-third to half of the transverse colon, the descending and sigmoid colon, the rectum, and superior part of the anal canal. The remainder of the anal canal develops from the anal pit or proctodeum. The caudal part of the hindgut is expanded into the *cloaca*, which is divided by the *urorectal septum* into the urogenital sinus and rectum. At first, the rectum is separated from the exterior by the *anal membrane*, but this normally breaks down at the end of the seventh week. Most anorectal malformations arise from abnormal partitioning of the cloaca by the urorectal septum into anorectal and urogenital parts.

SUGGESTED SUPPLEMENTARY READING

Crelin, E. S.: Development of the gastrointestinal tract. *Clin. Symp. 13*:67, 1961.

A well illustrated account of the development of the digestive system. It also includes a discussion of common congenital malformations.

Estrada, R. L.: *Anomalies of Intestinal Rotation and Fixation.* Springfield, IL, Charles C Thomas, 1968.

A good account of congenital malformations of the gut, with emphasis on abnormalities of rotation and fixation of the gut.

14

THE UROGENITAL SYSTEM

Development of the urinary (excretory) and genital (reproductive) systems is closely associated and parts of one system are used by the other and vice versa.

Both the urinary and genital systems develop from the intermediate mesoderm (see Fig. 5–5B), which extends along the entire length of the dorsal body wall of the embryo. During transverse folding of the embryo, the intermediate mesoderm is carried ventrally and loses its connection with the somites. This longitudinal mass of mesoderm on each side of the primitive aorta in the trunk region is called a *nephrogenic cord* (Fig. 14–1A).

Development of the urogenital system is easier to understand if the urinary and genital systems are described separately.

THE URINARY SYSTEM

THE KIDNEY AND URETER

Three successive sets of excretory organs develop in human embryos: the *pronephros,* the *mesonephros,* and the *metanephros.* The third set remains as the permanent kidneys.

The pronephros (or "forekidney") is a transitory, nonfunctional structure which appears early in the fourth week (Fig. 14–1A). The pronephros soon degenerates, but most of its duct is utilized by the next kidney (Fig. 14–1B).

The mesonephros (or "midkidney") appears later in the fourth week caudal to the rudimentary pronephros (Fig. 14–1). It may function while the permanent kidney is developing. By the end of the embryonic period, the mesonephros has degenerated and disappeared, except for its duct and a few tubules which persist as genital ducts in males or form vestigial remnants in females.

The metanephros (or "hindkidney") is the one which becomes the permanent kidney. It

appears in the fifth week and begins to function about three weeks later. Urine formation continues actively throughout fetal life. The urine mixes with the amniotic fluid which the fetus drinks (see Chapter 8).

The metanephros develops from two sources: the *metanephric diverticulum,* or ureteric bud, and a mass of *metanephric mesoderm* (Fig. 14–2A and B). The metanephric diverticulum is a dorsal bud from the mesonephric duct which grows into the mass of metanephric mesoderm (Fig. 14–2B). The stalk of the metanephric diverticulum becomes the ureter, and its expanded cranial end forms the renal pelvis. The pelvis divides into *major* and *minor calyces,* from which collecting tubules soon grow (Fig. 14–2C to E). Each collecting tubule undergoes repeated branching, forming successive generations of collecting tubules. Near the blind end of each arched collecting tubule (Fig. 14–3A), clusters of mesenchymal cells develop into metanephric tubules (Fig. 14–3B). The ends of these tubules are invaginated by an ingrowth of the fine blood vessels, the *glomerulus,* to form a double-layered cup, the glomerular (Bowman's) capsule. The renal corpuscle (glomerulus and capsule) and its associated tubules form a *nephron.* The distal convoluted tubule of the nephron contacts an arched collecting tubule, and the two tubules soon become confluent.

Positional Changes of the Kidney (Fig. 14–4). Initially, the kidneys are in the pelvis, but they gradually come to lie in the abdomen. This migration results mainly from growth of the embryo's body caudal to the kidneys. In effect, the caudal part of the embryo grows away from the kidneys so that they occupy progressively higher levels. Eventually, they come to lie posterior to the peritoneum on the posterior abdominal wall.

As the kidneys move out of the pelvis, they are supplied by arteries at successively

170

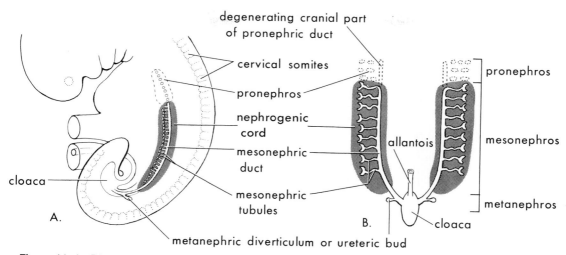

Figure 14–1   Diagrammatic sketches illustrating the three sets of excretory structures present in an embryo of about 29 days. *A*, Lateral view. *B*, Ventral view. The metanephros becomes the permanent kidney. For the sake of simplicity, the mesonephric tubules have been pulled out to the sides of the mesonephric ducts. Actually, the tubules lie medial to ducts as shown in *A*.

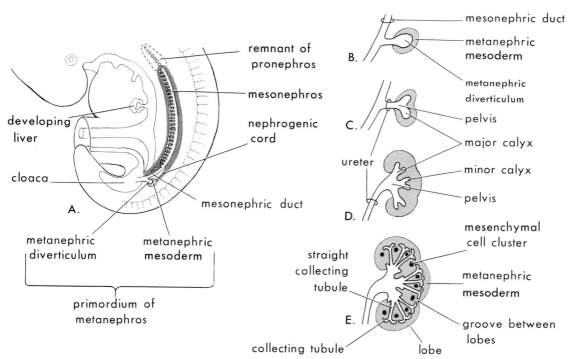

Figure 14–2   *A*, Sketch of a lateral view of a five-week embryo showing the primordium of the metanephros or permanent kidney. *B* to *E*, Sketches showing successive stages of development of the metanephric diverticulum (fifth to eighth weeks) into the ureter, pelvis, calyces, and collecting tubules. The renal lobes illustrated in *E* are visible in the kidneys of newborn infants. The external evidence of the lobes normally disappears by the end of the first year.

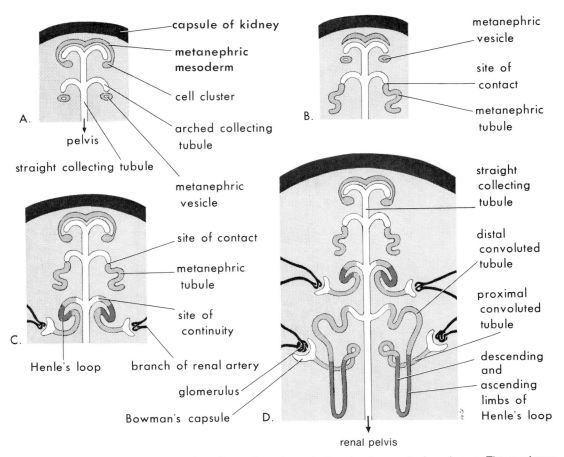

Figure 14–3   Diagrammatic sketches illustrating stages in the development of nephrons. The nephrons become continuous with the collecting tubules to form uriniferous tubules.

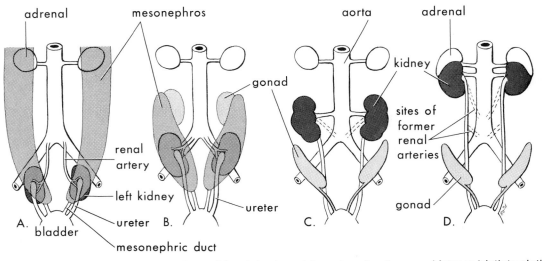

Figure 14–4   Diagrams of ventral views of the abdominopelvic region of embryos and fetuses (sixth to ninth weeks) showing the medial rotation and ascent of the kidneys from the pelvis to the abdomen. Note that as the kidneys ascend, they are supplied by arteries at successively higher levels.

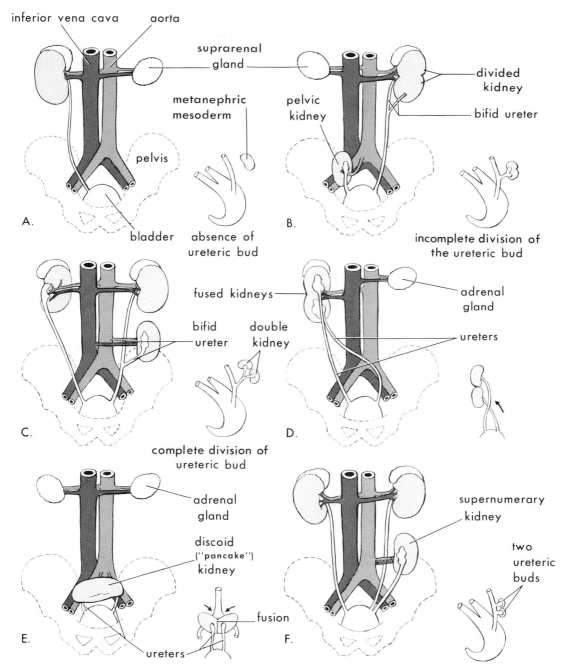

Figure 14–5   Drawings illustrating various abnormalities of the upper urinary tract. The small sketch to the lower right of each drawing illustrates the probable embryological basis of the malformation. *A*, Unilateral renal agenesis. *B*, Right side, pelvic kidney; left side, bifid ureter. *C*, Right side, malrotation of the kidney; left side, bifid ureter and two kidneys. *D*, Crossed renal ectopia. The left kidney crossed to the right side and fused with the right kidney. *E*, "Pancake" or discoid kidney resulting from fusion of the unascended kidneys. *F*, Supernumerary left kidney resulting from the development of two ureteric buds.

higher levels. The caudal arteries normally degenerate as the kidney ascends and new vessels form.

Abnormalities of the Kidneys and Ureters. These abnormalities occur in 3 to 4 per cent of the population and include variations in blood supply, abnormal positions, and upper urinary tract duplications.

Renal Agenesis (Fig. 14–5A). Unilateral absence of a kidney is relatively common, occurring about once in every 1000 births. *Unilateral renal agenesis* causes no symptoms and is usually not discovered in the neonatal period because the other kidney is able to perform the function of the missing kidney.

Bilateral renal agenesis is rare (about 0.3 per 1000 births), and is incompatible with postnatal life. Most infants afflicted with this malformation die during birth or a few hours later. Because no urine is excreted into the amniotic fluid, *bilateral renal agenesis is associated with oligohydramnios* (deficiency in the amount of amniotic fluid).

Renal agenesis results when the metanephric diverticulum fails to develop, or when early degeneration of this bud occurs. Failure of the metanephric diverticulum to penetrate the metanephric mesoderm results in absence of kidney development because no nephrons are induced to develop from the metanephric mesoderm.

Ectopic Kidneys (Fig. 14–5B and E). One or both kidneys may be in an abnormal position. They are lower than usual and malrotated. Most ectopic kidneys are located in the pelvis, but some are low in the abdomen.

Pelvic kidney and other forms of low kidney result from failure of the kidneys to "ascend." Pelvic kidneys may fuse to form a round mass known as a *pancake kidney* (Fig. 14–5E). Ectopic kidneys receive their blood supply from blood vessels near them, and they are often supplied by multiple vessels.

An unusual type of ectopic kidney is *unilateral fused kidney* (Fig. 14–5D). The developing kidneys fuse while in the pelvis, and one kidney "ascends" to its normal position, carrying the other one with it across the midline.

Horseshoe Kidney (Fig. 14–6). In 1 in about 600 persons, the kidneys are fused across the midline; usually the inferior poles are fused. The superior poles are fused in less

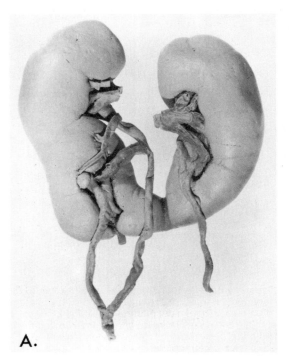

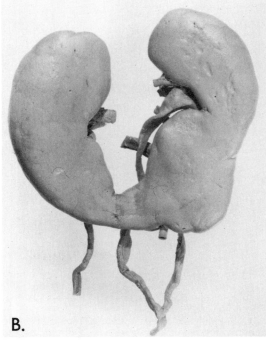

Figure 14–6 Photographs of a horseshoe kidney resulting from fusion of the lower poles of the kidneys. *A*, Anterior view. *B*, Posterior view. *Half actual size.* The larger right kidney has a bifid ureter.

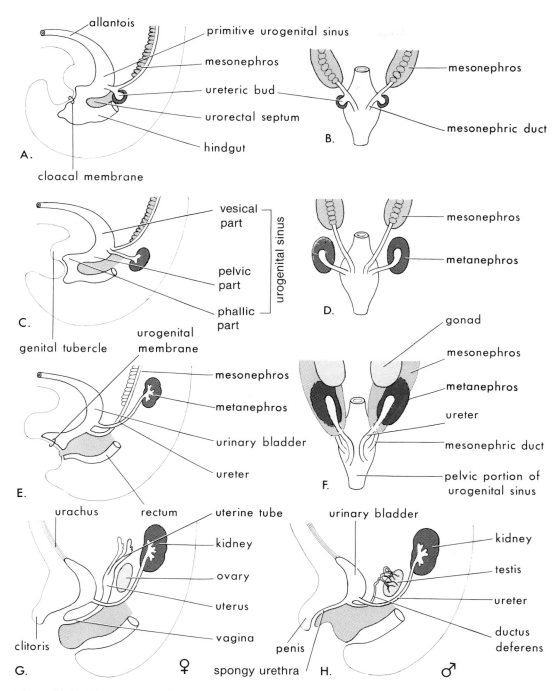

Figure 14–7 Diagrams showing (1) division of the cloaca into the urogenital sinus and the rectum, (2) absorption of the mesonephric ducts, (3) development of the urinary bladder, urethra, and urachus, and (4) changes in the location of the ureters. *A,* Lateral view of the caudal half of a five-week embryo. *B, D,* and *F,* Dorsal views. *C, E, G,* and *H,* Lateral views. The stages shown in *G* and *H* are reached by about 12 weeks.

than 10 per cent of cases. The large, U-shaped kidney usually lies in the hypogastrium at the level of the lower lumbar vertebrae, because normal ascent was prevented by the root of the inferior mesenteric artery. *Horseshoe kidney usually produces no symptoms,* because the collecting system usually develops normally and the ureters usually enter the bladder normally. If urinary outflow is impeded, signs and symptoms of obstruction and/or infection may appear.

Multiple Renal Vessels. Variations in the number of renal arteries and in their position with respect to the renal veins are common. About 25 per cent of kidneys have two or more renal arteries. Supernumerary arteries, usually two or three, are about twice as common as supernumerary veins, and they usually arise at the level of the kidney.

Accessory vessels may arise from the suprarenal artery and pass to the superior pole of the kidney. Polar vessels may also arise from the aorta and pass to the inferior pole of the kidney. Sometimes, an accessory renal artery supplying the inferior pole of the kidney compresses and obstructs the ureter at the ureteropelvic junction. Variations in the blood supply of the kidneys are most common in ectopic kidneys. As the kidney moves out of the pelvis, it is supplied by successively higher vessels, and the lower vessels normally degenerate (see Fig. 14–4). *Vascular variations result from persistence of embryonic vessels that normally disappear when the definitive renal arteries form.*

Duplications of the Upper Urinary Tract (Fig. 14–5). Duplications of the abdominal part of the ureter and renal pelvis are common, but a supernumerary kidney is rare. These abnormalities result from division of the metanephric diverticulum, or ureteric bud. The extent of ureteral duplication depends on how complete the division of the diverticulum is. Incomplete division of the diverticulum results in a divided kidney with a bifid ureter (Fig. 14–5B). Complete division of the diverticulum results in a supernumerary, or double, kidney with a bifid ureter (Fig. 14–5) or with separate ureters. A supernumerary kidney with its own ureter probably results from the formation of an extra ureteric bud (Fig. 14–5F).

THE BLADDER AND URETHRA

Division of the endodermal cloaca by the *urorectal septum* into a dorsal rectum and a ventral urogenital sinus is described in Chapter 13, and is illustrated in Figure 14–7. The urinary bladder and urethra are derived from the urogenital sinus and from the adjacent splanchnic mesenchyme. As the bladder enlarges, the caudal portions of the mesonephric ducts are incorporated into its dorsal wall (Fig. 14–7D). As the mesonephric ducts are absorbed, the ureters come to open separately into the urinary bladder (Fig. 14–7F).

Exstrophy of the Bladder (Fig. 14–8). Fortunately, this severe malformation occurs only about once in every 50,000 births. *Exposure and protrusion of the posterior wall of the urinary bladder* characterize this congenital abnormality, which occurs chiefly in males. The trigone of the bladder and the ureteric orifices are exposed, and urine dribbles intermittently on the mucous membrane of the everted bladder. *Epispadias* (see Fig. 14–16D) and wide separation of the pubic bones are associated with complete exstrophy of the bladder. In some cases, the penis or clitoris is divided and the halves of the scrotum or labia majora are widely separated.

Exstrophy of the bladder is caused by incomplete midline closure of the inferior part of the anterior abdominal wall. The fissure involves not only the anterior abdominal wall but also the anterior wall of the urinary bladder. The defective closure results from failure of mesenchymal cells to migrate between the surface ectoderm and the urogenital sinus during the fourth week. As a result, no muscle forms in the anterior abdominal wall over the urinary bladder. Later, the thin epidermis and the anterior wall of the bladder rupture, causing a wide communication between the exterior and the mucous membrane of the bladder, as shown in Figure 14–8.

THE SUPRARENAL GLAND

The cortex and medulla of the suprarenal (adrenal) glands have different origins. The *cortex* develops from mesoderm and the medulla from neuroectoderm (neural crest cells). The cells which form the medulla are derived from the neural crest which appears as the neural tube forms (see Chapters 5 and 17). The cells which form the *adrenal cortex* are derived from the coelomic epithelium lining the posterior abdominal wall. During the fifth week, cells migrate from adjacent sympathetic ganglia and form a cellular mass on the medial side of the fetal cortex (Fig. 14–

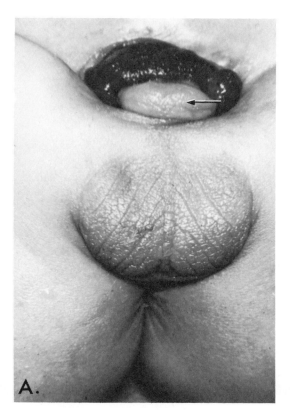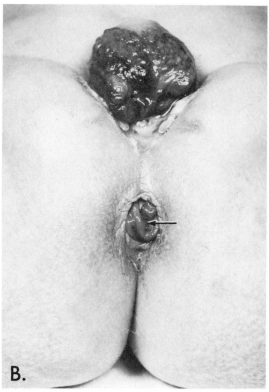

Figure 14–8 Photographs of infants with exstrophy of the bladder. Because of defective closure of the inferior portion of the anterior abdominal wall and the anterior wall of the bladder, the bladder appears as an everted bulging mass inferior to the umbilicus. *A,* Male. Epispadias is also present, and the penis (arrow) is small, flattened, and deeply fissured on the dorsal surface. (Courtesy of Dr. Colin C. Ferguson, Children's Centre, Winnipeg, Canada.) *B,* Female. The arrow indicates a slight prolapse of the rectum. (Courtesy of Mr. Innes Williams, Genitourinary Surgeon, The Hospital for Sick Children, Great Ormond Street, London, England.)

9*C*). These cells are gradually encapsulated by the fetal cortex as they differentiate into the *chromaffin cells* of the adrenal (suprarenal) medulla (Fig. 14–9*D*). Differentiation of the characteristic adrenal cortical zones begins during the late fetal period, but is not complete until the end of the third year.

Hyperplasia of the fetal adrenal cortex during the fetal period usually results in female pseudohermaphroditism (see Fig. 14–15). The adrenogenital syndrome associated with congenital adrenal hyperplasia manifests itself in various clinical forms that, in most aspects, can be correlated with certain *enzymatic deficiencies of cortisol biosynthesis.* Congenital adrenal hyperplasia is caused by a genetically determined deficiency of adrenal cortical enzymes that are necessary for the synthesis of various steroid

hormones. The reduced hormone output results in an increased release of ACTH, which causes adrenal hyperplasia and overproduction of androgens by the hyperplastic adrenal glands. In females, this causes masculinization. In males, the excess androgens may cause precocious sexual development.

THE GENITAL SYSTEM

Although the genetic sex of an embryo is determined at fertilization by the kind of sperm that fertilizes the ovum (see Chapter 3), there is no morphological indication of sex until the seventh week, when the *gonads* (future ovaries or testes) begin to acquire sexual characteristics.

The early genital system is similar in both sexes. This period of early genital develop-

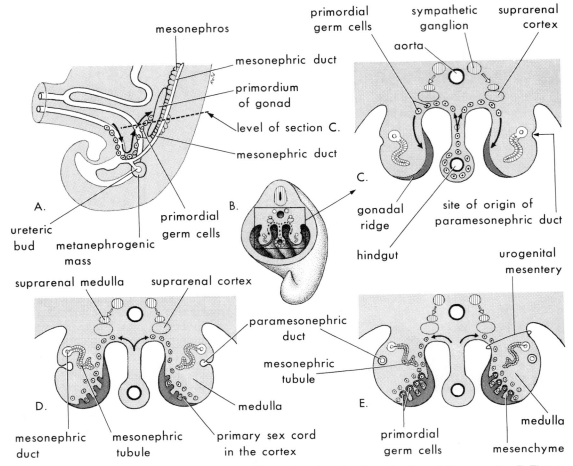

Figure 14–9   *A*, Sketch of five-week embryo illustrating the migration of primordial germ cells. *B*, Three-dimensional sketch of the caudal region of a five-week embryo showing the location and extent of the gonadal ridges on the medial aspect of the urogenital ridges. *C*, Transverse section showing the primordium of the adrenal glands, the gonadal ridges and the migration of primordial germ cells. *D*, Transverse section through a six-week embryo showing the primary sex cords and the developing paramesonephric ducts. *E*, Similar section at later stage showing the indifferent gonads and the mesonephric and paramesonephric ducts.

ment is referred to as the *indifferent stage* of the reproductive organs.

DEVELOPMENT OF TESTES AND OVARIES

The Indifferent Gonads (Figs. 14–9 and 14–10*A*). The gonads are first indicated during the fifth week, when a thickened area of coelomic epithelium develops on the medial aspect of the mesonephros. Proliferation of cells soon produces a bulge on the medial side of each mesonephros known as the *gonadal ridge*. Finger-like epithelial cords, called *primary sex cords*, soon grow into the underlying mesenchyme (Fig. 14–9*D*). The indifferent gonad now consists of an outer *cortex* and an inner *medulla*.

In embryos with an XX sex chromosome complex, the cortex normally differentiates into an ovary, and the medulla regresses. In embryos with an XY sex chromosome complex, the medulla normally differentiates into a testis, and the cortex regresses.

Large spherical primitive sex cells, called *primordial germ cells,* are visible early in the fourth week on the wall of the yolk sac. These cells later migrate along the dorsal mesentery of the hindgut to the gonadal ridges (Fig. 14–9), and become incorporated in the primary sex cords.

Sex Determination. *Genetic sex* is established at fertilization and depends upon whether an X-bearing sperm or a Y-bearing sperm fertilizes the ovum. *Gonadal sex* is determined by the sex chromosome complex. *The Y chromosome has a strong testis-determining effect* on the medulla of the indifferent gonad. Under its influence, the primary sex cords differentiate into seminiferous tubules (Fig. 14–10*B* and *D*). Absence of a Y chromosome results in formation of an ovary (Fig. 14–10*C* and *E*). Thus, the type of sex chromosome complex established at fertilization determines the type of gonad that develops from the indifferent gonad.

Development of Testes (Fig. 14–10*B, D,* and *F*). In embryos with a Y chromosome, the primary sex cords condense and branch. Their ends anastomose to form the *rete testis.* The prominent sex cords, now called *seminiferous cords,* lose their connections with the germinal epithelium as the thick fibrous capsule called the *tunica albuginea* develops (Fig. 14–10*B* and *D*). The seminiferous cords develop into the *seminiferous tubules,* the *tubuli recti,* and the *rete testis.* The walls of the seminiferous tubules are composed of two kinds of cells (Fig. 14–10*F*): supporting or *sustentacular cells of Sertoli,* derived from the surface epithelium, and *spermatogonia,* derived from the primordial germ cells.

The seminiferous tubules become separated by mesenchyme that gives rise to the *interstitial cells* (of Leydig). The interstitial cells produce the male sex hormone *testosterone,* which induces masculine differentiation of the external genitalia. In addition to testosterone, *genital duct inducer and suppressor substances* are produced by the interstitial cells. As described subsequently, these substances induce development of the mesonephric ducts and suppress development of the paramesonephric ducts.

Development of Ovaries (Figs. 14–10*C, E* and *G*). In embryos lacking a Y chromosome, gonadal development occurs very slowly. The ovary is not identifiable until about the tenth week. Thereafter the characteristic cortex begins to develop. The primary sex cords do not become prominent in the gonads of female embryos. The rete ovarii, comparable to the rete testis, is a transitory structure. During the fetal period, secondary sex cords, called *cortical cords,* extend from the germinal epithelium into the underlying mesenchyme (Fig. 14–10*C*). As these cords increase in size, *primordial germ cells* are incorporated into them. The cords break up into isolated cell clusters called *primordial follicles,* consisting of an *oogonium* derived from a primordial germ cell surrounded by a layer of follicular cells (Fig. 14–10*E* and *G*). Active mitosis of oogonia occurs during fetal life, producing thousands of these primitive germ cells. *No oogonia form postnatally.* All oogonia enlarge and become *primary oocytes* before birth (see Fig. 2–5).

DEVELOPMENT OF THE GENITAL DUCTS

The Indifferent Stage (Figs. 14–9 and 14–11). Two pairs of genital ducts develop in both sexes: *mesonephric ducts* and *paramesonephric ducts.* The paramesonephric ducts come together in the midline and fuse into a Y-shaped *uterovaginal primordium* or canal (Fig. 14–11*A*). The funnel-shaped openings of the ducts open into the coelomic or future peritoneal cavity. The uterovaginal primordium projects into the dorsal wall of the urogenital sinus and produces an elevation, called the *sinus tubercle* (Fig. 14–11*B*).

The fetal testes produce two hormones: one stimulates development of the mesonephric ducts into the male genital tract; the other suppresses development of the paramesonephric ducts which develop into female ducts in female fetuses.

Development of the Male Genital Ducts. When the mesonephros degenerates, some mesonephric tubules near the testis persist and are transformed into *efferent ductules* (Fig. 14–12*A*). These ductules open into the mesonephric duct which becomes the *ductus epididymidis* in this region. Beyond the epididymis, the mesonephric duct acquires a thick investment of smooth muscle and becomes the *ductus deferens.*

A lateral outgrowth from the caudal end of each mesonephric duct gives rise to a *seminal vesicle.* The part of the mesonephric duct between the duct of this gland and the urethra becomes the *ejaculatory duct.* The remainder of the male genital duct system consists of the urethra.

The Prostate Gland (Fig. 14–12*A*). Multiple endodermal outgrowths arise from the prostatic portion of the urethra and grow into the surrounding mesenchyme. The glandular epithelium of the prostate differentiates from the endodermal cells, and the associated mesenchyme differentiates into

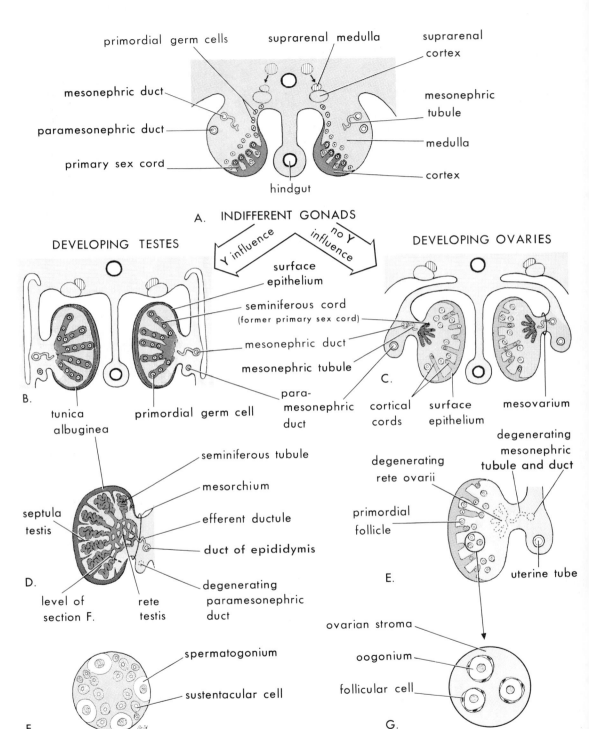

Figure 14–10 *See legend on opposite page*

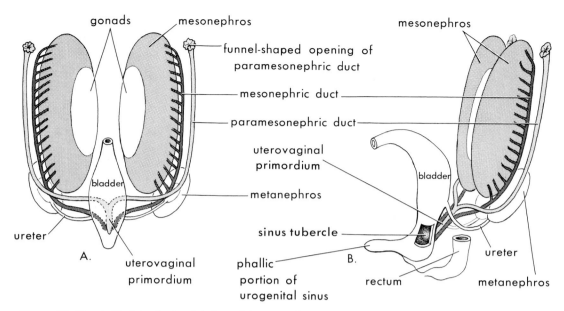

Figure 14–11 *A,* Sketch of a frontal view of the posterior abdominal wall of a seven-week embryo showing the two pairs of genital ducts present during the indifferent stage. *B,* Lateral view of a nine-week fetus showing the sinus tubercle on the posterior wall of the urogenital sinus. It becomes the hymen in females.

the stroma and smooth muscle fibers of the prostate.

The Bulbourethral Glands (Fig. 14–12*A*). These pea-sized structures develop from paired endodermal outgrowths from the membranous portion of the urethra. The smooth muscle fibers and the stroma differentiate from the adjacent mesenchyme.

Development of the Female Genital Ducts. In female embryos, the mesonephric ducts regress and the paramesonephric ducts develop into the female genital tract. The cranial unfused portions of the paramesonephric ducts develop into the uterine tubes, and the fused portions, or *uterova-*

ginal primordium, give rise to the epithelium and glands of the uterus (Fig. 14–12*B* and *C*). The endometrial stroma and the myometrium are derived from the adjacent mesenchyme.

Development of the Vagina. The vaginal epithelium is derived from the endoderm of the urogenital sinus, and the fibromuscular wall of the vagina develops from the uterovaginal primordium. A solid cord of endodermal cells, called the *vaginal plate* forms, and then the central cells break down and form the lumen of the vagina. The peripheral cells remain as the vaginal epithelium (Fig. 14–12*C*). Until late fetal life, the lumen of the vagina is separated from the

Figure 14–10 Schematic sections illustrating the differentiation of the indifferent gonads into testes or ovaries. *A,* Six weeks, showing the indifferent gonads composed of an outer cortex and an inner medulla. *B,* Seven weeks, showing testes developing under the influence of a Y chromosome. Note that the primary sex cords have become seminiferous cords and that they are separated from the surface epithelium by the tunica albuginea. *C,* 12 weeks, showing ovaries beginning to develop. Cortical (secondary sex) cords have extended from the surface epithelium, displacing the primary sex cords centrally into the mesovarium, where they form the rudimentary rete ovarii. *D,* Testis at 20 weeks, showing the rete testis and the seminiferous tubules derived from the seminiferous cords. An efferent ductule has developed from a mesonephric tubule, and the mesonephric duct has become the ductus epididymidis. *E,* Ovary at 20 weeks, showing the primordial follicles formed from the cortical cords. The rete ovarii derived from the primary sex cords and the mesonephric tubule and duct are regressing. *F,* Section of a seminiferous tubule from a 20-week fetus. Note that no lumen is present at this stage and that the seminiferous epithelium is composed of two kinds of cells. *G,* Section from the ovarian cortex of a 20-week fetus showing three primordial follicles.

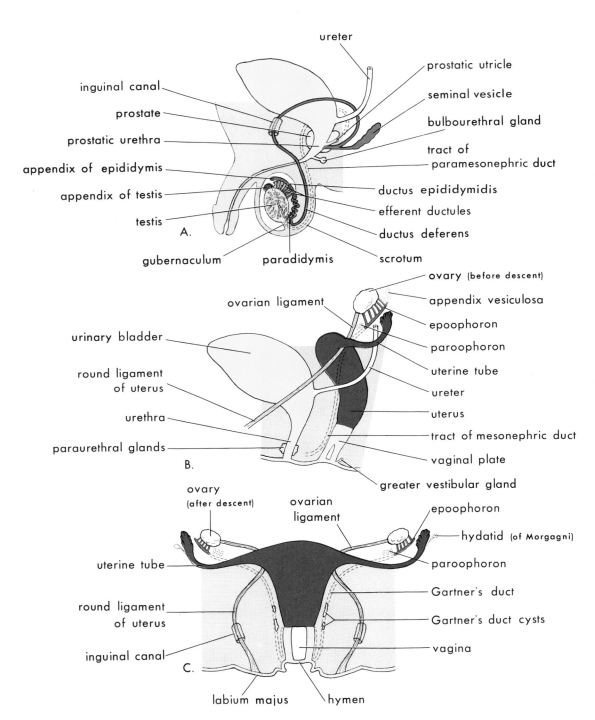

Figure 14–12 Schematic drawings illustrating development of the male and female reproductive systems from the primitive genital ducts. Vestigial structures (paradidymis, paroophoron, appendix of testis, appendix of epididymis, Gartner's duct, hydatid of Morgagni) are also shown. For more information about these, see Moore (1982). *A,* Reproductive system in a newborn male. *B,* Female reproductive system in a 12-week fetus. *C,* Reproductive system in a newborn female.

182

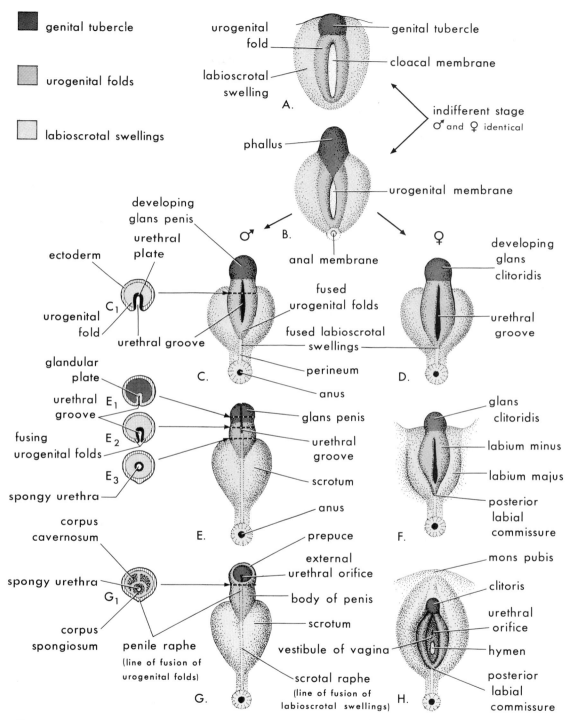

Figure 14–13 *A* and *B*, Diagrams illustrating development of the external genitalia during the indifferent stage (four to seven weeks). *C, E,* and *G,* Stages in the development of male external genitalia at about 9, 11, and 12 weeks, respectively. To the left are schematic transverse sections (*C₁, E₁* to *E₃,* and *G₁*) through the developing penis illustrating formation of the spongy urethra. *D, F,* and *H,* Stages in the development of female external genitalia at 9, 11, and 12 weeks, respectively.

cavity of the urogenital sinus by a membrane called the *hymen* (Figs. 14–12C and 14–13H). The hymen usually ruptures during the perinatal period.

Auxiliary Female Genital Glands. Buds grow out from the urethra into the surrounding mesenchyme and form the *urethral glands* and the paraurethral glands. These glands correspond to the prostate gland in the male. Similar outgrowths from the urogenital sinus form the greater vestibular glands, which are homologous with the bulbourethral glands in the male.

Descent of the Testes. Inguinal canals develop and later form pathways for the testes to descend through the abdominal wall into the scrotum. Inguinal canals develop in female embryos even though the ovaries do not enter the inguinal canals. Descent of the testes through the inguinal canals usually begins during the twenty-eighth week and takes about three days. About four weeks later, the testes enter the scrotum and the inguinal canals contract.

Cryptorchidism or Undescended Testes. This condition occurs in about 3 per cent of full-term male infants. A cryptorchid testis may be located in the abdominal cavity or anywhere along the usual path of descent of the testis; usually it lies in the inguinal canal. The cause of most cases of cryptorchidism is unknown, but failure of normal androgen production appears to be a factor.

DEVELOPMENT OF THE EXTERNAL GENITALIA

The Indifferent Stage (Fig. 14–13A and B). The external genitalia also pass through a stage that is not distinguishable as male or female. Early in the fourth week, a *genital tubercle* develops ventral to the cloacal membrane, and *labioscrotal swellings* and *urogenital folds* develop on each side of the cloacal membrane. The genital tubercle soon elongates and is called a *phallus*; initially it is as large in females as in males. A *urethral groove* forms on the ventral surface of the phallus (Fig. 14–13C and D).

Although external sexual characteristics begin to appear during the early fetal period, the external genitalia of males and females appear somewhat similar until the end of the ninth week. The final form is not established until the twelfth week (Fig. 14–13G and H).

Development of Male External Genitalia (Fig. 14–13C, E, and G). Masculinization of the indifferent external genitalia is caused by androgens produced by the fetal testes. As the phallus elongates to form a *penis,* the *urogenital folds* fuse with each other along the ventral surface of the penis to form the *spongy urethra.* As a result, the external urethral orifice moves to the *glans penis.*

Development of Female External Genitalia (Fig. 14–13D, F, and H). Feminization of the indifferent external genitalia occurs in the absence of hormones. The phallus becomes a relatively small *clitoris* which develops like the penis except that the urogenital folds do not fuse. The unfused urogenital folds form the *labia minora* and the unfused labioscrotal folds form the *labia majora.*

INTERSEXUALITY

Because an early embryo has the potential to develop as either a male or a female, errors in sex development may result in various degrees of intermediate sex, a condition known as *intersexuality* or *hermaphroditism.* A person with ambiguous external genitalia is called a hermaphrodite or *intersex.*

Intersexual conditions are classified according to the histological appearance of the gonads. *True hermaphrodites* have both ovarian and testicular tissue. Some *pseudohermaphrodites* have testes and are called male pseudohermaphrodites; others have ovaries and are known as female pseudohermaphrodites. Fortunately, intersexuality is uncommon.

True Hermaphrodites. Persons with this *extremely rare condition* usually have a 46,XX chromosome constitution. Both ovarian and testicular tissues are present, either in the same or in opposite gonads. The physical appearance may be male or female but the external genitalia are usually ambiguous. This condition results from an error in sex determination.

Male Pseudohermaphrodites. These persons have a 46,XY chromosome constitution. The external and internal genitalia are intersexual and variable, resulting from varying degrees of development of the phallus and the genital ducts. Either an inadequate amount of androgenic hormones is produced, or they are formed after the period of max-

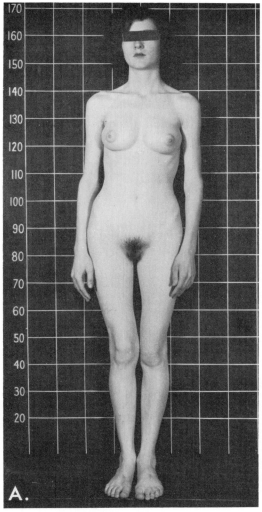

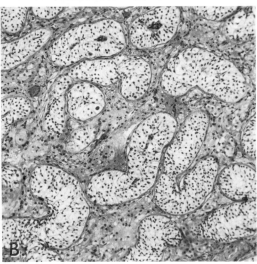

Figure 14–14 *A*, Photograph of a 17-year-old female with the syndrome of testicular feminization. *B*, Photomicrograph of a section through a testis removed from the inguinal region of this girl showing seminiferous tubules. There are no germ cells. (From Jones, H. W., and Scott, W. W.: *Hermaphroditism, Genital Anomalies and Related Endocrine Disorders*. Baltimore, Williams & Wilkins Company, 1958.)

185

imum tissue sensitivity of the sexual structures has passed.

Testicular Feminization (Fig. 14–14). Persons with this rare condition (related to intersexuality) appear as normal females despite the presence of testes and XY sex chromosomes. Normal breast development occurs at puberty. The vagina ends blindly and the other internal genitalia are absent or rudimentary. The testes are usually in the inguinal canals, but they may descend into the labia majora.

Embryologically, these females represent an extreme form of male pseudohermaphroditism, but they are not intersexes in the usual sense because they have normal feminine external genitalia. Although testes develop and secrete androgens, masculinization of the genitalia fails to occur apparently because the indifferent external genitalia were insensitive to androgens.

Female Pseudohermaphrodites. These persons have a 46,XX chromosome constitution. The most common cause of female

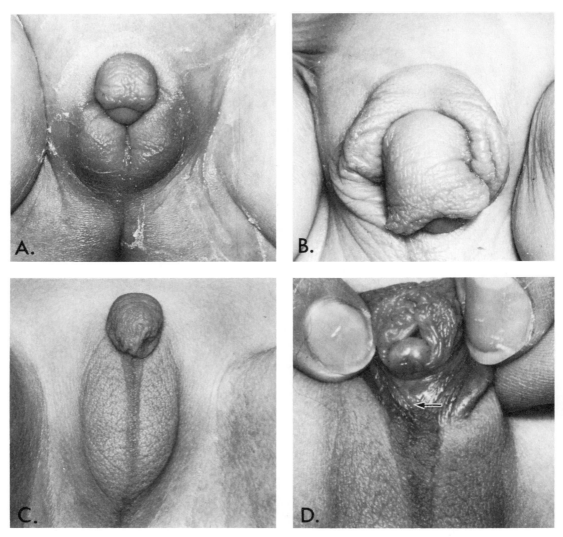

Figure 14–15 Photographs of the external genitalia of female pseudohermaphrodites resulting from congenital virilizing adrenal hyperplasia. *A*, External genitalia of a newborn female, exhibiting enlargement of the clitoris and fusion of the labia majora. *B*, External genitalia of a female infant, showing considerable enlargement of the clitoris. The labia majora have partially fused to form a scrotum-like structure. *C* and *D*, External genitalia of this six-year-old girl showing the enlarged clitoris and fused labia majora. In *D*, note the glans clitoridis and the opening of the urogenital sinus (arrow).

pseudohermaphroditism is the *adrenogenital syndrome,* resulting from congenital virilizing adrenal hyperplasia (Fig. 14–15). There is no ovarian abnormality, but the excessive production of androgens by the fetal suprarenal glands causes masculinization of the ex-

ternal genitalia, varying from enlargement of the clitoris to almost masculine genitalia (Fig. 14–15C). Commonly, there is clitoral hypertrophy and partial fusion of the labia majora. Persons with this syndrome are the most frequently encountered group of intersexes, ac-

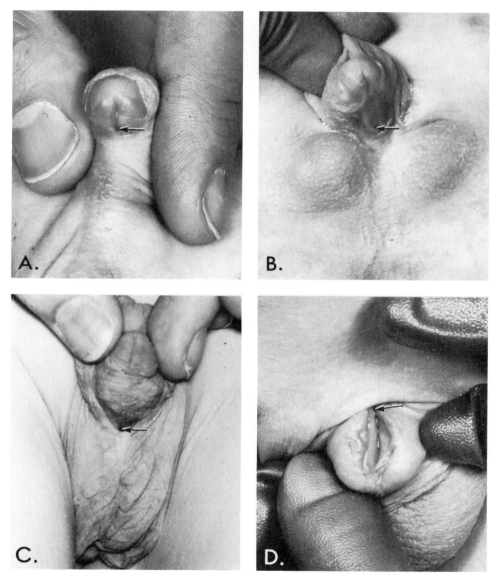

Figure 14–16 Photographs of penile malformations. *A*, Glandular hypospadias. The external urethral orifice is indicated by the arrow. There is a shallow pit at the usual site of the orifice. Note the moderate degree of chordee causing the penis to curve ventrally. (From Jolly, H.: *Diseases of Children*, 2nd ed. Oxford, Blackwell Scientific Publications, 1968.) *B*, Penile hypospadias. The penis is short and curved (chordee). The external urethral orifice (arrow) is near the penoscrotal junction. *C*, Penoscrotal hypospadias. The external urethral orifice (arrow) is located at the penoscrotal junction. *D*, Epispadias. The external urethral orifice (arrow) is on the dorsal (upper) surface of the penis near its origin. (Courtesy of Mr. Innes Williams, Genitourinary Surgeon, The Hospital for Sick Children, Great Ormond Street, London, England.)

counting for about half of all cases of ambiguous external genitalia.

Prompt recognition and treatment of the associated adrenal imbalance are most important. Congenital virilizing adrenal hyperplasia is caused by recessive mutant genes.

Female pseudohermaphrodites who do not have congenital virilizing adrenal hyperplasia are very rare. The administration of androgenic hormones to a mother during pregnancy may cause similar abnormalities of the female external genitalia (see Fig. 9–14).

Hypospadias (Fig. 14–16*A* to *C*). Once in about every 300 males, the external urethral orifice is on the ventral surface of the penis instead of at the tip of the glans. Usually the penis is curved downward or ventrally, a condition known as *chordee*.

There are four types of hypospadias: *glandular, penile, penoscrotal,* and *perineal*. The glandular and penile types constitute about 80 per cent of cases. Hypospadias results from an inadequate production of androgens by the fetal testes; this causes failure of fusion of the urogenital folds. Differences in the timing and degree of hormonal failure account for the variety of types of hypospadias.

Epispadias (Fig. 14–16*D*). Once in about 30,000 male infants, the urethra opens on the dorsal surface of the penis. Although epispadias may occur as a separate entity, it is often associated with exstrophy of the bladder (see Fig. 14–8) and has a similar cause.

Uterovaginal Malformations (Fig. 14–17). Various types of uterine duplication result from failure of the paramesonephric ducts to fuse normally during formation of the uterus. Double uterus results from failure of fusion of the caudal parts of the paramesonephric ducts and may be associated with a double or a single vagina (Fig. 14–17*A* and *B*). If the doubling involves only the superior portion of the body of the uterus, the condition is called *bicornuate (double-horned) uterus* (Fig. 14–17*C* and *D*). In some cases,

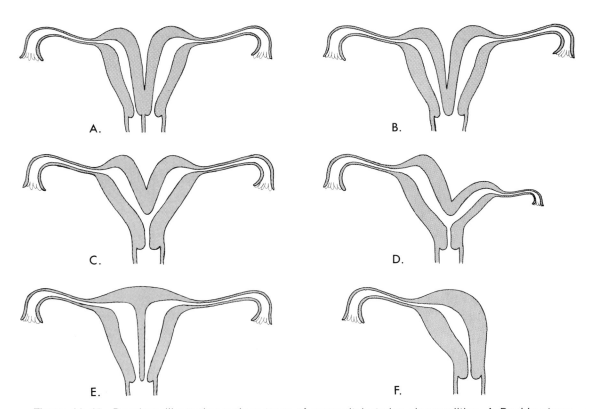

Figure 14–17 Drawings illustrating various types of congenital uterine abnormalities. *A*, Double uterus (uterus didelphys) and double vagina. *B*, Double uterus with single vagina. *C*, Bicornuate uterus. *D*, Bicornuate uterus with a rudimentary left horn. *E*, Septate uterus. *F*, Unicornuate uterus.

the uterus is divided internally by a thin septum (Fig. 14–17*E*). Very rarely, one paramesonephric duct degenerates or fails to form; this results in a *unicornuate (single-horned) uterus* (Fig. 14–17*F*).

Once in about every 4000 females *absence of the vagina* occurs. This results from failure of the vaginal plate to develop. When the vagina is absent, the uterus is usually also absent. Failure of canalization of the vaginal plate results in *vaginal atresia*. Failure of the hymen to rupture results in a condition known as *imperforate hymen*.

SUMMARY

Three successive sets of kidneys develop: (1) the transitory vestigial and nonfunctional *pronephros*, (2) the *mesonephros*, which may serve as a temporary excretory organ, and (3) the functional *metanephros* or permanent kidney.

The metanephros develops from two sources: (1) the metanephric diverticulum or ureteric bud, which gives rise to the ureter, the renal pelvis, the calyces, and the collecting tubules, and (2) a mass of metanephric mesoderm, which gives rise to the nephrons. At first the kidneys are located in the pelvis, but they gradually ascend to the abdomen.

The urinary bladder develops from the urogenital sinus and the surrounding splanchnic mesenchyme. The female urethra and almost all of the male urethra have a similar origin.

Developmental abnormalities of the kidney and excretory passages are relatively common. Incomplete division of the ureteric bud results in bifid or double ureter and supernumerary kidney. Failure of the kidney to ascend from its embryonic position in the pelvis results in ectopic kidney.

The genital or reproductive system develops in close association with the urinary or excretory system. *Genetic sex* is established at fertilization, but the gonads do not acquire sexual characteristics until the seventh week, and the external genitalia do not become distinctly masculine or feminine until the twelfth week.

The genital or reproductive organs in both sexes develop from primordia which appear identical at first. During this *indifferent stage,* an embryo has the potential to develop into a male or female.

Gonadal sex is controlled by the Y chromosome, which exerts a positive testis-determining action on the *indifferent gonad.* In the presence of a Y chromosome, testes develop and produce masculinizing hormones which stimulate development of the mesonephric ducts into the male genital ducts, and the indifferent external genitalia into the penis and scrotum. These androgens also suppress development of the paramesonephric ducts. In the absence of a Y chromosome and in the presence of two X chromosomes, ovaries develop, the mesonephric ducts regress, the paramesonephric ducts develop into the uterus and uterine tubes, the vagina develops from the urogenital sinus, and the indifferent external genitalia develop into the clitoris and labia.

Errors of the sex-determining mechanism produce true hermaphroditism, an extremely rare condition. Errors in sexual differentiation may cause pseudohermaphroditism. In the male, this results from failure of the fetal testes to produce adequate amounts of masculinizing hormones. In the female, pseudohermaphroditism usually results from a disorder of the fetal suprarenal glands which causes an excessive production of androgens.

SUGGESTED SUPPLEMENTARY READING

Moore, K. L.: *The Developing Human: Clinically Oriented Embryology*, 3rd ed. Philadelphia, W. B. Saunders Company, 1982, pp. 227–295.
A more comprehensive coverage of the development of the urogenital system, including many more illustrations. Several clinically oriented problems are presented.
Page, E. W., Villee, C. A., and Villee, D. B.: *Human Reproduction: Essentials of Reproductive and Perinatal Medicine*, 3rd ed. Philadelphia, W. B. Saunders Company, 1981.
Chapter 2 gives a concise, well-illustrated account of the embryological development of the urogenital system. There is also a good clinical discussion of the common congenital malformations.

15

THE CARDIOVASCULAR SYSTEM

The cardiovascular system is the first system to function in the embryo. Blood begins to circulate at the end of the third week. This early development is necessary because the rapidly growing embryo needs an efficient method of acquiring nutrients and disposing of waste products.

EARLY HEART DEVELOPMENT

Heart development is first indicated at 18 or 19 days in the *cardiogenic area* (Fig. 15–1A). A pair of *cardiogenic cords* appears and soon become canalized to form *endocardial heart tubes* (Fig. 15–2B). These heart tubes approach each other and fuse to form a single endocardial heart tube (Figs. 15–2C and 15–3).

With development of the head fold, the endocardial heart tube and pericardial cavity come to lie ventral to the foregut and caudal to the oropharyngeal membrane (Fig. 15–4). Concurrently, the heart elongates and develops alternate dilatations and constrictions: the *truncus arteriosus, bulbus cordis, ventricle, atrium,* and *sinus venosus* (Fig. 15–3C).

As the heart tubes fuse, the mesenchyme around them thickens to form a *myoepicardial mantle* (Fig. 15–2C and D). At this stage the developing heart is a simple tube, separated from another tube (the myoepicardial mantle) by gelatinous connective tissue called *cardiac jelly.* The inner endocardial tube is destined to become the internal endothelial lining of the heart, called the *en-*

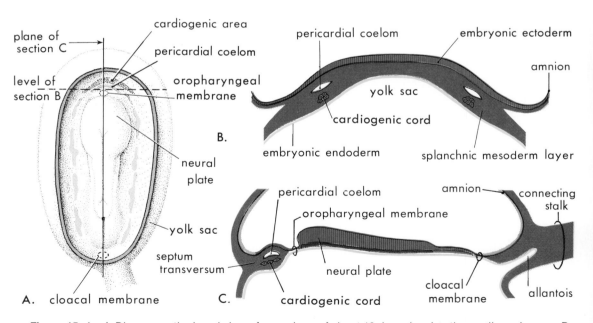

Figure 15–1 *A,* Diagrammatic dorsal view of an embryo of about 18 days showing the cardiogenic area. *B,* Transverse section of an embryo demonstrating the cardiogenic cords. *C,* Longitudinal section of the embryo illustrating the relationship of the developing heart to the oropharyngeal (buccopharyngeal) membrane, the pericardial coelom (cavity), and the septum transversum (future central part of the diaphragm).

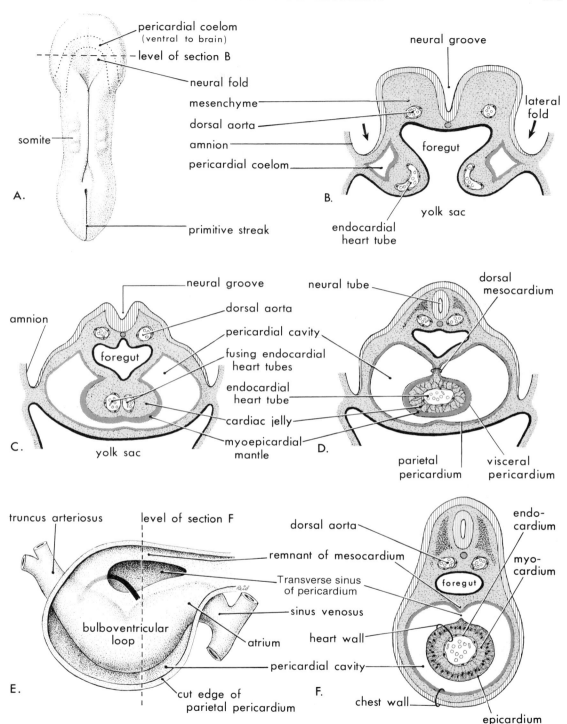

Figure 15–2   *A*, Dorsal view of an embryo of about 20 days. *B*, Transverse section through the heart region showing the widely separated heart tubes and the lateral folds (arrows). *C*, Transverse section of an embryo of about 21 days showing the formation of the pericardial cavity and the heart tubes about to fuse. *D*, Similar section at 22 days showing the single heart tube suspended by the dorsal mesocardium. *E*, Schematic drawing of the heart at about 28 days showing degeneration of the dorsal mesocardium and formation of the transverse pericardial sinus. *F*, Transverse section through this embryo after disappearance of the dorsal mesocardium, showing the layers of the heart wall.

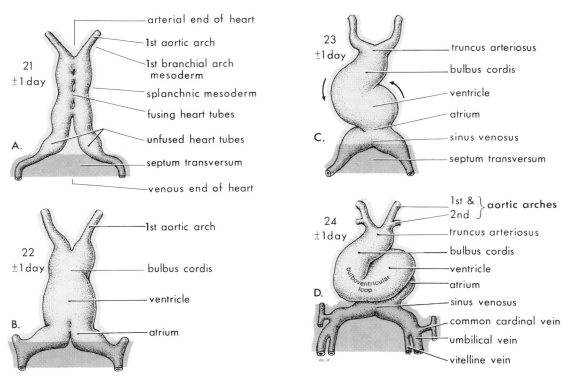

Figure 15-3 Sketches of ventral views of the developing heart during the fourth week, showing fusion of the heart tubes and bending of the single heart tube. Because the primitive heart grows within a confined space, the pericardial cavity (Figs. 15-2 and 15-4), it folds on itself and forms a bulboventricular loop.

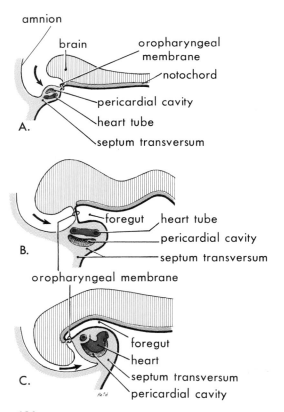

Figure 15-4 Schematic drawings of longitudinal sections through the cranial half of human embryos during the fourth week, showing the effect of the head fold (arrow) on the heart tube and other structures. As the head fold develops, the heart tube and the pericardial cavity come to lie ventral to the foregut and caudal to the oropharyngeal membrane.

192

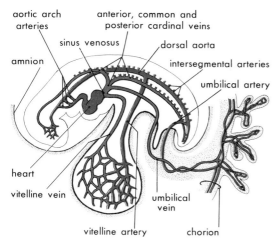

aortic arch arteries

anterior, common and posterior cardinal veins

sinus venosus

dorsal aorta

amnion

intersegmental arteries

umbilical artery

heart

vitelline vein

umbilical vein

vitelline artery   chorion

Figure 15–5   Sketch of the cardiovascular system in a 26-day embryo showing vessels of the left side only.

After releasing oxygen and nutrients to the developing tissues and organs of the embryo, and receiving carbon dioxide and waste products from them, the blood is returned to the heart mainly by the *cardinal veins* (Fig. 15–5).

The blood that passes from the heart to the chorion releases its waste products and carbon dioxide into the *maternal blood* and receives nutrients and oxygen from it. This well oxygenated blood is returned to the heart by the umbilical veins.

Contraction of the primitive heart begins by day 22 and originates in its muscle. Contractions occur in peristaltic waves that begin in the sinus venosus and force the blood through the tubular heart.

docardium. The myoepicardial mantle gives rise to the *myocardium* (muscular wall) and the *epicardium* or visceral pericardium (Fig. 15–2F).

The sinus venosus is a large venous sinus which receives blood from the *umbilical, vitelline*, and *common cardinal veins* (Fig. 15–3D and 15–5). Initially the heart is a fairly straight tube, but it soon bends upon itself, forming a U-shaped *bulboventricular loop* (Figs. 15–2E and 15–3D).

THE PRIMITIVE CIRCULATION

The primitive blood forms in the wall of the yolk sac during the third week (see Fig. 5–7), and passes via the *vitelline veins* to the sinus venosus of the heart (Fig. 15–5). The *sinus venosus* also receives blood from the chorion (embryonic part of placenta) via the *umbilical veins* (at first there are two). The blood from the *chorion* contains nutrients and oxygen derived from the mother's blood. Because *the yolk sac lacks yolk*, the embryo must obtain its nourishement and oxygen from its mother via the primitive placenta or chorion (see Fig. 8–5).

Blood from the primitive heart is distributed to the *branchial arches* (see Chapter 11) by the *aortic arches* and to the rest of the embryo's body by the *aortas* (initially there are two) and their branches. Blood from the primitive heart also passes to the yolk sac and the chorion via the vitelline and umbilical arteries, respectively.

LATER HEART DEVELOPMENT

The primitive heart has only one atrium and one ventricle. Partitioning of the atrioventricular canal, atrium, and ventricle begins around the middle of the fourth week and is essentially complete by the end of the sixth week. Although described separately, these processes occur concurrently.

Partitioning of the Atrioventricular Canal.   *Endocardial cushions* develop in the dorsal and ventral walls of the heart in the region of the atrioventricular canal (Fig. 15–6B). These cushions grow toward each other and fuse (Fig. 15–6C), dividing the atrioventricular canal into *right and left atrioventricular canals* (Fig. 15–6D).

Partitioning of the Primitive Atrium.   A crescent-shaped membrane, the *septum primum*, grows from the dorsocranial wall of the primitive atrium (Figs. 15–7B and 15–8A). A large opening, the *foramen primum*, exists between its caudal free edge and the endocardial cushions. As the septum primum grows toward the *endocardial cushions*, it reduces the size of the foramen primum (Fig. 15–8B and C). Before the foramen primum is obliterated, perforations appear in the dorsal part of the septum primum and soon coalesce to form another opening, the *foramen secundum* (Fig. 15–8B to D). Concurrently, the septum primum fuses with the left side of the fused endocardial cushions, thereby obliterating the foramen primum.

Subsequently, another crescentic membrane, the *septum secundum*, grows from the ventrocranial wall of the atrium on the right

Text continued on page 199

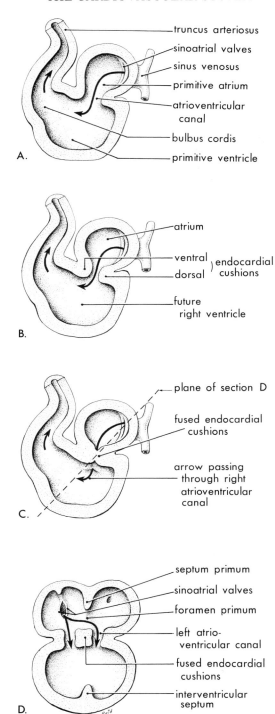

A.

- truncus arteriosus
- sinoatrial valves
- sinus venosus
- primitive atrium
- atrioventricular canal
- bulbus cordis
- primitive ventricle

B.

- atrium
- ventral ⎫ endocardial
- dorsal ⎭ cushions
- future right ventricle

C.

- plane of section D
- fused endocardial cushions
- arrow passing through right atrioventricular canal

D.

- septum primum
- sinoatrial valves
- foramen primum
- left atrio-ventricular canal
- fused endocardial cushions
- interventricular septum

Figure 15–6   *A* to *C,* Sketches of sagittal sections of the heart during the fourth and fifth weeks illustrating division of the atrioventricular canal. *D,* Frontal section of the heart at the plane shown in *C.* The interatrial and interventricular septa have also started to develop.

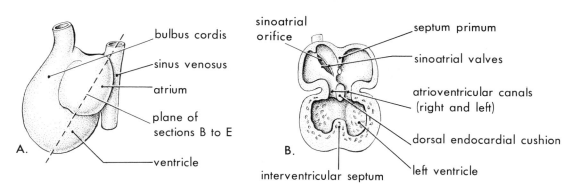

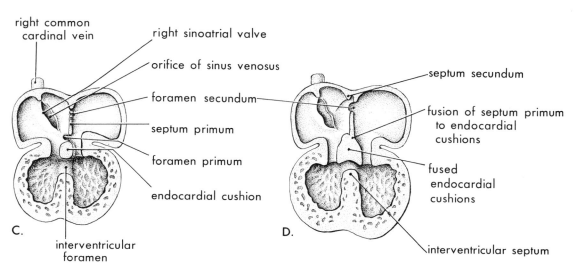

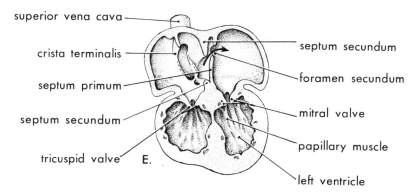

Figure 15–7 Drawings of the developing heart showing partitioning of the atrioventricular canal, the atrium, and the ventricle. *A,* Sketch showing the plane of frontal sections *B* to *E. B,* About 28 days, showing the early appearance of the septum primum, the interventricular septum, and the dorsal endocardial cushion. *C,* About 32 days, showing perforations in the dorsal part of the septum. *D,* About 35 days, showing the foramen secundum. *E,* About eight weeks, showing the heart after partitioning into four chambers. (Adapted from various sources, especially Patten, 1968.)

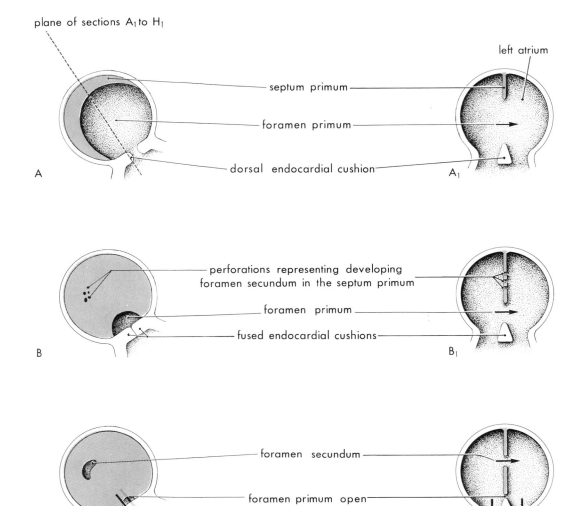

Figure 15–8 Diagrammatic sketches illustrating partitioning of the primitive atrium. *A* to *H* are views of the developing interatrial septum as viewed from the right side. *A₁* to *H₁* are frontal sections of the developing interatrial septum at the plane shown in *A*.

Illustration continued on opposite page

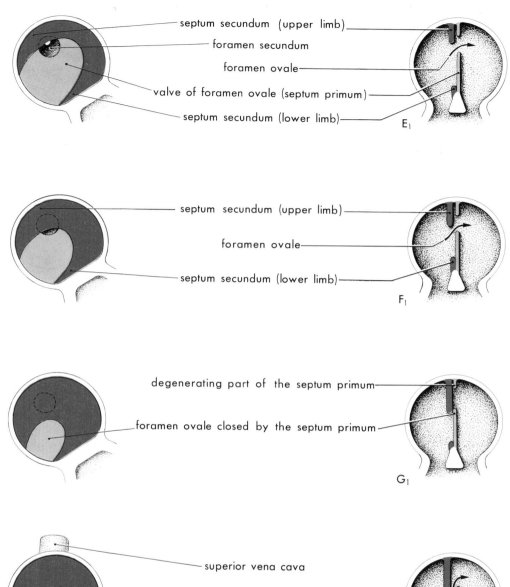

E — septum secundum (upper limb) — E₁
— foramen secundum
— foramen ovale
— valve of foramen ovale (septum primum)
— septum secundum (lower limb)

F — septum secundum (upper limb) — F₁
— foramen ovale
— septum secundum (lower limb)

G — degenerating part of the septum primum — G₁
— foramen ovale closed by the septum primum

H — superior vena cava — H₁
— foramen ovale open
— valve of foramen ovale
— inferior vena cava

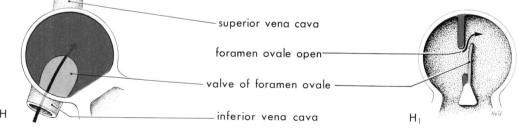

Figure 15–8 *Continued* The valvelike nature of the foramen ovale is illustrated in G_1 and H_1. When pressure in the right atrium exceeds that in the left atrium, blood passes from the right to the left side of the heart. When the pressures are equal, the septum primum closes the foramen ovale.

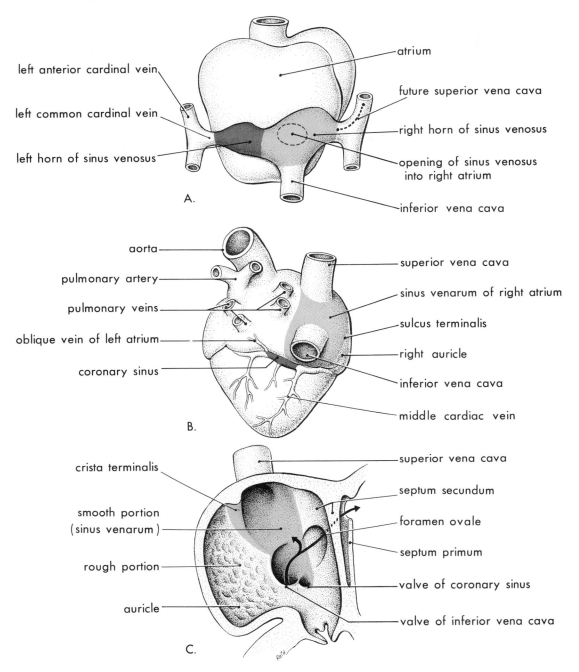

Figure 15–9 Diagrams illustrating the fate of the sinus venosus. *A*, Dorsal view of the heart at about 26 days showing the early appearance of the sinus venosus. *B*, Dorsal view at eight weeks after incorporation of the right horn of the sinus venosus into the right atrium. The left horn of the sinus venosus has become the coronary sinus. *C*, Internal view of the fetal right atrium showing (*1*) the smooth part (sinus venarum) of the wall of the right atrium derived from the right horn of the sinus venosus and (*2*) the crista terminalis and the valves of the interior vena cava and coronary sinus derived from the right sinoatrial valve. The primitive right atrium becomes the right auricle, a conical muscular pouch.

cside of the septum primum (Fig. 15–8*D*). This septum gradually covers the foramen secundum (Fig. 15–8*E* to *G*). The oval opening in the septum secundum is called the *foramen ovale* (Fig. 15–8*E*). The septum primum forms the *valve of the foramen ovale* (Fig. 15–8*G*₁ and *H*₁). *Before birth*, the foramen ovale allows most of the blood entering the right atrium to pass into the left atrium (see Fig. 15–20). *After birth*, the foramen ovale normally closes and the interatrial septum becomes a complete partition (see Fig. 15–21).

Fate of the Sinus Venosus and Formation of the Adult Right Atrium. Initially the sinus venosus is a separate chamber of the heart and opens into the caudal wall of the right atrium (see Figs. 15–5 and 15–6). The *left horn* of the sinus venosus forms the *coronary sinus* (Fig. 15–9*B*), and the right horn becomes part of the wall of the *right atrium* (Fig. 15–9*B* and *C*).

Formation of the Adult Left Atrium. The smooth part of the wall of the left atrium is derived from the *primitive pulmonary vein*. As the atrium expands, the terminal portion of this vein and its main branches are gradually incorporated into the wall of the left atrium. The remnant of the primitive atrium is the left auricle, an appendage of the atrium.

Partitioning of the Primitive Ventricle. Division of the primitive ventricle into right and left ventricles is first indicated by a muscular ridge, the *interventricular septum*, in the floor of the ventricle near its apex (see Figs. 15–6*D* and 15–7*B*).

A crescentic *interventricular foramen* between the free edge of the interventricular septum and the fused endocardial cushions permits communication between the right and left ventricles. The interventricular foramen closes around the end of the seventh week as the result of fusion of tissue from three sources (see Fig. 15–11). After closure of the interventricular foramen, the pulmonary trunk is in communication with the right ventricle and the aorta with the left ventricle.

Partitioning and Fate of the Bulbus Cordis and Truncus Arteriosus. During the fifth week, bulges form in the walls of the bulbus cordis (Fig. 15–10*B* and *C*). These bulges, called *bulbar ridges*, are first filled with cardiac jelly but are later invaded by mesenchymal cells. Similar *truncal ridges* form in the truncus arteriosus and are continuous with the bulbar ridges. The spiral ori-

entation of the ridges, possibly caused by the streaming of blood from the ventricles, results in a spiral *aorticopulmonary septum* when these ridges fuse (Fig. 15–10*D* to *G*). This septum divides the bulbus cordis and the truncus arteriosus into two channels, the *aorta* and the *pulmonary trunk*. Because of the spiral septum, the pulmonary trunk twists around the ascending aorta (Figs. 15–10*H* and 15–11).

The bulbus cordis is gradually incorporated into the walls of the ventricles. In the adult right ventricle, it is represented by the *conus arteriosus*, which gives origin to the pulmonary trunk. In the adult left ventricle, the bulbus cordis forms the walls of the *aortic vestibule*, the part of the ventricular cavity just inferior to the aortic valve.

CONGENITAL MALFORMATIONS OF THE HEART AND GREAT VESSELS

Because development of the heart and great vessels is complex, congenital heart defects are relatively common. The overall incidence is about 0.7 per cent of live births and 2.7 per cent of stillbirths.

The following malformations are relatively common and many are amendable to surgery:

Atrial Septal Defects (ASD). Atrial septal defect is among the most common of congenital heart defects. There are two main types:

Secundum Type ASD (Fig. 15–12*A* to *D*). The defect is in the area of the foramen ovale and may include defects of the septum primum and of the septum secundum. *Patent foramen ovale* may result from abnormal resorption of the septum primum during the formation of the foramen secundum. If resorption occurs in abnormal locations, the septum primum is fenestrated or netlike (Fig. 15–12*A*). If excessive resorption of the septum primum occurs, the resulting short septum primum does not cover the foramen ovale (Fig. 15–12*B*). If an abnormally large foramen ovale results from defective development of the septum secundum, a normal septum primum will not close the foramen ovale at birth (Fig. 15–12*C*). Large atrial septal defects may result from a combination of excessive resorption of the septum primum and a large foramen ovale (Fig. 15–12*D*). This heart defect is characterized by a *large opening between the left and right ventricles*. Obviously there is considerable interatrial shunting of blood.

Text continued on page 203

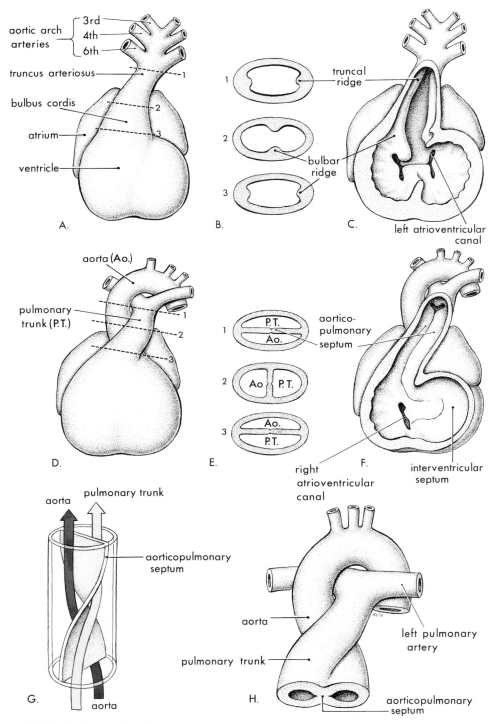

Figure 15–10 Schematic drawings illustrating partitioning of the bulbus cordis and truncus arteriosus. *A,* Ventral aspect of heart at five weeks. *B,* Transverse sections through the truncus arteriosus and bulbus cordis illustrating the truncal and bulbar ridges. *C,* The ventral wall of the heart has been removed to demonstrate the ridges. *D,* Ventral aspect of heart after partitioning of the truncus arteriosus. *E,* Sections through the newly formed aorta (Ao.) and pulmonary trunk (P.T.) showing the aorticopulmonary septum. *F,* Six weeks. The ventral wall of the heart and pulmonary trunk have been removed to show the aorticopulmonary septum. *G,* Diagram illustrating the spiral form of the aorticopulmonary septum. *H,* Drawing showing the great arteries twisting around each other as they leave the heart.

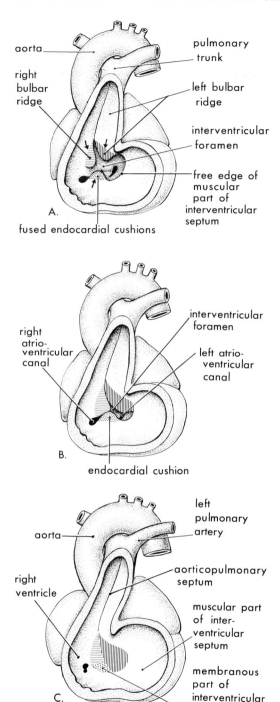

Figure 15–11   Schematic diagrams illustrating closure of the interventricular foramen and formation of the membranous part of the interventricular septum. The walls of the bulbus cordis and the right ventricle have been removed. *A*, Five weeks, showing the bulbar ridges and the fused endocardial cushions. *B*, Six weeks, showing how proliferation of subendocardial tissue diminishes the interventricular foramen. *C*, Seven weeks, showing the fused bulbar ridges and the membranous part of the interventricular septum formed by extensions of tissue from the right side of the endocardial cushions.

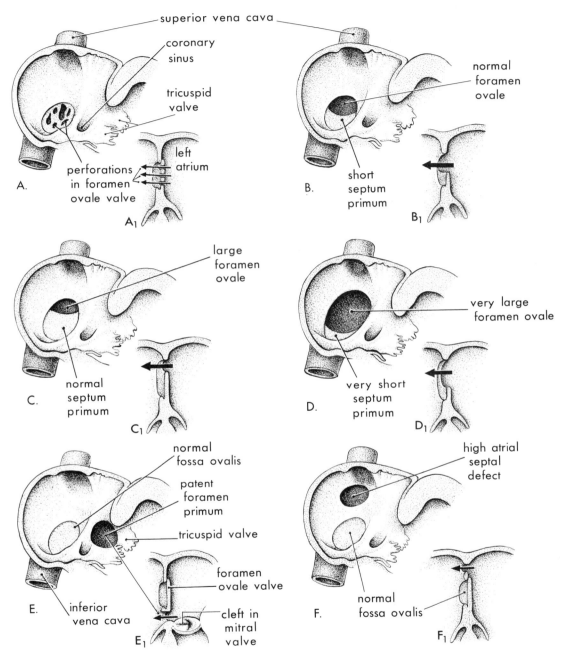

Figure 15–12 Drawings of the right aspect of the interatrial septum (*A* to *F*) and sketches of frontal sections through the septum (*A₁* to *F₁*) illustrating various types of atrial septal defect. *A*, Patent foramen ovale resulting from resorption of the septum primum in abnormal locations. *B*, Patent foramen ovale caused by excessive resorption of the septum primum, sometimes called the "short flap defect." *C*, Patent foramen ovale resulting from an abnormally large foramen ovale. *D*, Patent foramen ovale resulting from (1) an abnormally large foramen ovale, and (2) excessive resorption of the septum primum. *E*, Endocardial cushion defect with primum type atrial septal defect. The frontal section *E₁* also shows the cleft in the septal leaflet of the mitral valve. *F*, High septal defect resulting from abnormal absorption of the sinus venosus into the right atrium. This is a very rare defect. Note the fossa ovalis in *E* and *F* which forms when the foramen ovale closes normally.

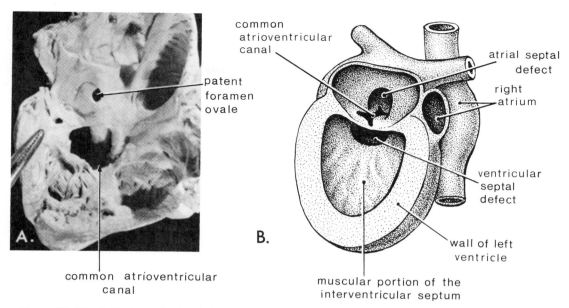

Figure 15–13 *A*, Photograph of an infant's heart, sectioned and viewed from the right side, showing a patent foramen ovale and a common atrioventricular canal. (From Lev, M.: *Autopsy Diagnosis of Congenitally Malformed Hearts*. Springfield, IL, Charles C Thomas, 1953.) *B*, Schematic drawing of a heart illustrating various defects of the cardiac septa.

Endocardial Cushion Defect with Primum Type ASD (Fig. 15–12*E*). The septum primum does not fuse with the endocardial cushions, leaving a *patent foramen primum*; usually there is also a cleft in the mitral valve.

Ventricular Septal Defects (VSD). This relatively common abnormality *ranks first in frequency on all lists of cardiac defects*. Membranous septal defect is the commonest type of VSD (Fig. 15–13*B*). Incomplete closure of the interventricular foramen and failure of the membranous part of the interventricular septum to develop result from failure of extensions of subendocardial tissue to grow from the right side of the fused endocardial cushions and fuse with the aorticopulmonary septum and the muscular part of the interventricular septum (see Fig. 15–11*C*). VSD is often associated with other defects of the cardiac septa (Fig. 15–13).

Persistent Truncus Arteriosus. This malformation results from failure of development of the aorticopulmonary septum. As a result the truncus arteriosus does not divide into the aorta and pulmonary trunk. The most common type is a single arterial vessel which gives rise to the pulmonary trunk and ascending aorta (Fig. 15–14*A* and *B*). The next most common type is for the right and left pulmonary arteries to arise close together from the dorsal wall of the persistent truncus arteriosus.

Complete Transposition of the Great Vessels. In typical cases, the aorta lies anterior to the pulmonary trunk and arises from the right ventricle, and the pulmonary trunk arises from the left ventricle. For survival, there must be a septal defect (ASD or VSD) or a patent ductus arteriosus (see Fig. 15–19*B*) to permit some interchange of blood between the pulmonary and systemic circulations. During partitioning of the truncus arteriosus, the aorticopulmonary septum fails to pursue a spiral course. As a result the origins of the great arteries are reversed.

Tetralogy of Fallot (Fig. 15–15*B*). This is a combination of four cardiac defects consisting of (1) pulmonary stenosis or narrowing of the region of the right ventricular outflow, (2) ventricular septal defect, (3) overriding aorta, and (4) hypertrophy of the right ventricle. This condition results in cyanosis (blueness) of the lips and fingernails; these infants are sometimes referred to as "blue babies."

For more details about *congenital heart defects*, see Moore (1982).

THE AORTIC ARCHES

As the branchial arches develop during the fourth week (Fig. 15–16), they receive arteries from the heart. These aortic arches (ar-

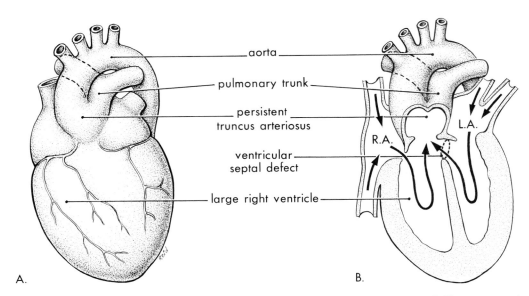

Figure 15–14 Drawing illustrating the main type of persistent truncus arteriosus. *A*, The common trunk divides into an aorta and short pulmonary trunk. *B*, Sketch showing circulation in this heart and a ventricular septal defect.

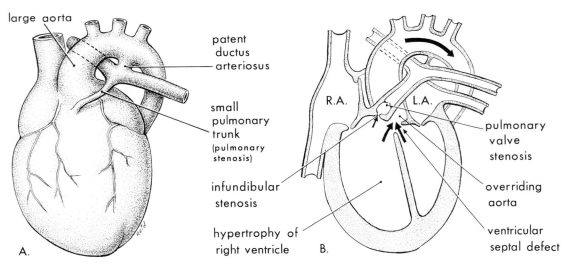

Figure 15–15 *A*, Drawing of an infant's heart showing a small pulmonary trunk (pulmonary stenosis) and a large aorta resulting from unequal partitioning of the truncus arteriosus. There is also hypertrophy of the right ventricle and a patent ductus arteriosus. *B*, Frontal section of a heart illustrating the tetralogy of Fallot. Note that the large aorta lies over the VSD and receives blood from both ventricles. There are two types of pulmonary stenosis. In *pulmonary valve stenosis*, the pulmonary valve cusps are fused, and a narrow opening remains. In *infundibular pulmonary stenosis*, the conus arteriosus (infundibulum) of the right ventricle is underdeveloped.

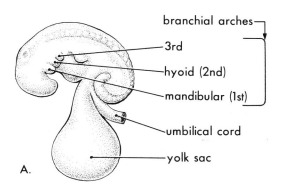

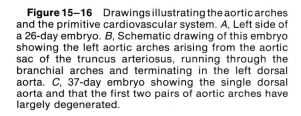

Figure 15–16 Drawings illustrating the aortic arches and the primitive cardiovascular system. *A*, Left side of a 26-day embryo. *B*, Schematic drawing of this embryo showing the left aortic arches arising from the aortic sac of the truncus arteriosus, running through the branchial arches and terminating in the left dorsal aorta. *C*, 37-day embryo showing the single dorsal aorta and that the first two pairs of aortic arches have largely degenerated.

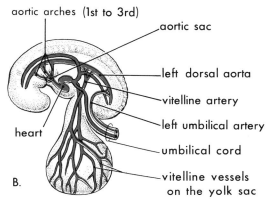

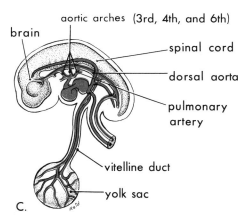

teries) arise from the truncus arteriosus and terminate in the dorsal aorta of the corresponding side (Fig. 15–16*B*). Although six pairs of aortic arches develop, they are not all present at the same time, e.g., when the sixth pair of aortic arches forms, the first two pairs have disappeared (Fig. 15–16*C*).

Derivatives of the Aortic Arches (Figs. 15–16 and 15–17). During the sixth to eighth weeks, the primitive aortic arch pattern is transformed into the basic adult arterial arrangement. The first and second pairs of aortic arches largely disappear. The proximal parts of the third pair of aortic arches

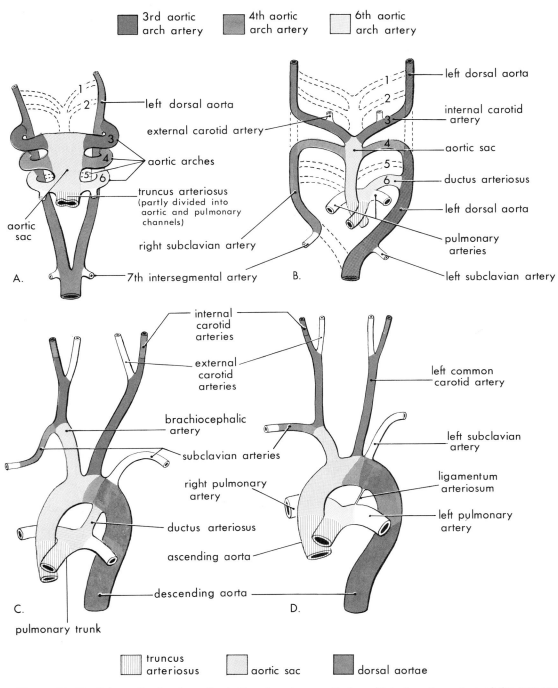

Figure 15–17 Schematic drawings illustrating the changes that result in transformation of the truncus arteriosus, aortic sac, aortic arches, and dorsal aortae into the adult arterial pattern. The vessels which are not shaded or colored are not derived from these structures. *A,* Aortic arches at six weeks; by this stage the first two pairs of aortic arches have largely disappeared. *B,* Aortic arches at seven weeks; the parts of the dorsal aortae and aortic arches that normally disappear are indicated with broken lines. *C,* Arterial arrangement at eight weeks. *D,* Sketch of the arterial vessels of a six-month infant.

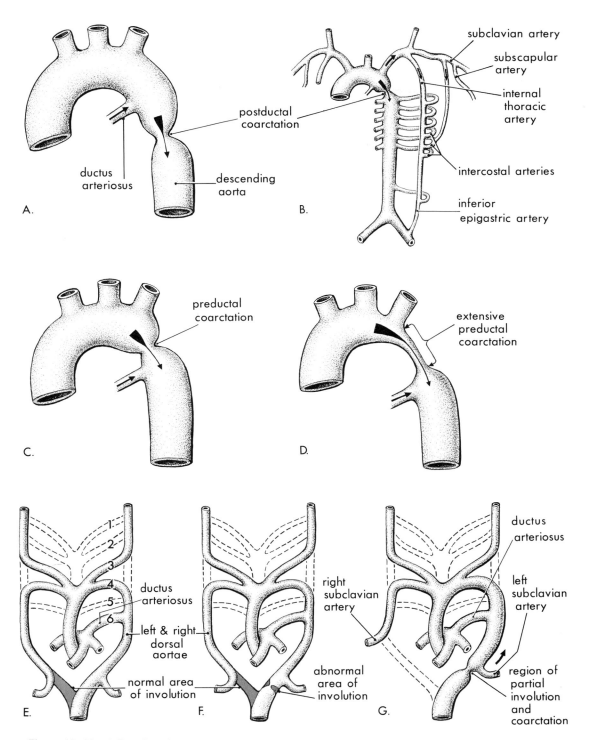

A.

ductus arteriosus

postductal coarctation

descending aorta

B.

subclavian artery

subscapular artery

internal thoracic artery

intercostal arteries

inferior epigastric artery

C.

preductal coarctation

D.

extensive preductal coarctation

E.

1
2
3
4
5
6

ductus arteriosus

left & right dorsal aortae

normal area of involution

F.

abnormal area of involution

G.

ductus arteriosus

right subclavian artery

left subclavian artery

region of partial involution and coarctation

Figure 15–18 *A*, Postductal coarctation of the aorta, the most common type. *B*, Diagrammatic representation of the common routes of collateral circulation that develop in association with coarctation of the aorta. *C* and *D*, Preductal coarctation. The type illustrated in *D* is usually associated with major cardiac defects. *E*, Sketch of the aortic arch pattern in a seven-week embryo showing the areas that normally involute. Note that the distal segment of the right dorsal aorta normally involves as the right subclavian artery develops. *F*, Localized abnormal involution of a small distal segment of the left dorsal aorta. *G*, Later stage showing the abnormally involuted segment appearing as a coarctation of the aorta. This moves (arrow) to the region of the ductus arteriosus with the left subclavian artery.

207

form the *common carotid arteries*, and distal portions join with the dorsal aortae to form the *internal carotid arteries*. The left fourth aortic arch forms part of the arch of the aorta. The right fourth aortic arch becomes the proximal portion of the *right subclavian artery*. The distal part of this artery forms from the right dorsal aorta and the right seventh intersegmental artery (Fig. 15–17*B*). The fifth pair of aortic arches have no derivatives. The left sixth aortic arch develops as follows: the proximal part persists as the proximal part of the left pulmonary artery, and the distal part persists as a shunt or passageway between the pulmonary artery and the aorta, called the *ductus arteriosus* (Fig. 15–17*C* and 15–18). The right sixth aortic arch develops as follows: the proximal part persists as the proximal part of the right pulmonary artery, and the distal part degenerates.

AORTIC ARCH ANOMALIES

Because of the many changes involved in transformation of the embryonic aortic arch system into the adult arterial pattern, it is understandable that variations may occur. Abnormalities result from the persistence of parts of aortic arches which normally disappear, from disappearance of other parts which normally persist, or from both.

Coarctation of the Aorta (Fig. 15–18).   This relatively common malformation is characterized by a narrowing of the aorta, just superior or inferior to the ductus arteriosus. The embryological basis of coarctation of the aorta is unclear. One explanation is illustrated (Fig. 15–18*E* to *G*). There is an abnormal involution of a small segment of the left dorsal aorta. Later this constricted segment (area of coarctation) moves cranially with the left subclavian artery to the region of the ductus arteriosus.

Postductal Coarctation.   In this common type, the constriction is inferior to the level of the ductus arteriosus (Fig. 15–18*A*). A collateral circulation develops during the fetal period, thus assisting with passage of blood to inferior parts of the body (Fig. 15–18*B*).

Preductal Coarctation.   In this less common type, the constriction is superior to the level of the ductus arteriosus (Fig. 15–18*C*). The ductus usually remains open, providing a communication between the pulmonary artery and the descending aorta. The narrowed segment is occasionally extensive (Fig. 15–18*D*).

Patent Ductus Arteriosus (Fig. 15–19*B*).   This malformation is two to three times more common in females than in males. The embryological basis of patent ductus arteriosus is failure of the ductus arteriosus to involute after birth and form the ligamentum arteriosum. Patent ductus arteriosus is the most common cardiac malformation associated with maternal rubella infection during early pregnancy (see Chapter 9).

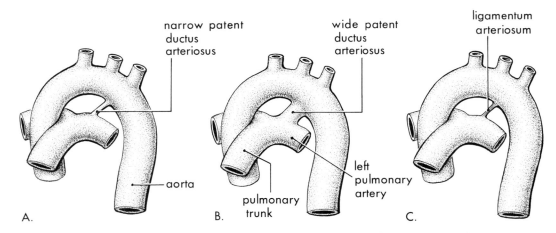

Figure 15–19   *A,* The ductus arteriosus of a newborn infant. The ductus is normally patent for about two weeks after birth. *B,* Abnormal patent ductus arteriosus in a six-month infant. In this case, some of the blood that should go through the aorta to the lower part of the body goes back to the lungs via the ductus arteriosus and the pulmonary arteries. The ductus is nearly the same size as the left pulmonary artery. *C,* The ligamentum arteriosum, normal remnant of the ductus arteriosus, in a six-month infant.

PRENATAL CIRCULATION

The fetal cardiovascular system is designed to serve prenatal needs and to permit modifications at birth which establish the postnatal circulatory pattern.

Course of the Fetal Circulation (Fig. 15–20). Well-oxygenated blood returns from the placenta in the *umbilical vein*. About half of this blood bypasses the liver, going through the *ductus venosus*. After a short course in the *inferior vena cava*, the blood enters the right atrium. Because the inferior vena cava also contains deoxygenated blood from the lower limbs, abdomen, and pelvis, the blood entering the right atrium is not so well oxygenated as that in the umbilical vein. The blood from the inferior vena cava is largely directed by the inferior border of the septum secundum through the *foramen ovale* into the left atrium. Here it mixes with a relatively small amount of deoxygenated blood returning from the lungs via the pulmonary veins. The blood passes into the left ventricle and leaves via the ascending aorta. Consequently, the vessels to the heart, head and neck, and upper limbs receive well-oxygenated blood.

A small amount of oxygenated blood from the inferior vena cava remains in the right atrium. This blood mixes with deoxygenated blood from the superior vena cava and coronary sinus and passes into the right ventricle. The blood leaves by the pulmonary trunk and most of it passes through the ductus arteriosus into the aorta. Very little blood goes to the lungs because they are nonfunctional and so require little blood. Most of the mixed blood in the descending aorta passes into the umbilical arteries and is returned to the placenta for reoxygenation. The blood remaining in the aorta circulates through the inferior part of the body and eventually enters the inferior vena cava.

POSTNATAL CIRCULATION

Changes in the Cardiovascular System at Birth (Fig. 15–21). Important circulatory adjustments occur at birth when the circulation of fetal blood through the placenta ceases and the lungs begin to function. The foramen ovale, the ductus arteriosus, the ductus venosus, and the umbilical vessels are no longer needed. Occlusion of the placental circulation causes an immediate fall of blood pressure in the inferior vena cava and the right atrium. Aeration of the lungs is associated with a dramatic fall in pulmonary vascular resistance, a marked increase in pulmonary blood flow, and a progressive thinning of the walls of the pulmonary arteries. As a result of this increased pulmonary blood flow, the pressure in the left atrium rises above that in the right atrium. This closes the foramen ovale by pressing its valve, the septum primum, against the septum secundum.

Because of the changes in the cardiovascular system at birth, certain vessels and structures are no longer required. They are transformed as follows (Fig. 15–21):

The intra-abdominal portion of the umbilical vein becomes the *ligamentum teres*, which passes from the umbilicus to the left branch of the portal vein.

The ductus venosus becomes the *ligamentum venosum*, which passes through the liver from the left branch of the portal vein to the inferior vena cava.

Most of the intra-abdominal portions of the umbilical arteries form the *medial umbilical ligaments*. The proximal parts of these vessels persist as the *superior vesical arteries*, which supply the superior part of the urinary bladder.

The foramen ovale normally closes functionally at birth. Later anatomical closure results from tissue proliferation and adhesion of the septum primum (the valve of the foramen ovale) to the left margin of the septum secundum.

The ductus arteriosus becomes the *ligamentum arteriosum*, which passes from the left pulmonary artery to the arch of the aorta. Anatomical closure of the ductus normally occurs by the end of the third postnatal month.

The change from the fetal to the adult pattern of circulation is not a sudden occurrence. It takes place over a period of days and weeks. During the transitional stage, there may be a right-to-left flow through the foramen ovale, and the ductus arteriosus usually remains patent for two or three months.

The closure of the fetal vessels and the foramen ovale is initially a functional change; later there is anatomical closure resulting from proliferation of endothelial and fibrous tissues.

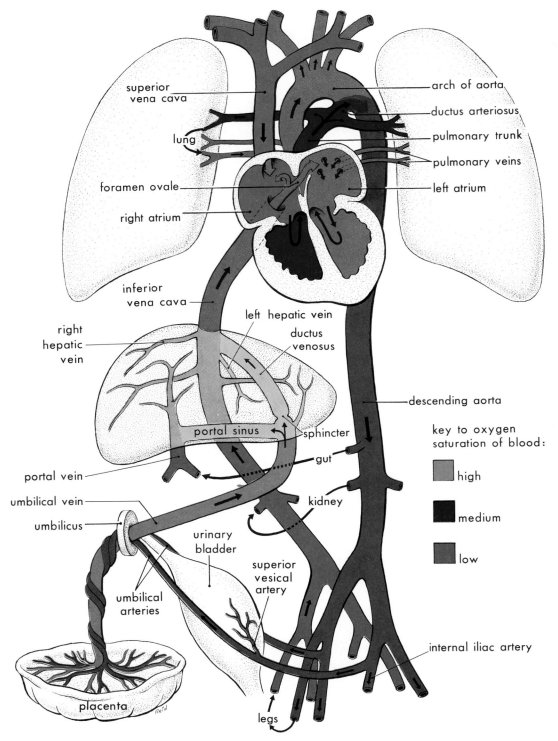

Figure 15–20 A simplified scheme of the fetal circulation. The colors indicate the oxygen saturation of the blood, and the arrows show the course of the fetal circulation. The organs are not drawn to scale.

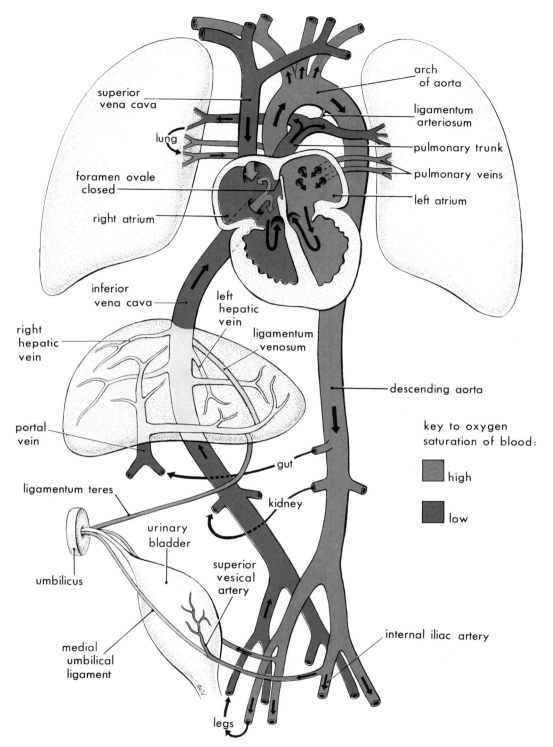

Figure 15–21 A simplified representation of the circulation after birth. The adult derivatives of the fetal vessels and structures that become nonfunctional at birth are also shown. The arrows indicate the course of the neonatal circulation. The organs are not drawn to scale.

SUMMARY

The cardiovascular system begins to develop during the third week from splanchnic mesoderm in the cardiogenic area. Paired heart tubes form and fuse into a single heart tube. By the end of the third week, a functional cardiovascular system is present. As the heart tube grows, it bends to the right and soon acquires the general external appearance of the adult heart. The heart becomes partitioned into four chambers between the fourth and seventh weeks.

The critical period of heart development is from about day 20 to day 50. Because partitioning of the heart is complex, *defects of the cardiac septa are relatively common*, particularly ventricular septal defects. Some congenital malformations result from abnormal transformation of the aortic arches into the adult arterial pattern.

Because the lungs are nonfunctional during prenatal life, the fetal cardiovascular system is structurally designed so that blood is oxygenated in the placenta and largely bypasses the lungs. The modifications which establish the postnatal circulatory pattern at birth are not abrupt, but extend into infancy. Failure of the normal changes in the circulatory system to occur at birth results in a *patent foramen ovale* or a *patent ductus arteriosus* or both.

SUGGESTED SUPPLEMENTARY READING

Duckworth, J. W. A.: Embryology of congenital heart disease; *in* Keith, J. D., Rowe, R. D., and Vlad, P. (Eds.): *Heart Disease in Infancy and Childhood*, 3rd ed. New York, The Macmillan Company, 1978.
The chapter cited gives a more comprehensive account of cardiovascular abnormalities. The remainder of the book gives clinical details of heart disease in infants and children.
Moore, K. L.: *The Developing Human. Clinically Oriented Embryology*, 3rd ed. Philadelphia, W. B. Saunders Company, 1982, pp. 298–339.
This account of normal and abnormal development of the cardiovascular system is more extensive. More details of the heart defects are given.

16

THE ARTICULAR, SKELETAL, AND MUSCULAR SYSTEMS

The articular, skeletal, and muscular systems develop from mesoderm, the formation of which is described in Chapter 5. With the formation of the notochord and the neural tube, the *intraembryonic mesoderm* lateral to these structures thickens to form two longitudinal columns of *paraxial mesoderm* (Fig. 16–1A). The somites arise from the paraxial mesoderm, beginning around 20 days. Externally, they appear as pairs of beadlike elevations along the dorsolateral surface of the embryo (see Fig. 6–3). The development and early differentiation of the *somites* are illustrated in Figure 16–1. Initially, the somites are composed of *compact aggregates of mesenchymal cells*. Each somite soon becomes differentiated into a ventromedial part called the *sclerotome* and a dorsolateral part called the *dermomyotome*.

Shortly after the somites form, their ventral and medial walls lose their organization and break up into sclerotomal cells, which are collectively referred to as the *sclerotomes* (Fig. 16–1). Sclerotomal cells soon surround the notochord and the neural tube, and form the primordia of the *vertebrae* and the ribs.

Cells of the sclerotomes give rise to the vertebral column and the ligaments associated with it. The *dermomyotome* (all but the sclerotome of a somite) gives rise to the dermis of the skin and to the dorsal musculature.

THE ARTICULAR SYSTEM

DEVELOPMENT OF JOINTS

The terms *articulation* and *joint* are used synonymously to refer to the structural arrangements that join two or more bones together at their place of meeting. Joints may be classified in several ways. Those with little or no movement are classified according to the type of material holding the bones together, e.g., the bones involved in *fibrous joints* are joined by fibrous tissue (Fig. 16–2D).

Synovial Joints (Fig. 16–2B). The mesenchyme between the developing bones, known as the *interzonal mesenchyme*, differentiates as follows: (1) Peripherally, it gives rise to the capsular and other ligaments. (2) Centrally, it disappears and forms the joint cavity. (3) Where it lines the capsule and the articular surfaces, it forms the synovial membrane. Probably as a result of joint movement, the mesenchymal cells subsequently disappear from the surfaces of the articular cartilages. Examples of this type of joint are the knee and elbow joints.

Cartilaginous Joints (Fig. 16–2C). The interzonal mesenchyme between the developing bones differentiates into hyaline cartilage (e.g., the costochondral joints) or fibrocartilage (e.g., the symphysis pubis). Hyaline cartilage caps the bones participating in the joint.

Fibrous Joints (Fig. 16–2D). The interzonal mesenchyme between the developing bones differentiates into dense fibrous connective tissue, e.g., the sutures of the skull.

THE SKELETAL SYSTEM

The skeletal system develops from mesoderm, the formation of which is described in Chapter 5. Most bones first appear as mesenchymal condensations and then as hyaline cartilage models which become ossified by endochondral ossification. Some bones develop in mesenchyme by intramembranous bone formation. For details about bone formation, see Ham and Cormack (1979).

213

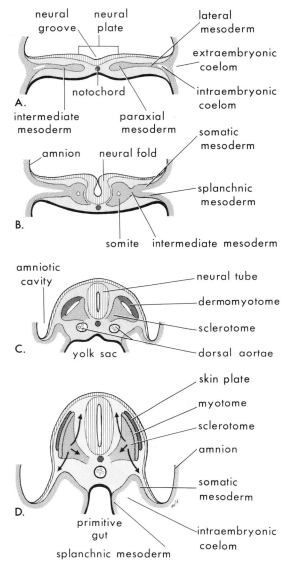

Figure 16–1 Transverse sections through embryos of various ages illustrating the formation and early differentiation of somites. See Figure 6–3 for the external appearance of these embryos. *A*, Presomite embryo showing the paraxial mesoderm from which the somites are derived. *B*, Embryo of about 22 days. *C*, Embryo of about 26 days. The dermomyotome region of the somite gives rise to a myotome and a skin plate (future dermis). *D*, Embryo of about 28 days. The arrows indicate the migration of cells from the sclerotome regions of the somites.

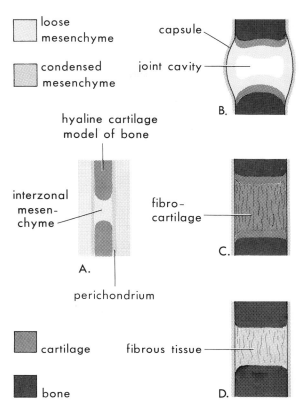

Figure 16–2 Schematic drawing illustrating the development of different types of joints. *A*, Condensed mesenchyme continues across the gap, or interzone, between the developing bones, enclosing some loose mesenchyme (the interzonal mesenchyme) between them. This primitive joint may differentiate into *B*, a synovial joint, *C*, a cartilaginous joint, or *D*, a fibrous joint. (From Moore, K. L.: *The Developing Human: Clinically Oriented Embryology,* 3rd ed. Philadelphia, W. B. Saunders Company, 1982.)

DEVELOPMENT OF VERTEBRAL COLUMN

Precartilaginous Stage. During the fourth week, mesenchymal cells from the somites migrate in three main directions (Figs. 16–1*D* and 16–3*A*):

1. Cells move ventromedially to surround the notochord. The body of each vertebra develops from the caudal part of one somite together with the cranial portion of the next somite. The notochord eventually degenerates and disappears where it is surrounded by the developing vertebral body. Between the vertebrae it expands to form the gelatinous center of the intervertebral disc, called the *nucleus pulposus.*

2. Cells migrate dorsally to cover the neural tube. These mesenchymal cells give rise to the *vertebral arch* of the vertebra.

3. Cells pass ventrolaterally into the body wall and form the costal processes which develop into ribs in the thoracic region.

Chondrification (Fig. 16–4). During the sixth week, chondrification centers appear in each mesenchymal vertebra. The two centers in each centrum fuse at the end of the embryonic period to form the cartilaginous centrum. Concomitantly, centers in the vertebral arches fuse with each other and with the centrum. The spinous and transverse processes are derived from extensions of chondrification centers in the vertebral arch.

Ossification of Typical Vertebrae (Fig. 16–4*C* to *F*). Ossification begins during the embryonic period and ends around the twenty-fifth year.

PRENATAL PERIOD. At first there are two *primary ossification centers*, ventral and dorsal, for the centrum. These differ from the chondrification centers that are side by side (Fig. 16–4*B*). The two primary ossification centers soon fuse to form one center. Hence, three primary centers appear by the end of the embryonic period: one in the centrum and one in each half of the vertebral arch (Fig. 16–4*C*). Ossification becomes evident in the vertebral arches around the eighth week. At birth, each vertebra consists of three bony parts connected by cartilage (Fig. 16–4*D*).

POSTNATAL PERIOD. The halves of the vertebral arch usually fuse during the first

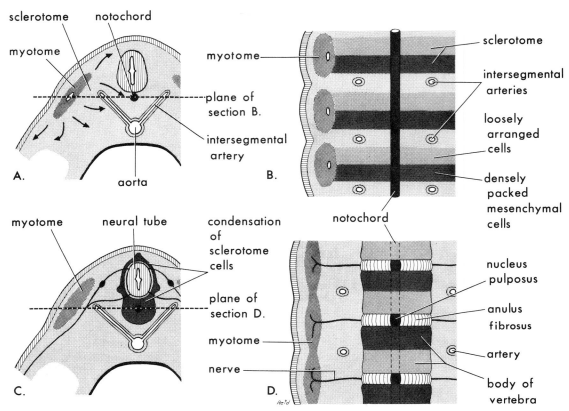

Figure 16–3 *A*, Partial transverse section through a four-week embryo. The arrows indicate the spread of mesenchymal cells from the sclerotome region of the somite on the right. *B*, Diagrammatic frontal section of this embryo, showing that the condensation of sclerotome cells around the notochord consists of a cranial area of loosely packed cells and a caudal area of densely packed cells. *C*, Partial transverse section through a five-week embryo showing the condensation of sclerotome cells around the notochord and the neural tube, forming a mesenchymal vertebra. *D*, Diagrammatic frontal section illustrating that the vertebral body forms from the cranial and caudal halves of two successive sclerotome masses. The intersegmental arteries now cross the bodies of the vertebrae, and the spinal nerves lie between the vertebrae. The notochord is degenerating except in the region of the intervertebral disc, where it forms the nucleus pulposus. (From Moore, K. L.: *The Developing Human: Clinically Oriented Embryology*, 3rd ed. Philadelphia, W. B. Saunders Company, 1982.)

three to five years. The laminae of the arches first unite in the lumbar region, and subsequent union progresses cranially. The vertebral arch articulates with the centrum at cartilaginous *neurocentral joints*, which permit the vertebral arches to grow as the spinal cord enlarges. These joints disappear when the vertebral arch fuses with the centrum during the third to sixth years.

During or shortly *after puberty*, five secondary centers appear: one for the tip of the spinous process, one for the tip of each transverse process, and two rim epiphyses (*anular epiphyses*), one on the superior and one on the inferior rim of the vertebral body (Fig. 16–4*E*).

The vertebral body is a composite of the superior and inferior anular epiphyses and the mass of bone between them. It includes the centrum, parts of the vertebral arch, and the facets for the heads of the ribs. The terms "body" and "centrum" are not, therefore, interchangeable. All secondary centers unite with the rest of the vertebra at about 25 years.

MALFORMATIONS OF VERTEBRAE

Variation in the Number of Vertebrae. About 95 per cent of normal people have 7 cervical, 12 thoracic, 5 lumbar, and 5 sacral vertebrae. About 3 per cent of people have one or two more vertebrae, and about

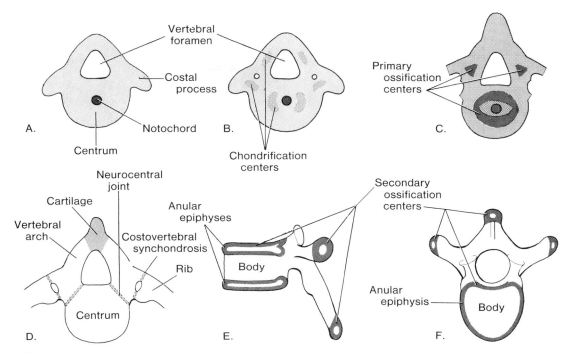

Figure 16–4   Drawings illustrating the stages of vertebral development. *A*, Precartilaginous (mesenchymal) vertebra at five weeks. *B*, Chondrification centers in a mesenchymal vertebra at six weeks. *C*, Primary ossification centers in a cartilaginous vertebra at seven weeks. *D*, A thoracic vertebra at birth, consisting of three bony parts. Note the cartilage between the halves of the vertebral (neural) arch and between the arch and the centrum (the neurocentral joint). *E* and *F*, Two views of a typical thoracic vertebra at puberty, showing the location of the secondary centers of ossification. (From Moore, K. L.: *The Developing Human: Clinically Oriented Embryology,* 3rd ed. Philadelphia, W. B. Saunders Company, 1982.)

2 per cent have one less. To determine the number of vertebrae, it is necessary to examine the entire vertebral column, because an apparent extra (or absent) vertebra in one segment of the column may be compensated for by an absent (or extra) vertebra in an adjacent segment, e.g., 11 thoracic-type vertebrae with 6 lumbar-type vertebrae.

Spina Bifida Occulta (see Fig. 17–10*A*). This defect of the vertebral arch results from failure of development and fusion of the halves of the vertebral arch. It is commonly observed in radiographs of the cervical, lumbar, and sacral regions. Frequently, only one vertebra is affected.

Spina bifida occulta of the first sacral vertebra occurs in about 10 per cent of people and usually causes no serious physiological disturbances. *The spinal cord and spinal nerves are usually normal* and neurological symptoms are commonly absent. The skin over the defect is intact and there may be no external evidence of the abnormality. Sometimes the malformation is indicated by a dimple or a tuft of hair.

In about 3 per cent of normal adults, there is *spina bifida occulta of the atlas.* At other cervical levels this condition is rare, and, when present, it is sometimes accompanied by other abnormalities of the cervical region of the vertebral column.

Rachischisis (see Fig. 16–8).   The term *rachischisis* (cleft of vertebral column) refers to the vertebral abnormalities encountered in a complex group of developmental malformations (*axial dysraphic disorders*) that affect primarily the axial structures of the body. In these cases, the neural folds fail to fuse, either because of faulty induction by the underlying notochord and its associated mesenchyme, or because of the action of teratogenic agents on the neuroepithelial cells making up the neural folds. The neural and vertebral defects may be extensive, or they may be restricted to a small area.

Hemivertebra (Fig. 16–5*B*).   The developing vertebral bodies have two juxtaposed chondrification centers (Fig. 16–4*B*) that soon unite. A hemivertebra results from failure of one of the chondrification centers to

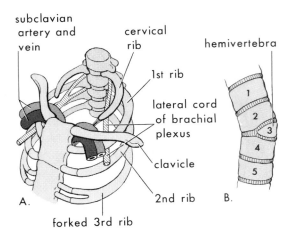

Figure 16–5 Drawings of vertebral and rib abnormalities. *A*, Cervical and forked ribs. Observe that the left cervical rib has a fibrous band passing posterior to the subclavian vessels and attaching to the sternum. Very likely, this condition produced neurovascular changes in the left upper limb. *B*, Anterior view of the vertebral column showing a hemivertebra (half vertebra). The right half of the third thoracic vertebra is absent. Note the associated lateral curvature, or scoliosis, of the vertebral column (From Moore, K. L.: *The Developing Human: Clinically Oriented Embryology,* 3rd ed. Philadelphia, W. B. Saunders Company, 1982.)

appear and subsequent failure of half of the vertebra to form. These defective vertebrae produce *scoliosis* (lateral curvature of the vertebral column).

DEVELOPMENT OF RIBS

The ribs develop from the mesenchymal costal processes of the thoracic vertebrae (Fig. 16–4*A*). They become cartilaginous during the embryonic period and later ossify. The original union of the costal processes with the vertebra is replaced by a synovial joint (Fig. 16–4*D*).

MALFORMATIONS OF RIBS

Accessory Ribs (Fig. 16–5*A*). Accessory ribs, which may be rudimentary or fairly well developed, result from the development of the costal processes of cervical or lumbar vertebrae. These processes form ribs in the thoracic region.

The most common type of accessory rib is a *lumbar rib*, but it causes no problems. *Cervical ribs* are less common, but are present in 0.5 to 1 per cent of people. A cervical rib

is attached to the seventh cervical vertebra and may be unilateral or bilateral. Pressure of a cervical rib on the brachial plexus or on the subclavian vessels may produce neurovascular symptoms.

Fused Ribs. Fusion of ribs occasionally occurs posteriorly when two or more ribs arise from a single vertebra. Fused ribs are often associated with a hemivertebra.

Forked or Bifid Ribs (Fig. 16–5*A*). Forking of a rib at its anterior (sternal) end is not uncommon. Usually the abnormality is unilateral and of no significance. Rib anomalies are often seen in combination with vertebral abnormalities and scoliosis (Fig. 16–5*B*).

DEVELOPMENT OF THE SKULL

The skull develops from mesenchyme around the developing brain. It consists of the *neurocranium*, a protective case for the brain, and the *viscerocranium*, the main skeleton of the jaws.

Cartilaginous Neurocranium (Chondrocranium). Initially, this consists of the cartilaginous base of the developing skull which forms by fusion of several cartilages (Fig. 16–6*A*). Later, endochondral ossification of this chondrocranium forms various bones in the base of the skull.

Membranous Neurocranium. Intramembranous ossification occurs in the mesenchyme investing the brain and forms the bones of the cranial vault (Fig. 16–6*D*). During fetal life and infancy, the flat bones of the skull are separated by dense connective tissue membranes or fibrous joints called *sutures* (Fig. 16–7). Six large fibrous areas, or "soft spots," called *fontanelles* are also present. The softness of the bones and their loose connections at the sutures enable the cranial vault (calvaria) to undergo changes of shape during birth, called *molding* (e.g., the forehead becomes flattened and the occiput (back of the head) drawn out as the bones overlap). This construction also enables the skull to enlarge rapidly with the brain during infancy and childhood.

Cartilaginous Viscerocranium (Fig. 16–6*D*). This consists of the cartilaginous skeleton of the first three *branchial arches* (see Chapter 11). During endochondral ossification, the dorsal end of the *first arch cartilage* (Meckel's cartilage) forms two middle ear bones, the malleus and incus. The dorsal end of the *second arch cartilage* (Reichert's cartilage) forms the stapes of the middle ear and

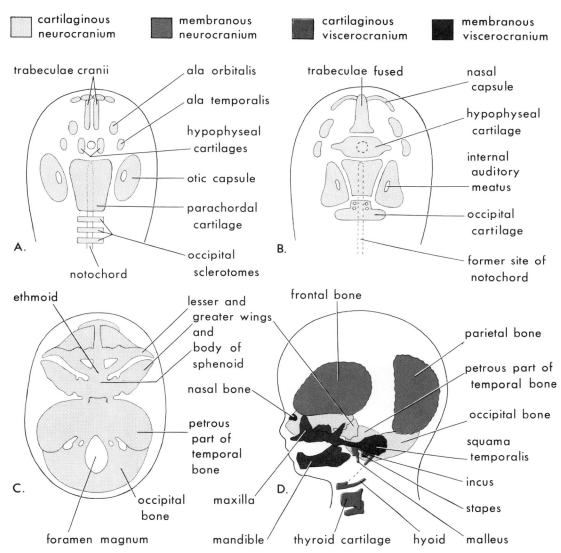

cartilaginous neurocranium

membranous neurocranium

cartilaginous viscerocranium

membranous viscerocranium

A.

trabeculae cranii

ala orbitalis

ala temporalis

hypophyseal cartilages

otic capsule

parachordal cartilage

occipital sclerotomes

notochord

B.

trabeculae fused

nasal capsule

hypophyseal cartilage

internal auditory meatus

occipital cartilage

former site of notochord

C.

ethmoid

lesser and greater wings and body of sphenoid

nasal bone

petrous part of temporal bone

maxilla

occipital bone

foramen magnum

mandible

D.

frontal bone

parietal bone

petrous part of temporal bone

occipital bone

squama temporalis

incus

stapes

malleus

thyroid cartilage

hyoid

Figure 16–6 Diagrams illustrating stages in the development of the skull. *A* to *C* are viewed from above; *D* is a lateral view. *A*, Six weeks, showing the various cartilages that will fuse to form the chondrocranium. *B*, Seven weeks, after fusion of some of the paired cartilages. *C*, 12 weeks, showing the cartilaginous base of the skull or chondrocranium formed by the fusion of various cartilages. *D*, 20 weeks, indicating the derivation of the bones of the fetal skull. The sides and roof of the skull (cranial vault or calvaria) develop from the mesenchyme investing the brain that undergoes intramembranous ossification.

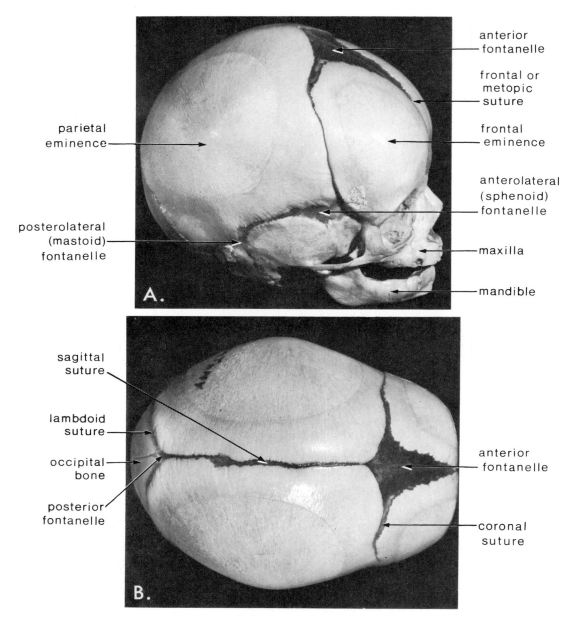

Figure 16–7 Photographs of a fetal skull showing the fontanelles, the bones, and the connecting sutures. *A*, Lateral view. *B*, Superior view. The posterior and anterolateral fontanelles close within two to three months after birth by growth of the surrounding bones. The posterolateral fontanelles close similarly by the end of the first year, and the anterior fontanelle closes about the middle of the second year. The two halves of the frontal bone normally begin to fuse during the second year, and the frontal or metopic suture is often obliterated by the eighth year. The other sutures begin to disappear during adult life, but the times when the sutures close are subject to wide variations.

the styloid process of the temporal bone. The ventral end ossifies to form the lesser cornu and superior part of the body of the hyoid bone. The ventral end of the *third arch cartilage* gives rise to the greater cornu and inferior part of the body of the hyoid bone.

Membranous Viscerocranium (Fig. 16–6*D*).   Intramembranous ossification occurs within the maxillary prominence (process) of the first branchial arch and forms the premaxilla, the maxilla, and the zygomatic and the squamous temporal bones. The mesenchyme of the mandibular prominence of this arch condenses around the first arch cartilage (Meckel's cartilage) and undergoes intramembranous ossification to form the mandible. This cartilage disappears ventral to the portion which forms the sphenomandibular ligament. Meckel's cartilage disappears and so does not give rise to the adult mandible.

The Newborn Skull (Fig. 16–7). The skull at birth is like the fetal skull; it is rather round and its bones are quite thin. The skull is large in proportion to the rest of the skeleton, and the face is relatively small compared with the cranial vault. The small facial region results from the small size of the jaws, the virtual absence of paranasal air sinuses, and the general underdevelopment of the facial bones.

Postnatal Growth of the Skull. The fibrous sutures of the newborn calvaria (cranial vault) permit the skull to enlarge during infancy and childhood. The increase in the size of the calvaria is greatest during the first two years, the period of most rapid postnatal growth of the brain. A person's calvaria normally increases in capacity until about 15 or 16 years of age. This growth is related to the rapid development of the brain. There is also rapid growth of the face and jaws, coinciding with the eruption of the primary or deciduous teeth; these changes are still more marked after the permanent teeth erupt (see Chapter 19). There is concurrent enlargement of the frontal and facial regions associated with the increase in the size of the paranasal air sinuses.

MALFORMATIONS OF THE SKULL

Acrania (Fig. 16–8). In this condition, the cranial vault is absent and a large defect of the vertebral column is usually present. Acrania is associated with *anencephaly* (absence of most of the brain); this condition is discussed in Chapter 17.

Craniosynostosis. Several rare skull deformities result from premature closure of the skull sutures. Prenatal closure results in the most severe abnormalities. The cause of

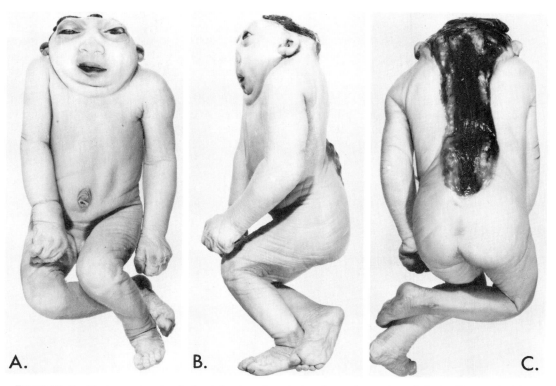

Figure 16–8 Photographs of anterior, lateral, and posterior views of a newborn infant with acrania (absence of cranial vault), anencephaly (absence of forebrain), rachischisis (extensive cleft in vertebral column), and myeloschisis (severe malformation of the spinal cord).

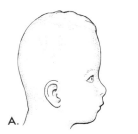 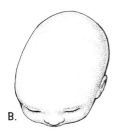

Figure 16–9 Drawing illustrating skull malformations. *A*, Oxycephaly, or turricephaly, showing the tower-like skull resulting from premature closure of the coronal suture. *B*, Plagiocephaly, illustrating a type of asymmetrical skull resulting from premature closure of the coronal and lambdoid sutures on the left side. (From Moore, K.L.: *The Developing Human: Clinically Oriented Embryology,* 3rd ed. Philadelphia, W. B. Saunders Company, 1982.)

craniosynostosis is unknown, but genetic factors appear to be important. These abnormalities are much more common in males than in females, and they are often associated with other skeletal malformations. The type of deformed skull produced depends upon which sutures close prematurely. If the sagittal suture closes early, the skull becomes long, narrow, and wedge-shaped (*scaphocephaly*); this type constitutes about half the cases of craniosynostosis. Another 30 per cent of cases involve premature closure of the coronal suture. This results in high, tower-like skull (*oxycephaly, or turricephaly*, Fig. 16–9*A*). If the coronal or the lambdoid suture closes prematurely on one side only, the skull is twisted and asymmetrical (*plagiocephaly*, Fig. 16–9*B*).

THE APPENDICULAR SKELETON

The appendicular skeleton consists of the pectoral (shoulder) and pelvic girdles and the limb bones. The general features of early limb development are described and illustrated in Chapter 6.

The *limb buds* first appear as small elevations of the ventrolateral body wall toward the end of the fourth week. The early stages of limb development are alike for the upper and lower limbs (Fig. 16–10), except that development of the *upper limb buds* precedes that of the *lower limb buds* by a few days. The upper limb buds develop opposite the caudal cervical segments, and the lower limb buds form opposite the lumbar and upper sacral segments. Each limb bud consists of a mass of mesenchyme derived from the somatic mesoderm and is covered by a layer of ectoderm.

The *apical ectodermal ridge* (Fig. 16–11*B*) exerts an inductive influence on this mesenchyme which promotes growth and development of the limbs. The ends of the flipper-like limb buds flatten into paddle-like hand or foot plates, and digits differentiate at the margins of these plates.

As the limbs elongate and the bones form, *myoblasts* (muscle-forming cells) aggregate and develop into a large muscle mass in each limb. In general, this muscle mass separates into dorsal (extensor) and ventral (flexor) components. Initially, the limbs are directed caudally; later they extend ventrally, and then the developing upper and lower limbs rotate in opposite directions and to different degrees (Fig. 16–11). Originally, the flexor

Figure 16–10 Drawing illustrating positional changes of the developing limbs: *A*, About 48 days, showing the extremities extending ventrally and the hand and foot plates facing each other. *B*, About 51 days, showing the arms bent at the elbows and the hands curved over the thorax. *C*, About 54 days, showing the soles of the feet facing each other. *D*, About 56 days. Note that the elbows now point caudally and the knees cranially.

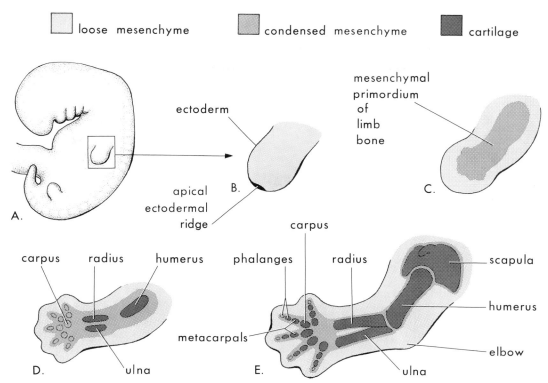

loose mesenchyme   condensed mesenchyme   cartilage

Figure 16–11   *A*, An embryo of about 28 days, showing the early appearance of the limb buds. *B*, Schematic drawing of a longitudinal section through an early arm bud. *The apical ectodermal ridge has an inductive influence on the loose mesenchyme in the limb bud; it promotes growth of the mesenchyme and appears to give it the ability to form specific cartilaginous elements. C*, Similar sketch of an arm bud at 33 days showing the mesenchymal primordium of a limb bone. *D*, Forelimb at six weeks showing the hyaline cartilage models of the various bones. *E*, Later in the sixth week, showing the completed cartilaginous models of the bones of the upper limb.

aspect of the limbs is ventral and the extensor aspect dorsal. The preaxial and postaxial borders are cranial and caudal, respectively (Fig. 16–12). The upper limb buds rotate laterally through 90 degrees on their longitudinal axes; thus the future elbows point backward or dorsally, and the extensor muscles come to lie on the lateral and dorsal aspect of the upper limb. The lower limb buds rotate medially through almost 90 degrees; thus the future knees point forward or ventrolaterally, and the extensor muscles lie on the ventral aspect of the lower limb. It should also be clear that the radius and tibia and the ulna and fibula are homologous bones, just as the thumb and the big toe are homologous digits.

During the sixth week, the mesenchymal primordia of bones in the limb buds undergo chondrification to form hyaline cartilage models of the future appendicular skeleton (see Fig. 16–11D and E). The models of the pectoral girdle and the upper limb bones appear slightly before those of the pelvic girdle and lower limbs, and the bone models in each limb appear in a proximodistal sequence. Ossification begins in the long bones by the end of the embryonic period; by 12 weeks primary centers have appeared in nearly all bones of the extremities. Secondary centers of ossification appear after birth.

Dermatomes and Cutaneous Innervation of the Limbs (Fig. 16–12).   Because of its relationship to the growth and rotation of the limbs, the cutaneous segmental nerve supply of the limbs is considered in this chapter rather than in the chapter dealing with the nervous system or the integumentary system.

A *dermatome is defined as the area of skin supplied by a single spinal nerve and its spinal ganglion.* The peripheral nerves grow from the limb plexuses (brachial and lum-

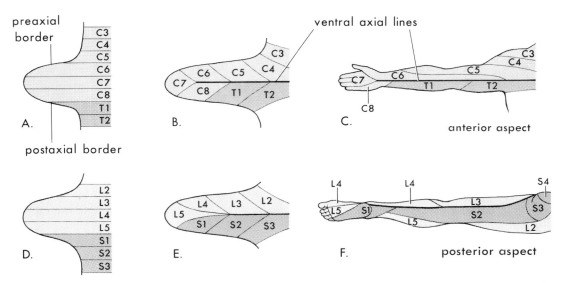

Figure 16–12 Diagrams illustrating development of the dermatomal patterns of the limbs. The *axial lines* indicate where there is no sensory overlap. *A* and *D*, Ventral aspect of the limb buds early in the fifth week. At this stage, the dermatomal patterns show the primitive segmental arrangement. *B* and *E*, Similar views later in the fifth week, showing the modified arrangement of dermatomes. *C* and *F*, The dermatomal patterns in the adult upper and lower limbs. The primitive dermatomal pattern has disappeared, but an orderly sequence of dermatomes can still be recognized. In *F*, note that most of the original ventral surface of the lower limb lies on the back of the adult limb. This results from the medial rotation of the lower limb that occurs toward the end of the embryonic period. In the upper limb, the ventral axial line extends along the anterior surface of the arm and forearm. In the lower limb, the ventral axial line extends along the medial side of the thigh and knee to the posteromedial aspect of the leg to the heel. (From Moore, K. L.: *The Developing Human: Clinically Oriented Embryology*, 3rd ed. Philadelphia, W. B. Saunders Company, 1982.)

bosacral) into the mesenchyme of the limb buds during the fifth week. The spinal nerves are distributed in segmental bands and supply both dorsal and ventral surfaces of the limb buds. As the limbs elongate, the cutaneous distribution of the spinal nerves migrates along the limbs and no longer reaches the surface in the distal part of the limbs. Although the original dermatomal pattern changes during growth of the limbs, an orderly sequence of distribution can still be recognized in the adult (Fig. 16–12*C* and *F*).

A *cutaneous nerve area is the area of skin supplied by a peripheral nerve.* Both cutaneous nerve areas and dermatomes show considerable overlapping. It should be emphasized that the dermatomal patterns indicate only that if the dorsal root of that segment is cut, there may be a slight deficit in the area indicated; however, because there is overlapping of dermatomes, a particular area is not exclusively innervated by a single segmental nerve. The limb dermatomes may be traced progressively down the lateral aspect of the upper limb and back up its medial aspect.

A comparable distribution of dermatomes occurs in the lower limbs, which may be traced down the ventral and then up the dorsal aspect of the lower limb. When the limbs descend, they carry their nerves with them; this explains the oblique course of the nerves of the brachial and lumbosacral plexuses.

MALFORMATIONS OF THE LIMBS

Minor defects are relatively common, but major limb malformations are generally rare. An "epidemic" of limb deformities occurred from 1957 to 1962 as a result of maternal ingestion of thalidomide (Fig. 16–13). This drug was withdrawn in 1961.

Absence of the Hands and Phalanges (Fig. 16–14*A* to *D*).   Absence of the fingers, and often part of the hand, is not too common. Often genetic factors cause these abnormalities.

Cleft Hand or Foot (Fig. 16–14*E* and *F*).   In this rare deformity, often called the lobster-claw deformity, there is absence of one or more central digits. Thus the hand or foot is divided into two parts that oppose

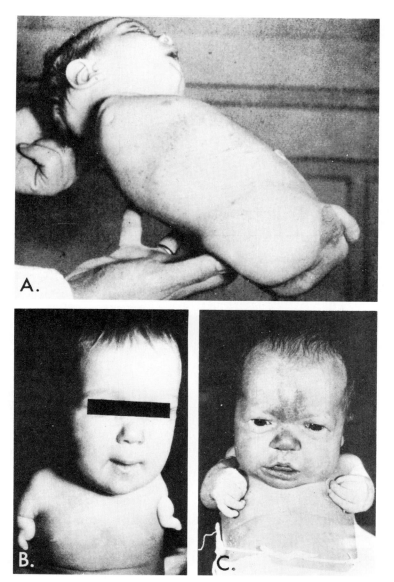

Figure 16–13 Limb malformations caused by thalidomide. *A,* Quadruple amelia. The upper and lower limbs are absent. *B,* Meromelia of the upper limbs. The arms are represented by rudimentary stumps. *C,* Meromelia, with the rudimentary upper limbs attached directly to the trunk. (From Lenz, W., and Knapp, K.: *German Med. Monthly 7*:253, 1962.)

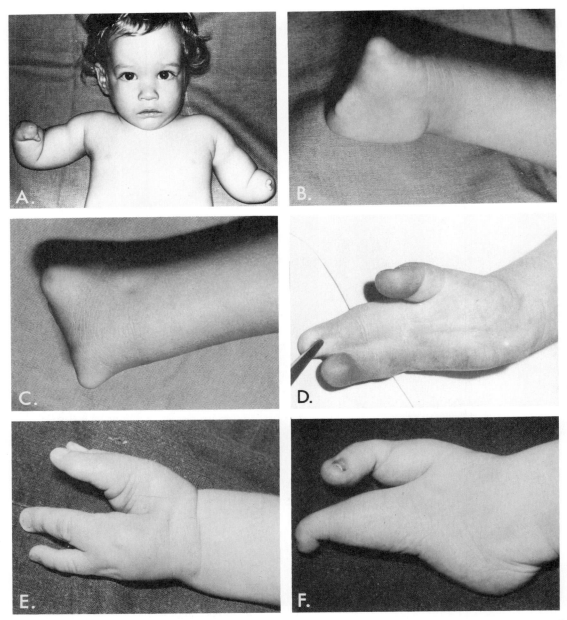

Figure 16–14   Photographs illustrating various types of meromelia. *A,* Absence of the hands and most of the forearms. *B,* Absence of the phalanges. *C,* Absence of the hand. *D,* Absence of the fourth and fifth phalanges and metacarpals. There is also syndactyly. *E,* Absence of the third phalanx, resulting in a cleft hand (lobster claw). *F,* Absence of the second and third toes, resulting in a cleft foot. (*D* from Swenson, O.: *Pediatric Surgery,* 1958. Courtesy of Appleton-Century-Crofts, Publishing Division of Prentice-Hall, Inc., Englewood Cliffs, NJ.)

each other like lobster claws. The remaining digits are partially or completely fused (syndactyly).

Brachydactyly (Fig. 16–15*A*). Abnormal shortness of the fingers or toes is uncommon. This results from reduction in the size of the phalanges. It is usually inherited as a dominant trait and is often associated with shortness of stature.

Polydactyly or Supernumerary Digits (Fig. 16–15*C* and *D*). Supernumerary (extra) fingers or toes are common. Often the extra digit is incompletely formed and is useless. If the hand is affected, the extra digit is most commonly ulnar or radial in position rather than central. In the foot, the extra toe is usually in the fibular position. Polydactyly is inherited as a dominant trait.

Syndactyly or Webbed Digits (Fig. 16–16). Fusion of the fingers or toes is a common limb malformation. Webbing of the skin between fingers or toes results from failure of the tissue to break down between the digits during development. Syndactyly is most frequently observed between the third and fourth fingers and the second and third toes. It is inherited as a simple dominant or simple recessive trait.

Clubfoot or Talipes Equinovarus (Fig. 16–16*C*). This type of clubfoot is relatively common and is about twice as frequent in males. The sole of the foot is turned medially and the foot is inverted. Although it is sometimes stated that this condition results from abnormal positioning or restricted movement of the lower limbs *in utero*, the evidence for

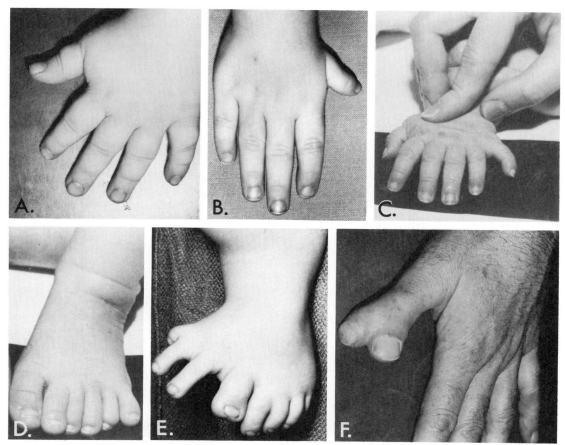

Figure 16–15 Photographs of various types of limb deformities. *A*, Brachydactyly. *B*, Hypoplasia (underdevelopment) of the thumb. *C*, Polydactyly showing a supernumerary finger. *D*, Polydactyly showing a supernumerary toe. *E*, Partial duplication of the foot. *F*, Partial duplication of the thumb. (*C* and *D* from Swenson, O.: *Pediatric Surgery.* 1958. Courtesy of Appleton-Century-Crofts, Publishing Division of Prentice-Hall, Inc., Englewood Cliffs, NJ.)

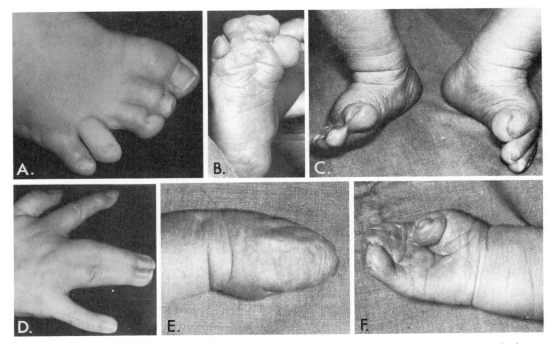

Figure 16–16 Photographs of various types of limb deformities. *A,* Syndactyly showing skin webs between the first and second and second and third toes. *B,* Syndactyly involving fusion of all the toes except the fifth. *C,* Syndactyly associated with clubfoot or talipes equinovarus. *D,* Syndactyly involving webbing of the third and fourth digits. *E* and *F,* Dorsal and palmar views of a child's right hand showing syndactyly or fusion of the second to fifth digits. (*A* and *D* from Swenson, O.: *Pediatric Surgery.* 1958. Courtesy of Appleton-Century-Crofts, Publishing Division of Prentice-Hall, Inc., Englewood Cliffs, NJ.)

this is inconclusive. Hereditary and environmental factors appear to be involved in most cases (*multifactorial inheritance*).

Any deformity of the foot involving the talus or ankle bone is called *talipes* or clubfoot. Talipes equinovarus is the most common type.

THE MUSCULAR SYSTEM

The muscular system develops from mesoderm, except for the muscles of the iris (see Chapter 18). Muscle tissue develops from primitive cells called *myoblasts.*

STRIATED SKELETAL MUSCULATURE

The myoblasts which form the skeletal musculature are derived from the myotome regions of the somites (see Fig. 16–1), the branchial arches, and the somatic mesoderm. The myoblasts elongate, aggregate to form parallel bundles, and then fuse to form multinucleated cells. During early fetal life, myo-

fibrils appear in the cytoplasm and show the characteristic cross striations by the end of the third month.

The migration of myoblasts from the branchial arches to form the muscles of mastication, of facial expression, and of the pharynx and larynx is described in Chapter 11 and is illustrated in Figures 11–5 and 16–17. Myoblasts from the *occipital myotomes* form the tongue muscles.

The musculature of the limbs develops from the mesenchyme surrounding the developing bones. It is now generally believed that there is no migration of mesenchyme from the somites to form limb muscles. The mesenchyme in the limbs which gives rise to the muscles is derived from the somatic layer of lateral mesoderm (Fig. 16–1).

VISCERAL MUSCULATURE

Smooth Muscle. Smooth muscle differentiates from splanchnic mesoderm surrounding the primitive gut and its derivatives (see Chapter 13). Elsewhere, smooth muscle

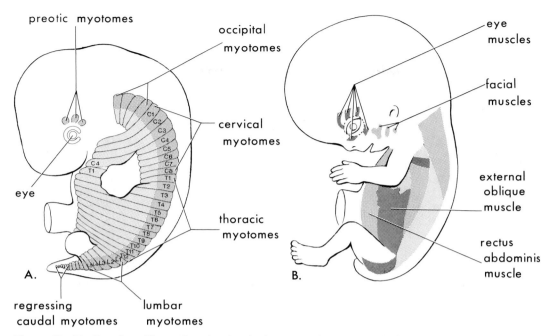

preotic myotomes

occipital myotomes

cervical myotomes

eye

thoracic myotomes

A.

regressing caudal myotomes

lumbar myotomes

eye muscles

facial muscles

external oblique muscle

rectus abdominis muscle

B.

Figure 16–17 Drawings illustrating the developing muscular system: *A*, Six-week embryo, showing the myotome regions of the somites that give rise to most skeletal muscles. *B*, Eight-week embryo, showing the developing superficial trunk musculature. (From Moore, K. L.: *The Developing Human: Clinically Oriented Embryology*, 3rd ed. Philadelphia, W. B. Saunders Company, 1982.)

develops from mesenchyme in the area concerned. The myoblasts elongate and develop contractile elements. The muscles of the iris and the myoepithelial cells of mammary and sweat glands appear to be derived from mesenchymal cells that originate from the ectoderm.

Striated Cardiac Muscle. Cardiac muscle develops from splanchnic mesoderm surrounding the heart (see Chapter 15). The myoblasts adhere to each other, as in developing skeletal muscle, but the intervening cell membranes do not disintegrate. These areas of adhesion become the *intercalated discs*. Usually there is a single central nucleus, and myofibrils develop as in skeletal muscle cells.

Late in the embryonic period, special bundles of muscle cells develop with relatively few myofibrils and relatively larger diameters than typical cardiac muscle cells. These atypical cardiac muscle cells, called *Purkinje fibers*, later form the conducting system of the heart.

SUMMARY

The articular, skeletal, and muscular systems are derived from mesoderm. The skeleton mainly develops from condensed mesenchyme which undergoes chondrification to form hyaline cartilage models of the bones. Ossification centers appear in these models by the end of the embryonic period. Some bones develop by intramembranous ossification.

The vertebral column and ribs develop from cells that originate in the somites. The developing skull consists of a neurocranium and a viscerocranium, each of which has membranous and cartilaginous components.

The limb buds appear during the fourth week as slight elevations of the ventrolateral body wall. The upper limb buds develop slightly before the lower limb buds. The tissues of the limb buds are derived from two main sources, the somatic layer of the lateral mesoderm and the ectoderm. The upper and lower limbs rotate in opposite directions and to different degrees.

Most skeletal muscle is derived from the myotome regions of the somites, but some head and neck muscles are derived from branchial arch mesoderm, and the limb musculature develops from mesenchyme derived from the somatic layer of lateral mesoderm. Cardiac muscle and smooth muscle are derived from splanchnic mesoderm.

The majority of malformations of the skeletal and muscular systems are caused by genetic factors; however, some deformities result from an interaction of genetic and environmental factors.

SUGGESTED SUPPLEMENTARY READING

Ham, A. W., and Cormack, D. H.: *Histology*, 8th ed. Philadelphia, J. B. Lippincott Company, 1979.
The descriptions of bones, joints, and muscles in this textbook are very good and there are many illustrations.
Smith, D. W.: *Recognizable Patterns of Human Malformation: Genetic, Embryologic and Clinical Aspects*, 3rd ed. Philadelphia, W. B. Saunders Company, 1982, pp. 224–238.
A good description of limb abnormalities and their causes is given.
Wolpert, L.: Mechanisms of limb development and malformation. *Br. Med. Bull. 32:*65, 1976.
A comprehensive discussion of normal and abnormal development of the limbs is presented.

17

THE NERVOUS SYSTEM

The nervous system develops from the *neural plate*, a thickened area of embryonic ectoderm which appears around the middle of the third week (Fig. 17–1). Formation of the *neural tube* and *neural crest* from the neural plate is described and also illustrated in Chapter 5. The neural tube differentiates into the *central nervous system*, consisting of the brain and spinal cord, and the neural crest gives rise to most of the *peripheral nervous system*. Neural crest cells also differentiate into other structures (see Fig. 17–8).

THE CENTRAL NERVOUS SYSTEM

The neural tube begins to form at 22 to 23 days and is temporarily open both cranially and caudally (Figs. 17–1C and 17–2). These openings, called *neuropores*, normally close during the fourth week. The walls of the neural tube thicken to form the brain and the spinal cord (Fig. 17–3). The *neural canal* becomes the ventricular system of the brain and the central canal of the spinal cord.

THE SPINAL CORD

The lateral walls of the neural tube thicken until only a minute *central canal* remains at 9 to 10 weeks (Fig. 17–4C). The wall of the neural tube is composed of a thick neuroepithelium which gives rise to all neurons and macroglial cells of the spinal cord (Fig. 17–5). The marginal zone of the neuroepithelium gradually becomes the white matter of the cord as axons grow into it and over it from nerve cell bodies in the spinal cord, in the spinal ganglia, and in the brain.

Some neuroepithelial cells differentiate into primitive neurons called *neuroblasts*. These cells form an *intermediate zone* between the ventricular and marginal zones (see Fig. 17–4E). When the neuroepithelial cells cease producing neuroblasts and glioblasts, they differentiate into ependymal cells

which give rise to the ependymal epithelium (ependyma) lining the central canal of the spinal cord.

The *microglial cells* (microglia), a smaller type of neuroglial cell, differentiate from mesenchymal cells surrounding the central nervous system (Fig. 17–5). They enter the spinal cord with developing blood vessels.

Thickening of the lateral walls of the spinal cord soon produces a shallow longitudinal groove called the *sulcus limitans* (Figs. 17–4B and 17–6). This groove demarcates the dorsal part or *alar plate* (lamina) from the ventral part or *basal plate* (lamina). The alar and basal plates are later associated with afferent and efferent functions, respectively.

The Alar Plates. Cell bodies in the alar plates form the dorsal gray matter in columns that extend the length of the spinal cord. In cross sections these columns are called *dorsal horns* (Fig. 17–7). As the alar plates enlarge, the *dorsal septum* forms and the central canal becomes small (Figs. 17–4C and 17–7).

The Basal Plates. Cell bodies in the basal plates form the ventral and lateral gray columns, which in cross sections are called *ventral* and *lateral horns*, respectively. Axons of ventral horn cells grow out of the spinal cord and form large bundles called *ventral roots* of the spinal nerves (see Fig. 17–6). As the basal plates enlarge, they produce the *ventral median septum* and a deep longitudinal groove on the ventral surface of the spinal cord known as the *ventral median fissure* (Figs. 17–4C and 17–7).

Spinal Ganglia (Figs. 17–6 to 17–8). The unipolar neurons in the spinal ganglia are derived from neural crest cells. Their axons divide in a T-shaped fashion into central and peripheral processes. The central branches or processes enter the spinal cord and constitute the *dorsal roots* of spinal nerves. The peripheral processes of spinal ganglion cells pass in the spinal nerves to special sensory endings in somatic or visceral structures.

Text continued on page 238

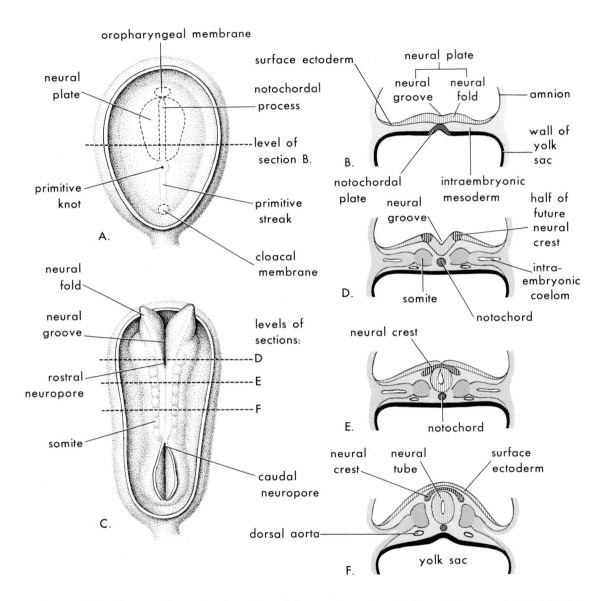

Figure 17–1 Diagrams illustrating formation of the neural crest and folding of the neural plate into the neural tube. *A,* Dorsal view of an embryo of about 18 days, exposed by removing the amnion. *B,* Transverse section of this embryo showing the neural plate and early development of the neural groove. *C,* Dorsal view of an embryo of about 22 days. The neural folds have fused opposite the somites, but are widely spread out at both ends of the embryo. *D, E,* and *F,* Transverse sections of this embryo at the levels shown in *C,* illustrating formation of the neural tube and its detachment from the surface ectoderm. Note that some neuroectodermal cells are not included in the neural tube but remain between it and the surface ectoderm as the neural crest. See Figure 17–8 for the derivatives of the neural crest. (From Moore, K. L.: *The Developing Human: Clinically Oriented Embryology,* 3rd ed. Philadelphia, W. B. Saunders Company, 1982.)

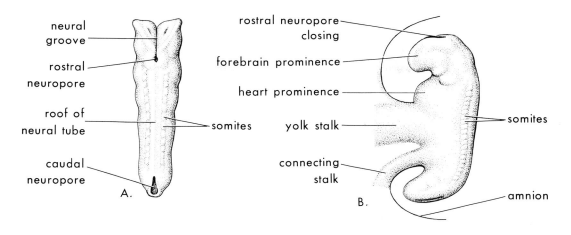

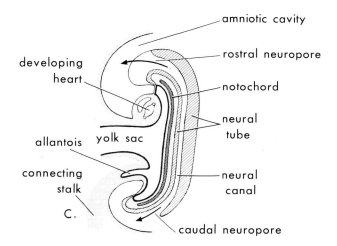

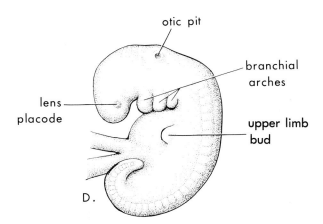

Figure 17–2 *A*, Dorsal view of an embryo of about 23 days showing advanced fusion of the neural folds. *B*, Lateral view of an embryo of about 24 days showing the forebrain prominence and closing of the rostral neuropore. *C*, Sagittal section of this embryo showing the transitory communication of the neural canal with the amniotic cavity (arrows). *D*, Lateral view of an embryo of 26 days after closure of the neuropores.

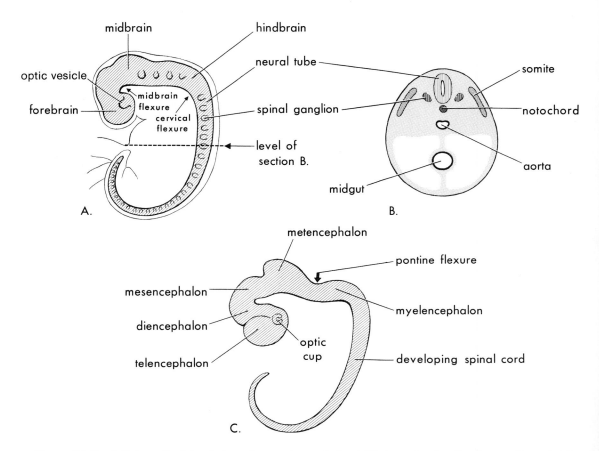

Figure 17–3 *A,* Schematic lateral view of an embryo of about 28 days showing the three primary brain vesicles. The two flexures demarcate the primary divisions of the brain. *B,* Transverse section of this embryo showing the neural tube which, in this region, will develop into the spinal cord. The spinal ganglia derived from the neural crest are also shown. *C,* Schematic lateral view of the central nervous system of a six-week embryo, showing the secondary brain vesicles and the pontine flexure. The flexures (bends) occur as the brain grows rapidly. They are important in determining the final shape of the brain.

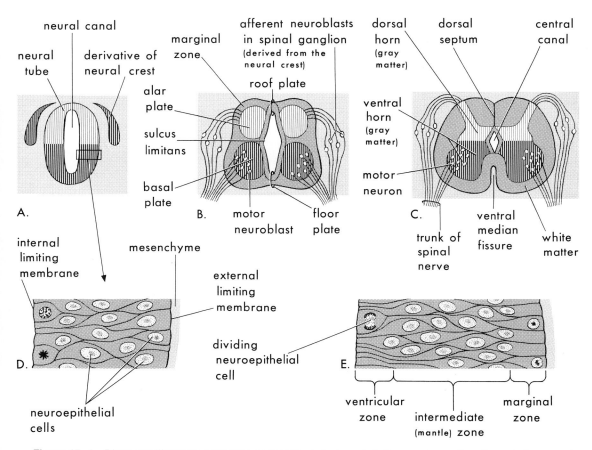

Figure 17–4 Diagrams illustrating development of the spinal cord. *A,* Transverse section through the neural tube of an embryo of about 23 days. *B* and *C,* Similar sections at six and nine weeks, respectively. *D,* Section through the wall of the early neural tube. *E,* Section through the wall of the developing spinal cord showing the three different zones. Note that the neural canal of the neural tube becomes the central canal of the spinal cord.

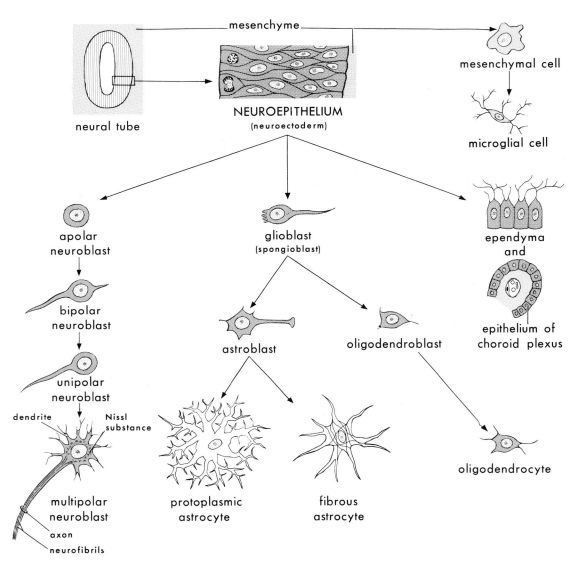

Figure 17–5 Schematic diagram illustrating the histogenesis of cells in the central nervous system. With further development, the multipolar neuroblast (lower left) becomes a nerve cell or neuron. Neuroepithelial cells give rise to all neurons and macroglial cells. Microglial cells are derived from mesenchymal cells which invade the developing nervous system.

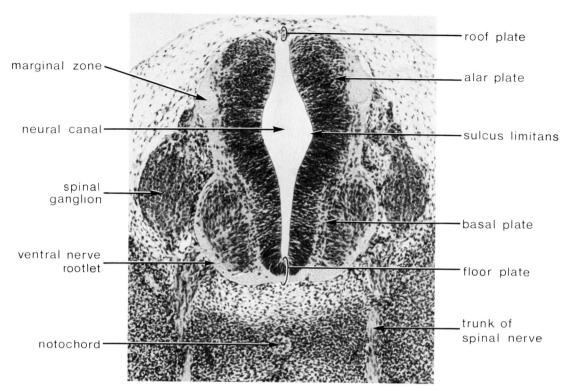

marginal zone

neural canal

spinal ganglion

ventral nerve rootlet

notochord

roof plate

alar plate

sulcus limitans

basal plate

floor plate

trunk of spinal nerve

Figure 17–6 Photomicrograph of a transverse section of the developing spinal cord in a 14-mm human embryo of about 36 days (×75). The dorsal wall (roof plate) and the ventral wall (floor plate) contain no neuroblasts and are relatively thin. (Courtesy of Dr. J. W. A. Duckworth, Professor Emeritus of Anatomy, University of Toronto.)

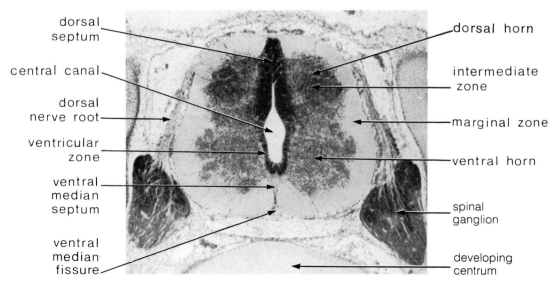

dorsal septum

central canal

dorsal nerve root

ventricular zone

ventral median septum

ventral median fissure

dorsal horn

intermediate zone

marginal zone

ventral horn

spinal ganglion

developing centrum

Figure 17–7 Photomicrograph of a transverse section of the developing spinal cord in a 20-mm human embryo of about 50 days (×60). (Courtesy of Professor Jean Hay, Department of Anatomy, Faculty of Medicine, University of Manitoba, Winnipeg, Canada.)

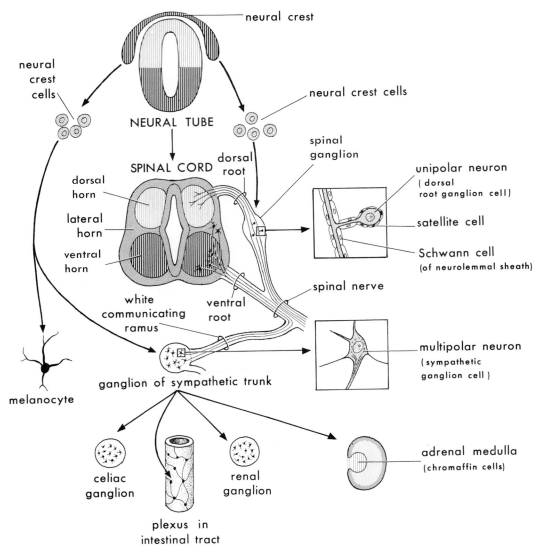

Figure 17–8 Diagram showing the derivatives of neural crest cells. Neural crest cells also differentiate into cells of the afferent ganglia of cranial nerves. Formation of a spinal nerve is also illustrated.

Positional Changes of the Spinal Cord. The spinal cord initially extends the entire length of the vertebral canal, and the spinal nerves pass through the intervertebral foramina at their levels of origin (Fig. 17–9A). This relationship does not persist because the vertebral column and the dura mater (outer covering of the spinal cord) grow more rapidly than the spinal cord. The caudal end of the spinal cord gradually comes to lie at relatively higher levels. As a result, the spinal roots, especially those of the lumbar and sacral segments, run obliquely from the spinal cord to the corresponding level of the vertebral column. The dorsal and ventral nerve roots inferior to the end of the cord form a sheaf of nerve roots called the *cauda equina* (Fig. 17–9D). Although the dura extends the entire length of the vertebral column in the adult, the other layers of the meninges do not. The pia mater inferior to the caudal end of the spinal cord forms a long fibrous thread, the *filum terminale*, which extends from the *conus medullaris* (conical extremity of the spinal cord) to the periosteum of the first coccygeal vertebra in the adult.

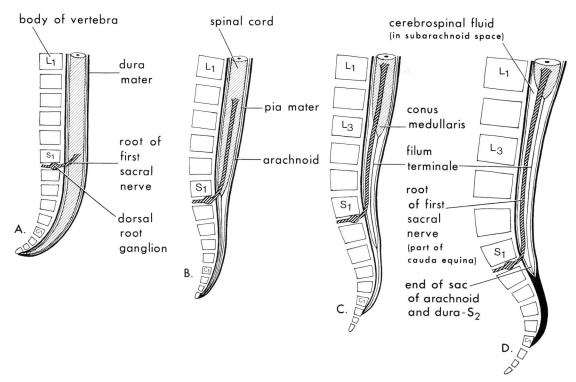

Figure 17–9 Diagrams showing the position of the caudal end of the spinal cord in relation to the vertebral column and the meninges at various stages of development. The increasing inclination of the root of the first sacral nerve is also illustrated. *A*, Eight weeks. *B*, 24 weeks. *C*, Newborn. *D*, Adult.

A portion of the subarachnoid space extends below the spinal cord (usually from L_1 to L_3) from which cerebrospinal fluid may be removed without damaging the cord. The removal of cerebrospinal fluid by insertion of a needle between L3 and L4 or L4 and L5 vertebrae and into the subarachnoid space is known as *lumbar puncture*.

Myelination. Myelin formation begins in the spinal cord during midfetal life and continues during the first postnatal year. The myelin sheath is formed around axons or axis cylinders by the plasma membranes of *Schwann cells*. The myelin sheath of axons in the central nervous system is formed in a somewhat similar manner by *oligodendrocytes*.

Malformations of the Spinal Cord and/ or its Meninges (Figs. 17–10 and 17–11). *Most congenital malformations of the spinal cord result from defective closure of the caudal neuropore* toward the end of the fourth week of development. Severe *neural tube defects* also involve the tissues overlying the spinal cord (meninges, vertebral arch, dorsal muscles, and skin).

Malformations involving the caudal end of the neural tube and the vertebral arches are referred to as *spina bifida* (divided spine). This term describes nonfusion of the vertebral arches common to all types of spina bifida.

Spina Bifida Occulta (Fig. 17–10A). This is a *vertebral defect* resulting from failure of the halves of the vertebral arch to develop fully and fuse, usually in the sacral, lumbar, and cervical regions (see also Chapter 16). *This defect is in L5 or S1 in about 10 per cent of people.* In its most minor form, there is no defect in the skin, and the only evidence of its presence may be a small dimple with a tuft of hair. *Spina bifida occulta produces no clinical symptoms*, but a small percentage of affected infants have associated developmental defects of the spinal cord and spinal roots which may produce symptoms.

Spina Bifida Cystica (Figs. 17–10B and C and 17–11). Severe types of spina bifida, involving protrusion of the spinal cord and/or the meninges through the defect in the vertebral arches, are referred to collectively as *spina bifida cystica* because of the cystlike

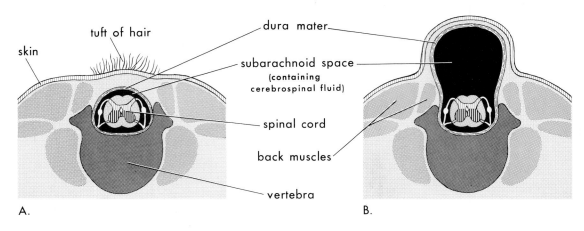

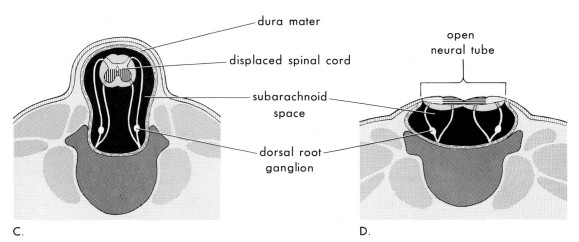

Figure 17–10   Diagrammatic sketches illustrating various types of spina bifida and the commonly associated malformations of the nervous system. *A,* Spina bifida occulta. The halves of the vertebral arch are not fully developed. As a result they are unfused and the spinous process has not formed. *B,* Spina bifida with meningocele. *C,* Spina bifida with meningomyelocele. *D,* Spina bifida with myeloschisis. Meningomyelocele is a more common and a very much more severe malformation than meningocele. Meningoceles and meningomyeloceles (*spina bifida cystica*) may occur anywhere along the spinal axis, but they are most common in the lumbar region. (Modified after Patten, 1968.)

protrusion, or sac, that is associated with these malformations. When the sac contains meninges and cerebrospinal fluid, the condition is called *spina bifida with meningocele* (Fig. 17–10*B*). The spinal cord and spinal roots are in their normal position, but there may be spinal cord abnormalities.

When the spinal cord and/or nerve roots are included in the sac, the malformation is called *spina bifida with meningomyelocele* (Fig. 17–10*C*). In meningomyeloceles, there is often a marked *neurological deficit* inferior to the level of the protruding sac. This deficit occurs because nervous tissue is often incorporated in the wall of the sac, a condition

that impairs early development of nerve fibers. Meningomyeloceles may be covered by skin or by a thin, easily ruptured membrane. *Spina bifida cystica occurs about once in every 1000 births.*

The most severe type of spina bifida is called spina bifida with myeloschisis (Figs. 17–10*D* and 17–11*B*). In these cases, the spinal cord is open because the neural folds failed to meet and fuse. As a result, the spinal cord in the area concerned is represented by a flattened mass of nervous tissue. Extensive *myeloschisis associated with rachischisis*, as shown in Figure 16–8, is rare. It is much more usual for a short part of the neural tube to

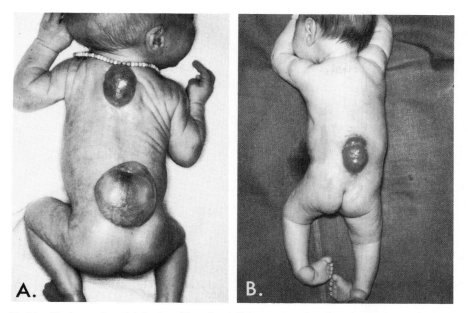

Figure 17–11 Photographs of infants with spina bifida cystica showing the common locations of these defects. *A,* Spina bifida with meningomyelocele in the thoracic and lumbar regions. *B,* Spina bifida with myeloschisis in the lumbar region. Note the nerve involvement affecting the lower limbs. (Courtesy of Dr. Dwight Parkinson, Children's Centre, Winnipeg.)

fail to form (Fig. 17–11*B*). Spinal bifida with myeloschisis (Fig. 17–10*D*) in the lumbosacral region probably results from *failure of the caudal neuropore to close* during the fourth week in the affected area.

THE BRAIN

The neural tube cranial to the fourth pair of somites develops into the brain. The adult brain is described as consisting of a number

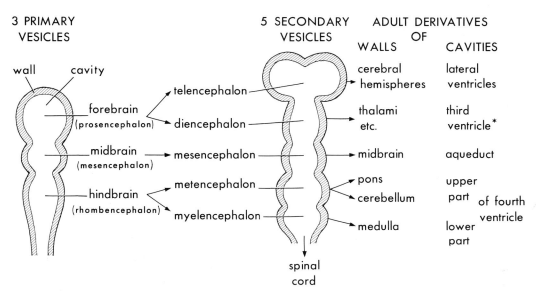

Figure 17–12 Diagrammatic sketches of the brain vesicles indicating the adult derivatives of their walls and cavities. The cerebrum comprises all the derivatives of the forebrain. *The extreme anterior part of the third ventricle forms from the cavity of the telencephalon.

of regions; the relation of these divisions to each other will be better understood after development of the brain has been considered.

Fusion of the neural folds in the cranial region and *closure of the rostral neuropore* result in the formation of three primary brain vesicles (Fig. 17–12), from which the brain develops.

Brain Vesicles. During the fourth week, the neural folds expand and fuse to form three primary brain vesicles: the *forebrain* or prosencephalon (Gr. *enkephalos*, brain), the *midbrain* or mesencephalon, and the *hindbrain* or rhombencephalon (Figs. 17–3*A* and 17–12). During the fifth week, the forebrain partly divides into two vesicles, the *telencephalon* and the *diencephalon*, and the hindbrain partly divides into the *metencephalon* and the *myelencephalon*. As a result, there are five secondary brain vesicles.

Brain Flexures (Figs. 17–3 and 17–13). During the fourth week the brain grows rapidly and bends or flexes ventrally. This produces the *midbrain flexure* in the midbrain region and the *cervical flexure* at the junction of the hindbrain and the spinal cord. Later, unequal growth in the hindbrain produces the *pontine flexure* between these flexures; this flexure causes thinning of the roof of the hindbrain.

Initially, the developing brain has the same basic structure as the developing spinal cord; however, the brain flexures produce considerable variation in the outline of transverse sections at different levels of the brain and in the position of the gray and white matter.

The Hindbrain. The cervical flexure demarcates the hindbrain vesicle from the developing spinal cord (Fig. 17–13*A*). The pontine flexure appears in the future pontine region. The bend of this flexure divides the hindbrain into caudal (myelencephalon) and rostral (metencephalon) parts.

The myelencephalon becomes the *medulla* (*oblongata*), and the metencephalon gives rise to the *pons* and *cerebellum*. The cavity

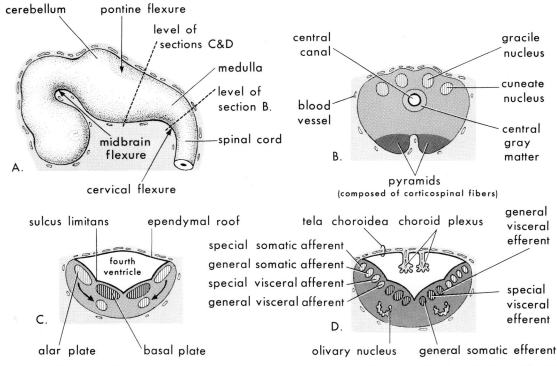

Figure 17–13 *A*, Sketch of the developing brain at the end of the fifth week, showing the three primary divisions of the brain and the brain flexures. *B*, Transverse section through the lower (caudal) part of the myelencephalon (developing closed part of the medulla). *C* and *D*, Similar sections through the upper (rostral) part of the myelencephalon (developing "open" part of the medulla) showing the position and successive stages of differentiation of the alar and basal plates. The arrows show the pathway taken by neuroblasts from the alar plates to form the olivary nuclei.

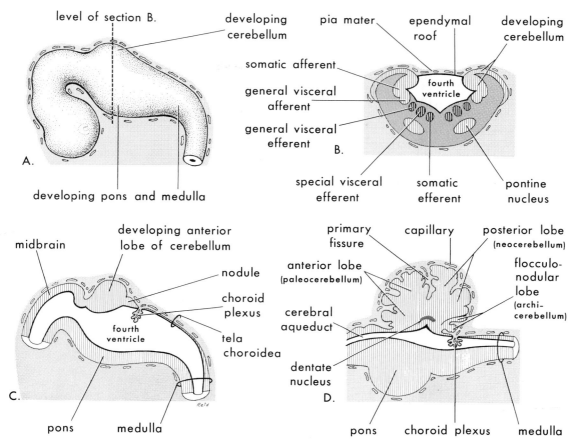

Figure 17–14 *A*, Sketch of the developing brain at the end of the fifth week. *B*, Transverse section through the metencephalon (developing pons and cerebellum) showing the derivatives of the alar and basal plates. *C* and *D*, Sagittal sections of the hindbrain at about 6 and 17 weeks, respectively, showing successive stages of development of the pons and cerebellum.

of the hindbrain becomes the fourth ventricle and the central canal of the caudal part of the medulla.

The Myelencephalon (Fig. 17–13). The caudal part of the myelencephalon (closed portion of medulla) resembles the spinal cord both developmentally and structurally. The lumen of the neural tube becomes a small central canal. Unlike the spinal cord, neuroblasts from the alar plates migrate into the marginal zone and form the *gracile nucleus* medially and the *cuneate nucleus* laterally (Fig. 17–13*B*). The ventral area contains a pair of fiber bundles, called the *pyramids*, consisting of nerve fibers from the developing cerebral cortex.

The rostral part of the myelencephalon (the developing "open" portion of the medulla) is wide and rather flat, especially opposite the pontine flexure (Fig. 17–13*A* and *C*). The pontine flexure causes the lateral walls of the medulla to fall outward like the pages of an opening book and the roof plate to become stretched and greatly thinned. The cavity of this part of the myelencephalon becomes the caudal half of the fourth ventricle.

The Metencephalon (Fig. 17–14). The walls of the metencephalon form the pons and the cerebellum, and its cavity forms the rostral part of the fourth ventricle. As in the rostral part of the myelencephalon, the pontine flexure causes divergence of the lateral walls of the medulla and spreads the gray matter in the floor of the fourth ventricle.

The *cerebellum* develops from thickenings of dorsal parts of the alar plates which enlarge and fuse in the midline. These cerebellar swellings soon overgrow the rostral half of the fourth ventricle and overlap the pons and medulla (Fig. 17–14D).

Nerve fibers connecting the cerebral and cerebellar cortices with the spinal cord pass through the marginal layer of the ventral region of the metencephalon. This region of the brainstem is called the *pons* (from Latin, meaning "bridge"), because of the band of nerve fibers thus formed.

Choroid Plexuses and Cerebrospinal Fluid (Figs. 17–13D and 17–14C and D). The thin ependymal roof of the fourth ventricle is covered externally by vascular *pia mater*. This pia mater together with the ependymal roof forms the *tela choroidea* which invaginates into the fourth ventricle and forms the *choroid plexus*.

Similar plexuses develop in the roof of the third ventricle and in the medial walls of the lateral ventricles. Four choroid plexuses are formed and are responsible for the secretion of cerebrospinal fluid. The thin roof of the fourth ventricle bulges outward in three locations and ruptures to form foramina. The median and lateral apertures permit the cerebrospinal fluid from the fourth ventricle to enter the *subarachnoid space* (see Fig. 17–9D).

The Midbrain. The midbrain undergoes less change than any other part of the developing brain, except the caudal part of the hindbrain. The neural canal narrows to form the cerebral aqueduct (Figs. 17–14D and 17–15D), which joins the third and fourth ven-

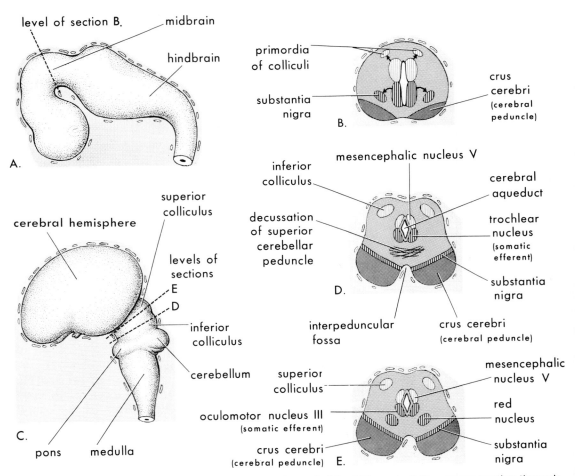

Figure 17–15 *A,* Sketch of the developing brain at the end of the fifth week. *B,* Transverse section through the mesencephalon (developing midbrain) showing basal and alar plates. *C,* Sketch of the developing brain at about 11 weeks. *D* and *E,* Transverse sections of the developing midbrain at the level of the inferior and superior colliculi, respectively.

tricles. Neuroblasts migrate from the alar plates into the roof or *tectum* and aggregate to form four large groups of neurons, the paired *superior* and *inferior colliculi* (concerned with visual and auditory reflexes, respectively). The basal plates give rise to neurons of the *tegmentum* (red nuclei, nuclei of the third and fourth cranial nerves, and neu-

rons of the reticular nuclei). Fibers growing from the cerebrum form the cerebral peduncles. The *substantia nigra* (black nucleus), a broad layer of gray matter adjacent to the *cerebral peduncle*, differentiates from the basal plate.

The Forebrain. Before closure of the rostral neuropore, two lateral outgrowths, or

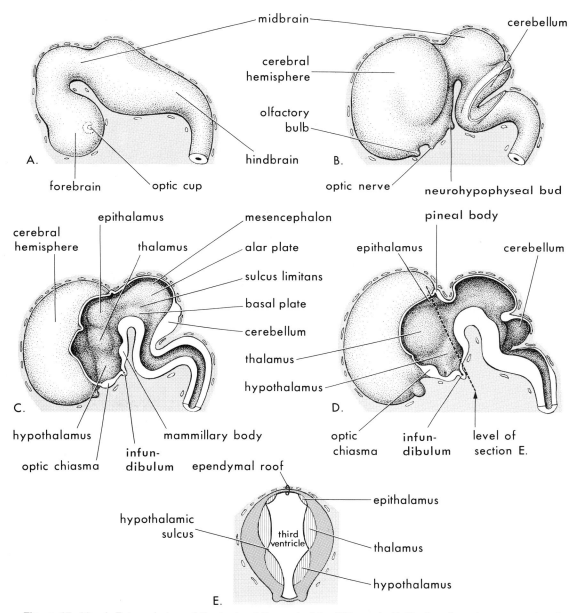

Figure 17–16 *A,* External view of the brain at the end of the fifth week. *B,* Similar view at seven weeks. *C,* Median sagittal section of this brain showing the medial surface of the forebrain and midbrain. *D,* Similar section at eight weeks. *E,* Transverse section through the diencephalon showing the epithalamus dorsally, the thalamus laterally, and the hypothalamus ventrally.

diverticula, called *optic vesicles* (see Fig. 17–3A) appear, one on each side of the forebrain. The optic vesicles are the primordia of the *retinae* and *optic nerves* (see Chapter 18).

A second pair of diverticula soon arise more dorsally and rostrally; these are called the *telencephalic vesicles* (Fig. 17–15C). They are the primordia of the *cerebral hemispheres*, and their cavities become the *lateral ventricles*.

The anterior part of the forebrain, including the primordia of the cerebral hemispheres, is known as the *telencephalon*, and the posterior part of the forebrain is called the *diencephalon*. The cavities of the telencephalon and diencephalon both contribute to the formation of the *third ventricle*, although the cavity of the diencephalon contributes more. (see Fig. 17–12).

The Diencephalon (Fig. 17–16). Three swellings develop in the lateral walls of the third ventricle which later become the *epithalamus*, the *thalamus*, and the *hypothalamus*. The *thalamus* on each side develops rapidly and bulges into the cavity of the third ventricle, reducing it to a narrow cleft. The *hypothalamus* arises by proliferation of neuroblasts in the intermediate zone of the diencephalic walls inferior to the hypothalamic sulcus (Fig. 17–16E). The *pineal body* (epiphysis) develops as a midline diverticulum of the caudal part of the diencephalic roof (Fig. 17–16D).

The Telencephalon (Fig. 17–17). The telencephalon consists of a median part and two cerebral vesicles. The cavity of the median portion forms the extreme anterior part of the third ventricle. At first the cerebral vesicles are in wide communication with the cavity of the third ventricle through the *interventricular foramina* (Fig. 17–18B). As the hemispheres expand, somewhat like inflating balloons, they cover the diencephalon, the midbrain, and the hindbrain. The hemispheres eventually meet each other in the midline, flattening their medial surfaces.

The *corpus striatum* appears as a prominent swelling in the floor of each hemisphere (Fig. 17–18B). The floor of the hemisphere expands more slowly than the thin cortical wall because it contains the rather large corpus striatum. Consequently, the cerebral hemispheres assume a C-shape (Fig. 17–17). Backward extension of the hemispheres is limited; thus its caudal end turns downward and forward, forming the temporal lobe.

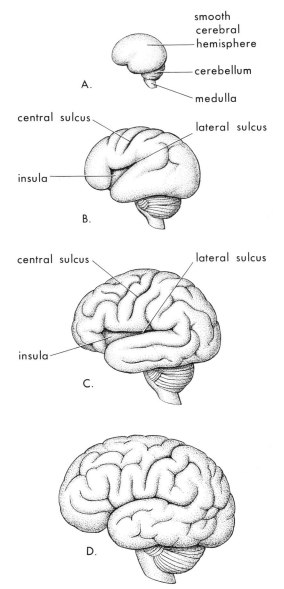

Figure 17–17 Sketches of lateral views of the left cerebral hemisphere showing successive stages in the development of sulci and gyri. *Half actual size.* Note the gradual narrowing of the lateral sulcus and formation of the insula. *A*, 13 weeks. *B*, 26 weeks. *C*, 35 weeks. *D*, Newborn.

As the cerebral cortex differentiates, fibers passing to and from it through the corpus striatum divide it into *caudate* and *lentiform nuclei*. This important fiber pathway is called the *internal capsule* (Fig. 17–18C).

The Cerebral Cortex. The walls of the developing cerebral hemispheres initially show

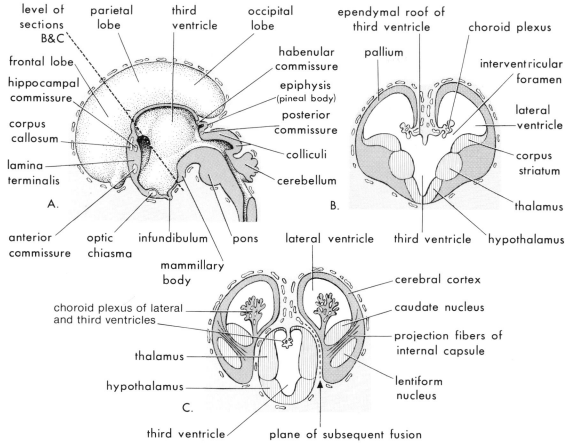

Figure 17–18 *A*, Drawing of medial surface of the forebrain of a 10-week embryo showing the diencephalic derivatives, the main commissures, and the expanding telencephalic (cerebral) vesicle. *B*, Transverse section through the forebrain at the level of the interventricular foramen showing the corpus striatum and the choroid plexus of the lateral ventricle. *C*, Similar section at about 11 weeks showing division of the corpus striatum into caudate and lentiform nuclei by the internal capsule. The developing relationship of the cerebral hemispheres to the diencephalon is also illustrated.

the typical zones of the neural tube. Cells of the intermediate zone migrate into the marginal zone and give rise to the cortical layers. Thus, the gray matter is located marginally, and axons from its cell bodies pass centrally and not peripherally as in the spinal cord.

Initially the surface of the hemispheres is smooth (Fig. 17–17*A*), but as growth proceeds, sulci and gyri develop. These permit increase in the area of the cerebral cortex without requiring an extensive increase in cranial size.

As a hemisphere grows, the cortex lying over the outer surface of the corpus striatum grows relatively slowly and is soon overgrown (Fig. 17–17*C*). This buried cortex, hidden from view in the depths of the lateral sulcus (fissure) of the cerebral hemisphere, is known as the *insula*.

The Pituitary Gland (Fig. 17–19). The pituitary gland (hypophysis cerebri) develops from two sources: oral ectoderm of the primitive mouth cavity and neuroectoderm of the diencephalon (Table 17–1). This double origin explains why the pituitary is composed of two completely different types of tissue. The *adenohypophysis* (glandular portion) arises from the oral ectoderm, and the neurohypophysis (nervous portion) originates from the neuroectoderm.

During the third week, a diverticulum called *Rathke's pouch* arises from the roof of the primitive mouth cavity and grows toward the brain. By the fifth week, this pouch has

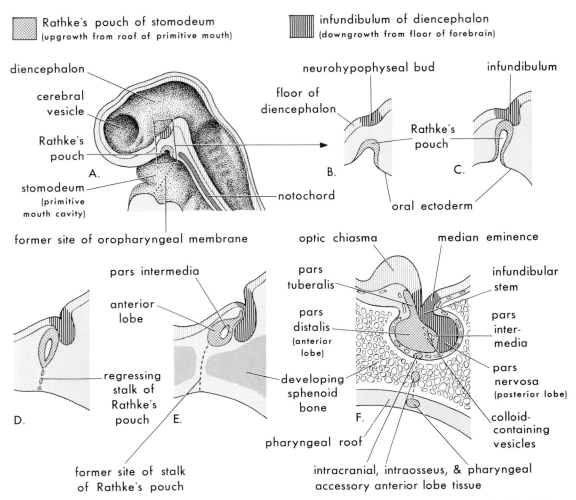

Figure 17–19 Diagrammatic sketches illustrating development of the pituitary gland (hypophysis). *A,* Sagittal section of the cranial end of an embryo at four weeks showing Rathke's pouch as an upgrowth from the roof of the primitive mouth cavity, and the neurohypophyseal bud from the forebrain. *B* to *D,* Successive stages of the developing pituitary gland. By eight weeks, Rathke's pouch loses its connection with the oral cavity. *E* and *F,* Later stages, showing proliferation of the anterior wall of Rathke's pouch and obliteration of its lumen.

TABLE 17–1.   DERIVATION AND TERMINOLOGY OF THE PITUITARY GLAND

Oral Ectoderm (From roof of primitive mouth [stomodeum]) ──────▶ Adenohypophysis (glandular portion)	Pars distalis ⎫ Pars tuberalis ⎬ Pars intermedia ⎭	Anterior lobe
		Posterior lobe
Neuroectoderm (From floor of diencephalon) ──────────────▶ Neurohypophysis (nervous portion)	Pars nervosa ⎫ Infundibular stem ⎬ Median eminence ⎭	

elongated and come into contact with the *infundibulum*, which develops as a ventral diverticulum of the floor of the diencephalon (Figs. 17–18*A* and 17–19*B*).

Adenohypophysis. Early during the sixth week, the connection of Rathke's pouch with the oral cavity disappears (Fig. 17–19*D* and *E*). Cells of the anterior wall of Rathke's pouch proliferate actively and give rise to the *pars distalis* of the pituitary gland. Later a small extension, the *pars tuberalis*, extends around the *infundibular stem*. Proliferation of the anterior wall of Rathke's pouch reduces its lumen to a narrow residual cleft (Fig. 17–19*E*). The posterior wall does not proliferate; it remains as the poorly defined *pars intermedia* which becomes an inconspicuous, discontinuous layer.

Neurohypophysis. The small infundibulum gives rise to the *median eminence*, the *infundibular stem*, and the *pars nervosa* (Fig. 17–19*F*). Nerve fibers grow into the pars nervosa from the hypothalamic area to which the infundibular stem is attached.

Malformation of the Brain and/or Its Meninges. *Abnormal development of the brain is not uncommon*, owing to the complexity of its embryological history. Most major congenital malformations of the brain result from *defective closure of the rostral neuropore* during the fourth week and involve the overlying tissues (future meninges and calvaria). The factors causing the faulty development may be primarily either genetic or environmental in nature.

Congenital abnormalities of the brain can result from alterations in the morphogenesis or the histogenesis of the nervous tissue, or they can result from developmental failures occurring in associated structures (notochord, somites, mesenchyme, and skull). Faulty development or histogenesis of the cerebral cortex can result in various types of congenital mental retardation.

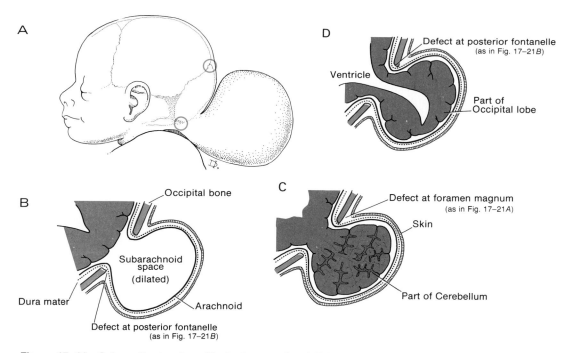

Figure 17–20   Schematic drawings illustrating cranium bifidum and the various types of herniation of the brain and/or cranial meninges associated with it. *A,* Sketch of the head of a newborn infant with a large protrusion from the occipital region of the skull, similar to that shown in Figure 17–21. The *upper red circle* indicates a cranial defect at the posterior fontanelle, and the *lower red circle* indicates a cranial defect at the foramen magnum. *B, Meningocele* consisting of a protrusion of the cranial meninges that is filled with cerebrospinal fluid. *C, Meningoencephalocele* consisting of a protrusion of part of the cerebellum that is covered by cranial meninges and skin. *D, Meningohydroencephalocele* consisting of a protrusion of part of the occipital lobe that contains part of the posterior horn of a lateral ventricle. (From Moore, K. L.: *The Developing Human: Clinically Oriented Embryology,* 3rd ed. Philadelphia, W. B. Saunders Company, 1982.)

Defects in the formation of the cranium (*cranium bifidum*) are often associated with congenital malformations of the brain and/or meninges. Such defects of the cranium are usually in the median plane of the calvaria (cranial vault). The defect is often in the squamous part of the occipital bone and may include the posterior lip of the foramen magnum.

When the defect in the cranium is small, usually only the meninges herniate, and the malformation is called a *meningocele* (Fig. 17–20*B*). When the cranial defect is large, the meninges and part of the brain herniate, forming a *meningoencephalocele* (Fig. 17–20*C*). If the protruding part of the brain contains part of the ventricular system, the malformation is called a *meningohydroencephalocele* (Figs. 17–20*D* and 17–21). The part of the brain in the sac is dependent on the location of the cranial defect. Cranium bifidum associated with herniation of the brain and/or its meninges occurs about once in every 2000 births.

Exencephaly and Anencephaly (see Fig. 16–8).   These severe malformations of the brain result from failure of the rostral neuropore to close properly during the fourth week. As a result, the forebrain primordium is abnormal or absent and the calvaria is defective or absent. Most of the embryo's brain is exposed or extruding from the skull, a condition known as *exencephaly*. Exencephaly is occasionally observed in aborted human embryos, but not at birth.

Owing to the abnormal structure and vascularization of the embryonic exencephalic brain, the nervous tissue undergoes degeneration until most of it is replaced in fetuses by a spongy, vascular mass consisting mostly of hindbrain structures. Although this condition is called *anencephaly* (Gr. *an*, without + *enkephalos*, brain), a rudimentary brain stem and traces of the basal ganglia are usually present.

Anencephaly is a common malformation, occurring about once in every 1000 births, and it is about four times more common in females than in males. It is always associated with *acrania* and may be associated with *rachischisis* (see Fig. 16–8) when defective neural tube closure is extensive.

Sustained extrauterine life is impossible in infants born with anencephaly. Infants afflicted with this defect survive for a few hours after birth, at most.

Microcephaly (Fig. 17–22).   In this uncommon condition, the calvaria is small, but the face is normal-sized. Generally, these infants are grossly mentally retarded because the brain is small and underdeveloped, a condition known as *microencephaly*. Microcephaly (Gr. *mikros*, small + *kephalē*, head) results from *microencephaly* (Gr. *mikros*,

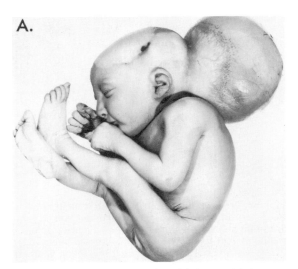
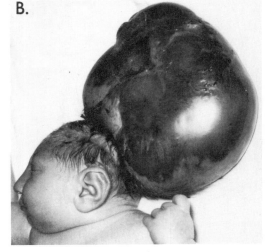

Figure 17–21   Photographs of infants with large meningoencephaloceles. *A, Occipital area. B,* Occipital and parietal areas, similar to that illustrated in Figure 17–20. (Courtesy of Dr. Dwight Parkinson, Children's Centre, Winnipeg.)

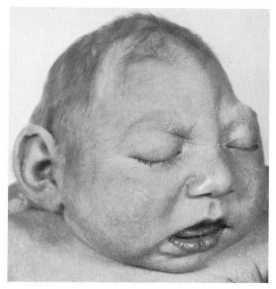

Figure 17–22 Photograph of an infant with microcephaly showing the typical normal-sized face and small cranial vault covered with loose wrinkled skin (From Laurence, K. M., and Weeks, R.: Abnormalities of the central nervous system; *in* Norman, A. P. (Ed.): *Congenital Abnormalities in Infancy,* 2nd ed. Oxford, Blackwell Scientific Publications, 1971.)

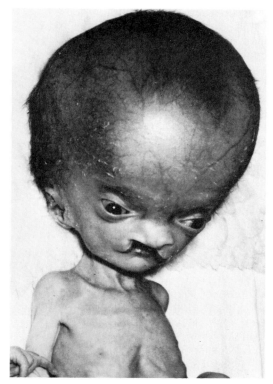

Figure 17–23 Photograph of an infant with hydrocephalus, bilateral cleft lip, and deformed limbs. (Courtesy of Dr. T. V. N. Persaud, Professor of Anatomy and Head of the Anatomy Department, University of Manitoba, Winnipeg, Canada.)

small + *enkephalos*, brain) because growth of the *calvaria* (*cranial vault*) is largely due to pressure from the growing brain.

The cause of these conditions is often uncertain; some cases appear to be genetic in origin, and others seem to be associated with environmental factors. Exposure to large amounts of ionizing radiation during the embryonic and fetal periods and to infectious agents during the fetal period is a possible contributing factor (see Chapter 9). Microcephaly can be detected in utero by ultrasound (see Chapter 7).

Hydrocephalus (Fig. 17–23). Overproduction of cerebrospinal fluid (CSF), obstruction of its flow, or interference with its absorption results in *an excess of CSF*, a condition known as hydrocephalus (Gr. *hydōr*, water + *kephalē*, head).

In *obstructive hydrocephalus* there is interference with the circulation of cerebrospinal fluid *inside the brain*. Obstructive hydrocephalus often results from *congenital aqueductal stenosis*, in which the cerebral aqueduct is narrow or consists of several minute channels. Blockage of CSF circulation results in dilation of the ventricles superior to the obstruction and in pressure on the cerebral hemispheres. This squeezes the brain between the ventricular fluid and the bones of the cranium. In infants, the internal pressure results in expansion of the brain and the calvaria because the sutures and fontanelles are still open.

Hydrocephalus usually refers to obstructive hydrocephalus, in which all or part of the ventricular system is enlarged. All ventricles are enlarged if the apertures of the fourth ventricle or the subarachnoid spaces are blocked, whereas the lateral and third ventricles are dilated when the cerebral aqueduct is obstructed. Although rare, obstruction of one interventricular foramen can produce dilation of one ventricle.

In *communicating hydrocephalus* there is an accumulation of CSF *outside the brain*, between the brain and the dura mater (i.e, in the subarachnoid space) owing to interference with the absorption of CSF. *The CSF pathways inside the brain are open.*

Hydrocephalus is often associated with spina bifida cystica, although the hydrocephalus may not be obvious at birth. Hydrocephalus often produces thinning of the bones of the calvaria, prominence of the forehead, atrophy of the cerebral cortex and white matter, and compression of the basal nuclei (ganglia) and diencephalon.

Mental Retardation. Congenital impairment of intelligence may result from various genetically determined conditions. The relation of chromosomal abnormalities to mental retardation is briefly discussed in Chapter 9. Disorders of metabolism may also cause mental retardation. Maternal and fetal infections (syphilis, German measles, toxoplasmosis, and cytomegalic inclusion disease), fetal irradiation, and cretinism are commonly associated with mental retardation.

The period of 8 to 16 weeks of human development appears to be its period of greatest sensitivity for fetal brain damage resulting from *high doses* of radiation. (see Chapter 9). Cell depletion of sufficient degree in the cerebral cortex results in mental retardation.

THE PERIPHERAL NERVOUS SYSTEM

The peripheral nervous system consists of the cranial, spinal, and visceral nerves and the cranial, spinal, and autonomic ganglia. Afferent neurons in the spinal ganglia and ganglia of cranial nerves develop from *neural crest cells* (see Figs. 17–1 and 17–8). Cells of the neural crest also differentiate into multipolar neurons of the *autonomic ganglia*, including ganglia of the sympathetic trunks along the sides of the vertebral bodies, collateral or prevertebral ganglia in plexuses of the thorax and abdomen (e.g., the cardiac, celiac, and mesenteric plexuses), and parasympathetic or terminal ganglia in or near the viscera (e.g., the Meissner's or submucosal plexus). *Chromaffin cells* of the paraganglia are also derived from the neural crests. The carotid and aortic bodies also have small islands of chromaffin cells associated with them. These widely scattered groups of chromaffin cells constitute the *chromaffin system*.

SUMMARY

The central nervous system develops from a dorsal thickening of ectoderm known as the *neural plate*. This plate becomes infolded to form a *neural groove* and *neural folds*. When the neural folds fuse to form the *neural tube*, some neuroectodermal cells are not included but remain between the neural tube and the surface ectoderm as the *neural crest*.

The cranial end of the neural tube forms the brain, consisting of the forebrain, the midbrain, and the hindbrain. The forebrain gives rise to the cerebral hemispheres and the diencephalon; the midbrain becomes the adult midbrain; and the hindbrain gives rise to the pons, cerebellum, and medulla (oblongata).

The remainder and longest part of the neural tube becomes the spinal cord. The lumen of the neural tube becomes the ventricles of the brain and the central canal of the spinal cord. The walls of the neural tube become thickened by proliferation of neuroepithelial cells which give rise to all nerve and macroglial cells in the central nervous system. The microglia are believed to differentiate from mesenchymal cells which enter

the central nervous system with the blood vessels.

Cells in the cranial, spinal, and autonomic ganglia are derived from the neural crest. *Schwann cells*, which myelinate the axons, also arise from the neural crest. Similarly, most of the autonomic nervous system and all chromaffin tissue, including the suprarenal (adrenal) medulla, develop from the neural crest.

Congenital malformations of the central nervous system are common. Defects of closure of the neural tube (*neural tube defects*) account for most abnormalities. The defects may be limited to the nervous system, or they may include overlying tissues (bone, muscle, and connective tissue).

Some malformations are caused by genetic abnormalities; others result from such environmental factors as infectious agents, drugs, and metabolic disease. However, most malformations are probably caused by an interaction of genetic and environmental factors.

Most gross abnormalities (e.g., anencephaly) are usually incompatible with life. Other severe malformations (e.g., spina bifida cystica) often cause functional disability (e.g., muscle paralysis).

There are two main types of *hydrocephalus*: obstructive hydrocephalus (blockage of cerebrospinal fluid flow in the ventricular system) and communicating hydrocephalus (blockage of cerebrospinal fluid in the subarachnoid space).

Mental retardation may result from chromosomal abnormalities, metabolic disorders, maternal and fetal infections, and high levels of radiation occurring during prenatal life.

SUGGESTED SUPPLEMENTARY READING

Crelin, E. S.: Development of the nervous system. A logical approach to neuroanatomy. *Clin. Symp. 26*:1, 1974.
A good account of the normal development of the nervous system which is beautifully illustrated by Dr. Netter.
Lemire, R. J., Loeser, J. D., Leech, R. W., and Alvord, E. C.: *Normal and Abnormal Development of the Human Nervous System.* Hagerstown, MD, Harper & Row, 1975.
A comprehensive account of normal development of the nervous system. There is also a good discussion of the causes of abnormalities of the nervous system.

18

THE EYE AND THE EAR

THE EYE

The eyes develop from three sources: neuroectoderm of the forebrain, surface ectoderm of the head, and mesoderm between these layers.

Eye development is first evident early in the fourth week when a pair of *optic sulci* appears in the neural folds at the cranial end of the embryo (Fig. 18–1A and B). As the neural folds fuse to form the forebrain, these sulci become a pair of hollow diverticula called *optic vesicles*, which project from the sides of the forebrain (Fig. 18–1C). As the bulblike optic vesicles grow, their distal ends expand and their connections with the forebrain become constricted to form *optic stalks* (Fig. 18–1D).

As the optic vesicles grow outward, the surface ectoderm adjacent to the optic vesicles thickens and forms *lens placodes* (Fig. 18–1C). The central region of each lens placode rapidly invaginates, forming a *lens pit* (Fig. 18–1D). The edges of these pits gradually approach each other and fuse to form *lens vesicles* (Fig. 18–1F). Meanwhile the optic vesicles invaginate and become double-layered *optic cups*. The lens vesicles soon separate from the surface ectoderm and grooves, called *optic fissures*, develop on the inferior surfaces of the optic cups and along the optic stalks (Fig. 18–1E to H). Hyaloid blood vessels develop in the mesenchyme in these fissures. The *hyaloid artery* supplies the inner layer of the optic cup, the lens vesicle, and the mesenchyme within the optic cup. The hyaloid vein returns blood from these structures. As the edges of the optic fissure come together and fuse, the hyaloid vessels are enclosed within the optic nerves (Fig. 18–2E and F). The distal portions of the hyaloid vessels eventually degenerate, but their proximal portions persist as the *central artery and vein of the retina*.

The Retina (Figs. 18–1, 18–3, and 18–4). The retina develops from the walls of the optic cup: the outer, thinner layer of the cup becomes the pigment epithelium and the inner, thicker layer differentiates into the neutral layer of the retina. During the embryonic and early fetal periods, the two retinal layers are separated by an intraretinal space representing the cavity of the original optic vesicle. This space gradually disappears as the retina forms. The pigment epithelium becomes firmly fixed to the choroid, but its attachment to the neural layer of the retina is not so firm. Hence, detachment of the retina may follow a blow to the eye. It often occurs during fixation and preparation of an eye for histological study. The detachment consists of separation of the pigment epithelium from the neural layer of the retina, i.e., at the site of embryonic adherence of the outer and inner layers of the optic cup.

Because the optic vesicle is an outgrowth of the forebrain, the layers of the optic cup which form from the vesicle are continuous with the wall of the brain. Under the influence of the lens, the inner layer of the optic cup proliferates and forms a thick neuroepithelium. Subsequently, the cells of this layer differentiate into rods and cones, bipolar cells, and ganglion cells. The neural layer of the developing retina is continuous with the inner layer of the optic stalk (Figs. 18–1F and G and 18–2D). Consequently, axons of the ganglion cells pass into the inner wall of the optic stalk and gradually convert it into the *optic nerve* (Fig. 18–2B, D, and F).

The Ciliary Body (Fig. 18–3). Because the pigmented portion of the epithelium of the ciliary body is derived from the outer layer of the optic cup, it is continuous with the pigment epithelium of the retina. The nonpigmented portion of the ciliary epithelium represents the forward prolongation of the neural layer of the retina in which no neural elements differentiate. The ciliary muscle and connective tissue develop from mesenchyme at the edge of the optic cup.

The eyes of most Caucasians are blue at birth because the small amount of dark melanin pigment in the epithelial layers on the

Text continued on page 258

254

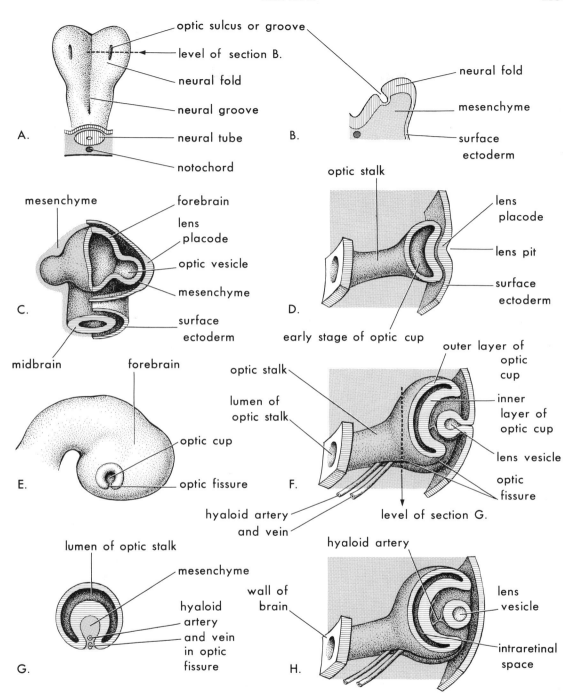

Figure 18–1 Drawings illustrating early eye development. *A*, Dorsal view of the cranial end of a 22-day embryo showing the first indication of eye development. *B*, Transverse section through an optic sulcus. *C*, Schematic drawing of the forebrain, its covering layers of mesoderm and surface ectoderm from an embryo of about 28 days. *D, F,* and *H,* Schematic sections of the developing eye illustrating successive stages in the development of the optic cup and the lens vesicle. *E,* Lateral view of the brain of an embryo of about 32 days showing the external appearance of the optic cup. *G,* Transverse section through the optic stalk showing the optic fissure and its contents.

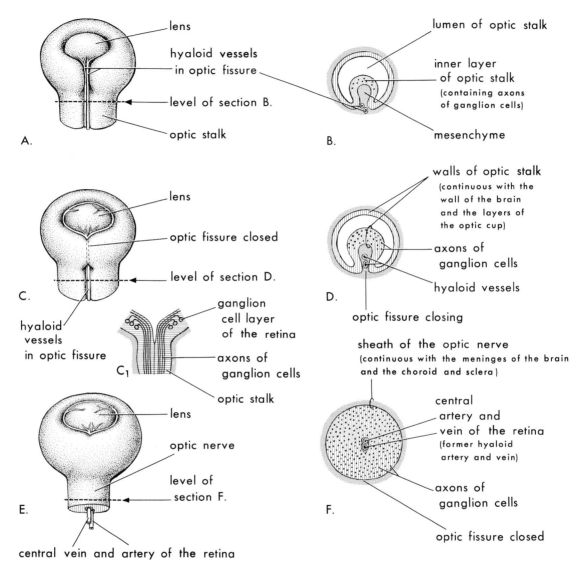

A.
lens
hyaloid vessels in optic fissure
level of section B.
optic stalk

B.
lumen of optic stalk
inner layer of optic stalk (containing axons of ganglion cells)
mesenchyme

C.
lens
optic fissure closed
level of section D.
hyaloid vessels in optic fissure

D.
walls of optic stalk (continuous with the wall of the brain and the layers of the optic cup)
axons of ganglion cells
hyaloid vessels
optic fissure closing

C₁
ganglion cell layer of the retina
axons of ganglion cells
optic stalk

E.
lens
optic nerve
level of section F.
central vein and artery of the retina

F.
sheath of the optic nerve (continuous with the meninges of the brain and the choroid and sclera)
central artery and vein of the retina (former hyaloid artery and vein)
axons of ganglion cells
optic fissure closed

Figure 18–2 Diagrams illustrating closure of the optic fissure and formation of the optic nerve. *A, C,* and *E,* Views of the inferior surface of the optic cup and stalk showing progressive stages in the closure of the optic fissure. *C₁,* Schematic sketch of a longitudinal section of a portion of the optic cup and optic stalk showing axons of ganglion cells of the retina growing through the optic stalk to the brain. *B, D,* and *F,* Transverse sections through the optic stalk showing successive stages in the closure of the optic fissure and in formation of the optic nerve. Note that the lumen of the optic stalk is gradually obliterated as axons of ganglion cells accumulate in the inner layer of the optic stalk. Formation of the optic nerve occurs between the sixth and eighth weeks. (From Moore, K. L.: *The Developing Human: Clinically Oriented Embryology,* 3rd ed. Philadelphia, W. B. Saunders Company, 1982.)

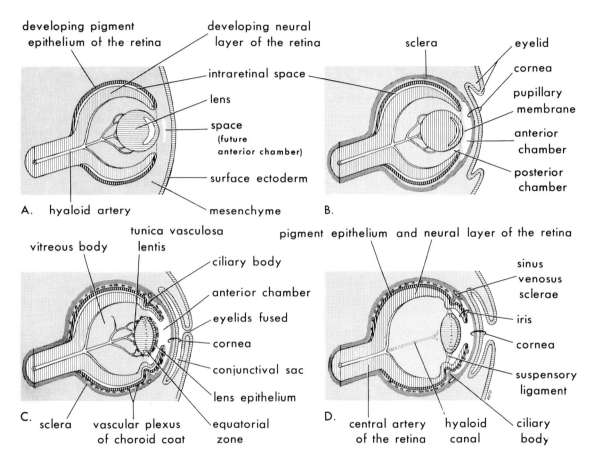

developing pigment epithelium of the retina

developing neural layer of the retina

intraretinal space

lens

space (future anterior chamber)

surface ectoderm

mesenchyme

A. hyaloid artery

sclera

eyelid

cornea

pupillary membrane

anterior chamber

posterior chamber

B.

vitreous body

tunica vasculosa lentis

ciliary body

anterior chamber

eyelids fused

cornea

conjunctival sac

lens epithelium

equatorial zone

C. sclera vascular plexus of choroid coat

pigment epithelium and neural layer of the retina

sinus venosus sclerae

iris

cornea

suspensory ligament

D. central artery of the retina hyaloid canal ciliary body

Figure 18–3 Drawings of sagittal sections of the eye showing successive developmental stages. *A*, Five weeks. *B*, Six weeks. *C*, 20 weeks. *D*, Newborn. Note that the layers of the optic cup are fused and form the pigment epithelium and neural layer of the retina and that they extend anteriorly as the double epithelium of the ciliary and iridial parts of the retina. At the end of the fifth week the developing eye is completely surrounded by loose mesenchyme (*A*). This embryonic connective tissue soon differentiates into an inner layer continuous with the pia mater of the brain, and an outer layer which is continuous with the dura mater covering the brain. Observe that the cornea is formed (from outside in) by (1) surface ectoderm; (2) substantia propria or stroma which is continuous with the sclera; and (3) an epithelial layer bordering the anterior chamber.

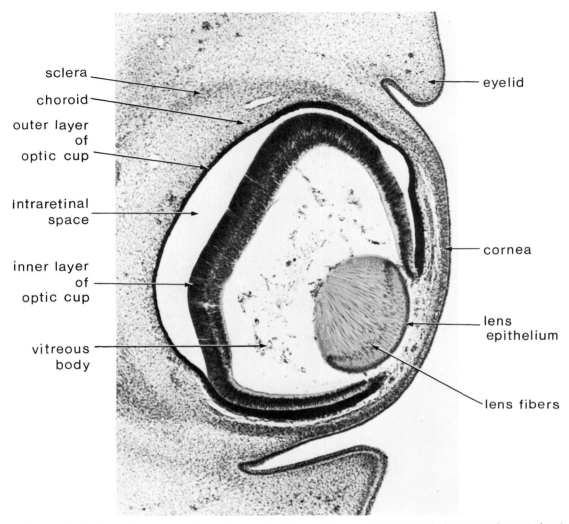

sclera

choroid

outer layer
of
optic cup

intraretinal
space

inner layer
of
optic cup

vitreous
body

eyelid

cornea

lens
epithelium

lens fibers

Figure 18–4 Photomicrograph of a sagittal section through the developing eye of a human embryo at about 50 days (×75). The relatively large intraretinal space, representing the cavity of the optic vesicle, gradually disappears as the inner and outer layers of the optic cup fuse to form the retina (Courtesy of Professor Jean Hay, Department of Anatomy, Faculty of Medicine, University of Manitoba, Winnipeg, Canada.)

posterior aspect of the iris appears blue through the stroma anterior to it. Pigment begins to form in the stroma during the first few days after birth. The final color of the eye depends on the density of the stroma and on how much pigment is deposited in it and in the two layers of epithelial cells at the posterior aspect of the iris. If very little pigment is deposited, the eye remains blue. When the stroma is dense, the eye appears gray. If more pigment is deposited, the eye appears brown. The eyes of deeply-pigmented races may look blue, hazel, or brown at birth, depending upon the amount of pigment present in the iris. They become darker during the first few days as more pigment is deposited in the iris. Changes in eye color may be noticeable for several weeks.

The Iris (Fig. 18–3).   The iris is derived from the edge of the optic cup which bends inward and partially covers the lens. The epithelium of the iris represents both layers of the optic cup and is continuous with the double-layered epithelium of the ciliary body and with the pigmented and neural layers of the retina.

The dilator and sphincter pupillae muscles of the iris are derived from the neuroectoderm of the outer layer of the optic cup. The vascular connective tissue of the iris is derived from mesenchyme located anterior to the rim of the optic cup.

The Lens (Figs. 18–1 to 18–4). The lens develops from the lens vesicle. The anterior wall becomes the *anterior epithelium* of the adult lens; cells of the posterior wall lengthen to form *lens fibers* which grow into and gradually obliterate the cavity of the lens vesicle. New lens fibers are continuously added to the lens from epithelial cells at the *equatorial zone* of the lens.

The Aqueous Chambers and Cornea (Figs. 18–3 and 18–4). The anterior chamber develops from a space which forms in the mesenchyme located between the developing lens and the surface ectoderm. The mesenchyme superficial to this space forms the substantia propria of the cornea.

The epithelium of the cornea and the conjunctiva are derived from the surface ectoderm. The mesenchyme deep to the developing anterior chamber forms the stroma of the iris. The posterior chamber develops from a space which forms in the mesenchyme posterior to the developing iris and anterior to the developing lens.

The Sclera and Choroid (Figs. 18–3 and 18–4). The mesenchyme surrounding the optic cup differentiates into an inner vascular layer, the choroid, and an outer fibrous layer, the sclera.

The Eyelids (Figs. 18–3 and 18–4). The eyelids develop from two ectodermal folds that have cores of mesenchyme. The eyelids meet and adhere by about the tenth week and remain closed until about the twenty-sixth week (see Chapter 7). While the eyelids are adherent, a closed conjunctival sac exists anterior to the cornea. When the eyes open (21 to 26 weeks), the *conjunctiva* covers the "white" of the eye and lines the eyelids.

The eyelashes and glands are derived from the surface ectoderm in a manner similar to that described for other parts of the integument (see Chapter 19). The muscles and tarsal plates develop from mesenchyme in the cores of the eyelids.

EYE ABNORMALITIES

The critical period of human eye development is from about 22 to 50 days after fertilization. Most congenital abnormalities of the eye appear to be caused by genetic factors and intrauterine infections.

Congenital Cataract (see Fig. 9–17A). The lens is opaque and frequently appears grayish white in this condition. Many lens opacities are inherited, but some are caused by noxious agents which affect early lens development. Congenital cataract is likely to follow *maternal rubella* infections which occur during the fourth to sixth weeks when the lens is developing (see Chapter 9).

Congenital Glaucoma (see Fig. 9–17B). High intraocular pressure and enlargement of the eye result from abnormal development of the drainage mechanism of the aqueous humor. *Intraocular tension* rises as a result of imbalance between production of aqueous humor and its outflow. This probably results from absence of or abnormal development of the *sinus venosus sclerae* (Fig. 18–3D). Congenital glaucoma is usually caused by recessive mutant genes, but the condition sometimes results from maternal rubella infection during early pregnancy.

Cyclopia. In this very rare condition, the eyes are partially or completely fused into a single median eye enclosed in a single orbit. Usually there is a tubular nose (proboscis) above the single eye. The abnormality is frequently associated with other severe malformations which are incompatible with life.

For descriptions and illustrations of other congenital malformations of the eye, see Mann (1974).

THE EAR

The ear consists of internal, middle, and external parts.

The Internal Ear (Figs. 18–5 and 18–6). Early in the fourth week a thickened plate of surface ectoderm, the *otic placode*, appears on each side of the developing hindbrain (Fig. 18–5A and B). Each placode soon invaginates and forms an *otic pit* (Fig. 18–5C and D). The edges of the pit come together and fuse to form an *otic vesicle* (otocyst), the primordium of the *membranous labyrinth*. The otic vesicle soon loses its connection with the surface ectoderm.

Two regions of each otic vesicle soon become recognizable: a dorsal *utricular portion* from which the endolymphatic duct arises, and a ventral *saccular portion*.

Three flat disclike diverticula grow out from the utricular portion, and soon the cen-

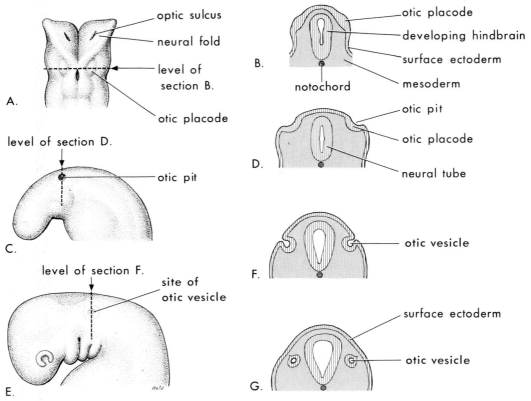

Figure 18–5 Drawings illustrating early development of the internal ear. *A*, Dorsal view of an embryo of 22 days showing the otic placodes. *B, D, F,* and *G*, Schematic sections illustrating successive stages in the development of the otic vesicles. *C* and *E*, Lateral views of the cranial region of embryos of about 24 and 28 days, respectively, showing the external appearance of the developing otic vesicle.

tral portions of the walls of these diverticula fuse and then disappear (Fig. 18–6*B* to *E*). The peripheral unfused portions of the diverticula become the *semicircular ducts*, which are later enclosed in the *semicircular canals*. From the ventral saccular portion of the otic vesicle, a tubular diverticulum, the *cochlear duct*, grows and coils to form the *cochlea* (Fig. 18–6*C* to *E*). The *organ of Corti* differentiates from cells in the wall of the cochlear duct (Fig. 18–6*F* to *I*).

The mesenchyme around the otic vesicle differentiates into a cartilaginous *otic capsule* (Fig. 18–6*F*). As the membranous labyrinth enlarges, vacuoles appear in the cartilaginous otic capsule and soon coalesce to form the *perilymphatic space*. The membranous labyrinth is soon suspended in a fluid, the *perilymph*, in the perilymphatic space. The perilymphatic space related to the cochlear duct develops in two divisions, the *scala tympani* and the *scala vestibuli* (Fig. 18–6*H* and *I*).

The cartilaginous otic capsule ossifies to form the *bony labyrinth* of the internal ear.

The Middle Ear (Fig. 18–7). The tubotympanic recess of the first pharyngeal pouch, described in Chapter 11, expands and becomes the *tympanic cavity*. The unexpanded portion becomes the *auditory tube*.

The *auditory ossicles* (malleus, incus, and stapes) develop by endochondral ossification of the cartilages of the first two pairs of branchial arches (see Fig. 11–4).

The External Ear (Figs. 18–7 and 18–8). The *external acoustic meatus* develops from the dorsal end of the first branchial groove. The cells at the bottom of this funnel-shaped tube extend inward as a solid epithelial plate called the *meatal plug*. Late in the fetal period, the central cells of this plug degenerate, forming a cavity which becomes the inner part of the external acoustic meatus.

The early *tympanic membrane* forms from

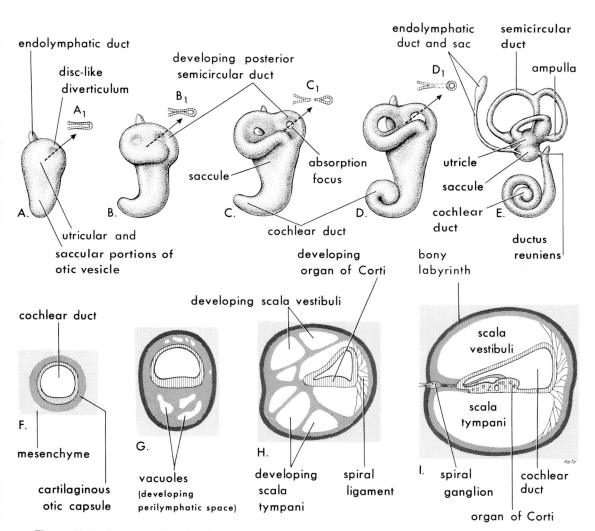

Figure 18-6 Diagrams showing development of the membranous and bony labyrinths of the internal ear. *A* to *E*, Lateral views showing successive stages in the development of the otic vesicle into the membranous labyrinth from the fifth to eighth weeks. *A₁* to *D₁*, Diagrammatic sketches illustrating the development of a semicircular duct. *F* to *I*, Sections through the cochlear duct showing successive stages in the development of the organ of Corti and the perilymphatic space from the eighth to the twentieth weeks.

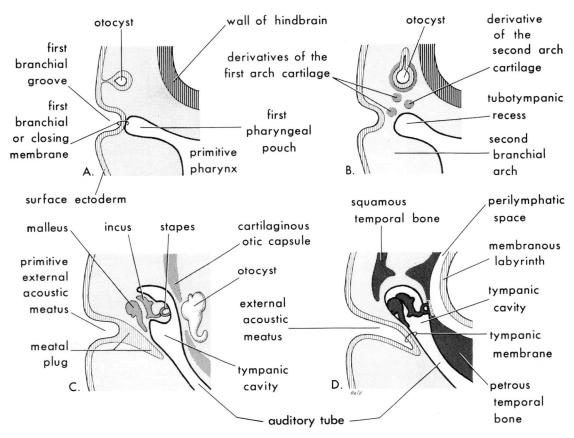

Figure 18–7 Schematic drawings showing development of the middle ear. *A,* Four weeks, illustrating the relation of the otocyst to the branchial apparatus. *B,* Five weeks, showing the tubotympanic recess and branchial arch cartilages. *C,* Later stage, showing the tubotympanic recess (future tympanic cavity) beginning to envelop the ossicles. *D,* Final stage of ear development, showing the relationship of the middle ear to the perilymphatic space and the external acoustic meatus. Observe that the epithelium lining the tympanic cavity is of endodermal origin and is derived from the first pharyngeal pouch. During late fetal life the tympanic cavity expands dorsally to form the mastoid antrum. Most mastoid air cells develop after birth when the bone of the developing mastoid processes is invaded by the epithelium of the mastoid antrum.

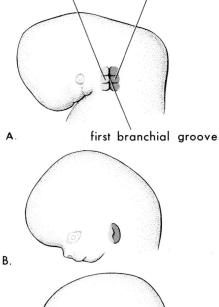

auricular hillocks derived from the
first and second branchial arches

A.   first branchial groove

B.

C.

D.

Figure 18–8 Drawings illustrating development of
the auricle of the external ear. *A,* Five weeks. *B,* Six
weeks. *C,* Eight weeks. *D,* 32 weeks. As the auricle
develops, it moves from the neck to the side of the
head at level of the eyes.

The *auricle* develops from six swellings,
called *auricular hillocks,* which develop
around the first branchial groove (Fig. 18–
8*A*). As the mandible develops, the auricles
ascend to the level·of the eyes.

EAR ABNORMALITIES

Congenital Deafness. Congenital impairment of hearing may be the result of
maldevelopment of the sound-conducting apparatus of the middle ear or of the neurosen-
sory or perceptive structures of the internal
ear. Most types of congenital deafness are
caused by genetic factors. Maternal *rubella
infection* during the critical period of development of the internal ear can cause maldevelopment of the organ of Corti (see Chapter 9).

Congenital fixation of the stapes results in
severe congenital conductive deafness in an
otherwise normal ear. Defects of two of the
middle ear bones (malleus and incus) are
often associated with the first arch syndrome
(discussed in Chapter 11).

Auricular Abnormalities. There is a
wide normal variation in the shape of the au-

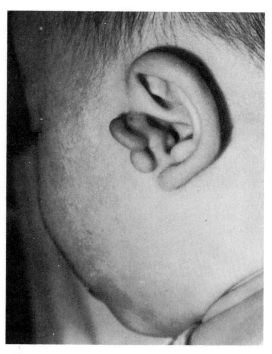

Figure 18–9 Photograph of a child with two auricular appendages or tags. (From Swenson, O.: *Pediatric Surgery.* 1958. Courtesy of Appleton-Century-
Crofts, Publishing Division of Prentice-Hall, Englewood Cliffs, NJ.)

the first branchial membrane (Fig. 18–7*A*).
As development proceeds, mesenchyme extends between the branchial membrane and
differentiates into the fibrous stratum of the
tympanic membrane.

ricle. Minor variations are not classified as malformations. The auricles are often abnormal in shape and low-set in malformed infants, especially in chromosomal syndromes (see Table 9–1 and Fig. 9–5A).

Auricular appendages or tags (Fig. 18–9) anterior to the auricle are relatively common and result from the development of accessory auricular hillocks. Usually they consist of skin only.

Atresia of the External Acoustic Meatus. Congenital blockage of the meatus results from failure of the meatal plug to canalize. Most cases are associated with the *first arch syndrome* (see Fig. 11–9).

SUMMARY

The eyes and the ears begin to develop during the fourth week. These special sense organs are very sensitive to teratogenic agents, especially viral infections. The most serious defects result from disturbances of development during the fourth to sixth weeks, but defects of sight and hearing may result from developmental disturbances by certain microorganisms during the fetal period.

The Eye. The first indications of the eyes are the *optic sulci*. Soon, these sulci form an *optic vesicle* on each side of the forebrain. The optic vesicles contact the surface ectoderm and induce development of the lens placodes, the primordia of the lenses. As the *lens placodes* invaginate to form *lens vesicles*, the optic vesicles invaginate to form *optic cups*. The retina forms from both layers of the optic cup.

The retina, the optic nerve fibers, the iris muscles, and the epithelium of the iris and ciliary body are derived from the *neuroectoderm*. The lens and the epithelium of the lacrimal glands and ducts, the eyelids, the conjunctiva, and the cornea are derived from the *surface ectoderm*. The mesoderm gives rise to the eye muscles (except those of the iris) and all connective and vascular tissues of the cornea, iris, ciliary body, choroid, and sclera.

There are many congenital ocular abnormalities, but most of them are rare. Some malformations are caused by defective closure of the optic fissure. Congenital cataract and glaucoma may result from intrauterine *rubella infections*.

The Ear. The surface ectoderm gives rise to the *otic vesicle*, which becomes the *membranous labyrinth* of the internal ear. The bony labyrinth develops from the surrounding mesenchyme. The epithelium lining the tympanic cavity, the mastoid antrum, the mastoid air cells, and the *auditory tube* is derived from endoderm of the tubotympanic recess of the first pharyngeal pouch.

The middle ear bones or *auditory ossicles* develop from the cartilages of the first two branchial arches. The external acoustic meatus develops from ectoderm of the first branchial groove. The tympanic membrane develops from endoderm of the first pharyngeal pouch, ectoderm of the first branchial groove, and mesenchyme between these layers. The auricle develops from six auricular hillocks or swellings around the first branchial groove.

Congenital deafness may result from abnormal development of the membranous labyrinth or the bony labyrinth or both, as well as from abnormalities of the auditory ossicles. Recessive inheritance is the most common cause of congenital deafness, but prenatal rubella virus infection is a major environmental factor known to cause defective hearing. There are many minor anomalies of the auricle. Low-set malformed ears are often associated with chromosomal abnormalities.

SUGGESTED SUPPLEMENTARY READING

Mann, I. C.: *The Development of the Human Eye*, 3rd ed. London, British Medical Association, 1974.
A classic reference on the embryology of the eye.
Wright, I.: Hearing and balance; *in* Davis, J. A., and Dobbing, J. (Eds.): *Scientific Foundation of Paediatrics.* Philadelphia, W. B. Saunders Company, 1974, pp. 661–680.
A very good description of the development of the internal and middle ear. Abnormalities leading to congenital deafness are also described.

19

THE SKIN, CUTANEOUS APPENDAGES, AND TEETH

SKIN

The epidermis is derived from surface ectoderm and the dermis from the mesenchyme deep to it.

Epidermis (Fig. 19–1). The surface ectodermal cells proliferate and form a protective layer, the *periderm*. Cells from this layer slough off and form part of the *vernix caseosa*, a cheeselike protective substance that covers the skin before birth.

By about 11 weeks, cells from the basal layer, or stratum germinativum, have formed an intermediate layer. All layers of the adult epidermis are present at birth.

During the early fetal period, neural crest cells (see Fig. 17–8) migrate into the dermis and differentiate into *melanoblasts* (Fig. 19–1C). These cells soon enter the epidermis and differentiate into *melanocytes* which lie at the epidermal-dermal junction (Fig. 19–1D). The melanocytes produce melanin and distribute it to the epidermal cells. Very few melanocytes develop in the skin of the palms and the soles. *Melanin pigment formation* occurs mainly after birth when the process is stimulated, e.g., by utraviolet radiation.

Dermis (Fig. 19–1). The dermis is derived from the mesenchyme underlying the surface ectoderm. By 11 weeks, the mesenchymal cells have begun to produce collagenous and elastic connective tissue fibers. The dermis projects upward into the epidermis and forms *dermal papillae*. Capillary loops develop in some dermal papillae and sensory nerve endings occur in others.

Disorders of Keratinization. *Ichthyosis* (Gr. *ichthys*, fish) is a general term applied to a group of disorders characterized by dryness and *fishskin-like scaling of the skin*. Scaling is often pronounced, involving the entire body surface.

A *harlequin fetus* results from a very rare keratinizing disorder that is inherited as an autosomal recessive trait. The skin is markedly thickened, ridged, and cracked. Affected infants have a grotesque appearance, and most of them die within the first week of life.

A *collodion baby* is covered at birth by a thick, taut membrane resembling collodion. This membrane cracks with the first respiratory efforts and begins to fall off in large sheets, but complete shedding may take several weeks.

HAIR

A hair follicle begins as a solid downgrowth of the epidermis into the underlying dermis (Fig. 19–2A). The deepest part of the *hair bud* soon becomes club-shaped to form a *hair bulb* (Fig. 19–2B). The epithelial cells of the hair bulb constitute the *germinal matrix* which later gives rise to the hair. The hair bulb is then invaginated by a small mesenchymal *hair papilla* (Fig. 19–2C). The peripheral cells of the developing hair follicle form the *epithelial root sheath*. The surrounding mesenchymal cells differentiate into the *dermal (connective tissue) root sheath* (Fig. 19–2D). As the cells in the *germinal matrix* proliferate, they are pushed upward and become keratinized to form the *hair shaft* (Fig. 19–2C). The hair grows, pierces the epidermis and protrudes above the surface of the skin.

Congenital Alopecia (Atrichia Congenita). Fetal absence or loss of hair may occur alone or with other abnormalities of the skin and its derivatives. The hair loss may be caused by failure of hair follicles to develop or result from follicles producing poor-quality hairs.

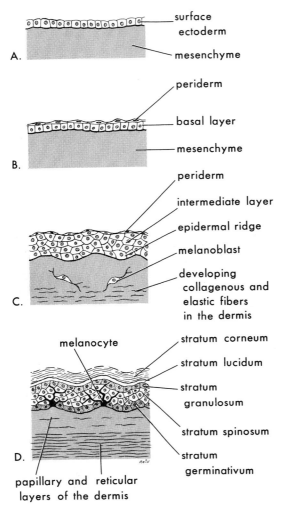

Figure 19–1 Drawings illustrating successive stages in the development of thick skin. *A,* Four weeks. *B,* Seven weeks. *C,* 11 weeks. *D,* Newborn. The epidermis is derived from the surface ectoderm and the dermis develops from mesenchyme that is derived from the somatic layer of mesoderm.

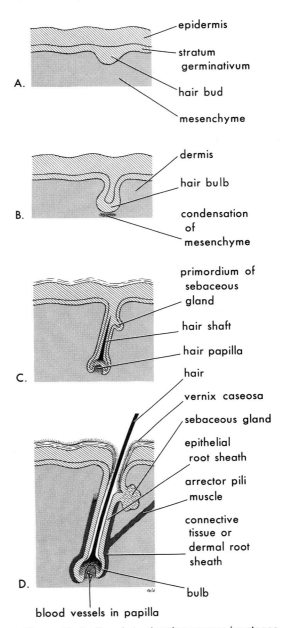

Figure 19–2 Drawings showing successive stages in the development of a hair and its associated sebaceous gland. *A,* 12 weeks. *B,* 14 weeks. *C,* 16 weeks. *D,* 18 weeks.

Hypertrichosis. Excessive hairiness results from the development of excess hair follicles or from the persistence of hairs that normally disappear during the fetal period. Localized hypertrichosis is often associated with spina bifida occulta (see Chapter 17).

SEBACEOUS GLANDS

These glands develop as buds from the side of the developing hair follicle (Fig. 19–2C). The glandular buds grow into the surrounding connective tissue and branch to form the primordia of several alveoli and their associated ducts (Fig. 19–2D).

The whitish, creamlike paste, called *vernix caseosa,* covering the skin of the fetus is formed from the secretion of the sebaceous glands and degenerated epidermal cells and hairs. It *protects the skin* against the macerating action of the amniotic fluid.

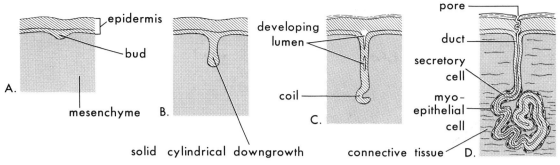

Figure 19–3 Diagrams illustrating successive stages in the development of a sweat gland.

SWEAT GLANDS

These glands develop as solid epidermal downgrowths into the underlying dermis (Fig. 19–3). As the bud elongates, its end becomes coiled to form the primordium of the secretory portion of the gland. The epithelial attachment of the developing gland to the epidermis forms the primordium of the duct.

NAILS

The nails begin to develop at about 10 weeks. Development of fingernails precedes that of toenails. The nails first appear as thickened areas of epidermis on the dorsal aspect of each digit (Fig. 19–4A). These *nail fields* are surrounded laterally and proximally by folds of epidermis called *nail folds*. Cells from the proximal nail fold grow over the nail field and become keratinized to form the *nail* or *nail plate* (Fig. 19–4B and C).

MAMMARY GLANDS

The mammary glands develop as solid downgrowths of the epidermis into the un-derlying mesenchyme (Fig. 19–5C). These occur along two thickened strips of ecto-derm, the *mammary ridges* (Fig. 19–5A). Each mammary bud soon gives rise to several secondary buds which develop into the *lactiferous ducts* and their branches (Fig. 19–5F). The epidermis at the origin of the mammary gland becomes depressed to form a shallow *mammary pit* (Fig. 19–5E). The mammary glands of newborn males and females are often enlarged and may produce secretions (often called "witch's milk"). These transitory changes are caused by maternal hormones passing into the fetal circulation via the placenta.

Supernumerary Breasts and Nipples (Fig. 19–6). An extra breast (*polymastia*) or nipple (*polythelia*) occurs in about 1 per cent of the female population and is an inheritable condition. Supernumerary nipples may also occur in males. An extra breast or nipple usually develops just below the normal breast. In these positions, the extra nipples or breasts develop from extra mammary buds along the mammary ridges. Accessory breasts may have normal breast tissue and become functional during pregnancy.

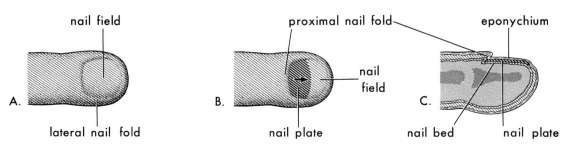

Figure 19–4 Diagrams illustrating successive stages in the development of a fingernail. The fingernails reach the fingertips by 32 weeks and extend beyond them in full-term infants.

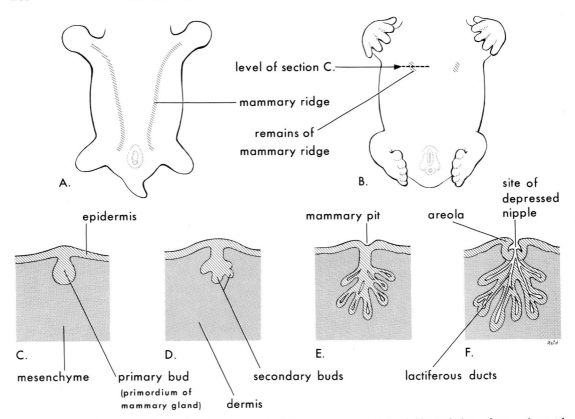

Figure 19–5　Drawings illustrating development of the mammary glands. *A*, Ventral view of an embryo of about 28 days showing the mammary ridges. *B*, Similar view at six weeks showing the remains of these ridges. *C*, Transverse section through the mammary ridge at the site of a developing mammary gland. *D, E,* and *F*, Similar sections showing successive stages of development between the twelfth week and birth.

TABLE 19–1　ORDER AND TIME OF ERUPTION OF TEETH AND TIME OF SHEDDING OF DECIDUOUS TEETH*

	Deciduous Teeth				
	Medial Incisor	*Lateral Incisor*	*Canine*	*First Molar*	*Second Molar*
Eruption (months)	6 to 8	8 to 10	16 to 20	12 to 16	20 to 24
Shedding (years)	6 to 7	7 to 8	10 to 12	9 to 11	10 to 12

	Permanent Teeth							
	Medial Incisor	*Lateral Incisor*	*Canine*	*First Premolar*	*Second Premolar*	*First Molar*	*Second Molar*	*Third Molar*
Eruption (years)	7 to 8	8 to 9	10 to 12	10 to 11	11 to 12	6 to 7	12	13 to 25

* (From Moore, K. L. *Clinically Oriented Anatomy*. © 1980. Courtesy of The Williams & Wilkins Company, Baltimore.)

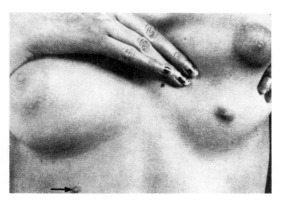

Figure 19–6 Photograph of an adult female with a supernumerary nipple on the right (arrow) and a supernumerary breast below the normal left one. (From Haagensen, C. D.: *Diseases of the Breast*, rev. 2nd ed. Philadelphia, W. B. Saunders Company, 1974.)

TEETH

Two sets of teeth normally develop: the *primary dentition*, or deciduous teeth, and the *secondary dentition*, or permanent teeth (Table 19–1).

The teeth develop from ectoderm and mesoderm. The enamel is derived from ectoderm of the oral cavity; all other tissues differentiate from mesenchyme.

The Dental Lamina and the Bud Stage. Tooth development begins early in the sixth week as linear U-shaped bands of oral epithelium, called *dental laminae* (Fig. 19–7A). Localized proliferations of cells in the dental laminae produce round or oval swellings called *tooth buds* (Fig. 19–7B). These buds grow into the mesenchyme and develop into the deciduous teeth. The first teeth are called deciduous teeth because they are shed during childhood. There are 10 tooth buds in each jaw, one for each deciduous ("milk") tooth. The tooth buds for the permanent teeth with deciduous predecessors begin to appear at about 10 weeks (Fig. 19–7D).

The Cap Stage. The tooth bud becomes slightly invaginated by mesenchyme called the *dental papilla* (Fig. 19–7C). The dental papilla gives rise to the *dentin* and the *dental pulp*. The developing tooth, called an *enamel organ*, later produces enamel. As the enamel organ and the dental papilla form, the mesenchyme surrounding them condenses and forms a capsule-like structure called the *dental sac* or follicle (Fig. 19–7E and F). It gives rise to the cementum and the *periodontal ligament*.

The Bell Stage. As invagination of the enamel organ continues, the developing tooth assumes a bell shape (Fig. 19–7D). Mesenchymal cells in the dental papilla adjacent to the inner enamel epithelium differentiate into *odontoblasts*. These cells produce *predentin* and deposit it adjacent to the inner enamel epithelium. Later the predentin calcifies and becomes *dentin*. As the dentin thickens, the odontoblasts regress toward the center of the dental papilla, but processes of the odontoblasts, called *odontoblastic processes*, remain embedded in the dentin (Fig. 19–7F and I). Cells adjacent to the dentin differentiate into *ameloblasts*. These cells produce enamel prisms (rods) over the dentin (Fig. 19–7I). As the enamel increases, the ameloblasts regress toward the outer enamel epithelium. The inner cells of the dental sac differentiate into *cementoblasts* and produce cementum which is deposited over the dentin of the root.

As the teeth develop and the jaws ossify, the outer cells of the dental sac also become active in bone formation. Each tooth soon becomes surrounded by bone, except over its crown. The tooth is held in its bony socket or *alveolus* by the *periodontal ligament*, a derivative of the dental sac (Fig. 19–7G). Some fibers of this ligament are embedded in the cementum, others in the bony wall of the socket.

Tooth Eruption (Fig. 19–7 and Table 19–1). As the root grows, the crown gradually erupts through the oral mucosa. Eruption of the deciduous teeth usually occurs between the sixth and twenty-fourth months after birth.

The mandibular teeth usually erupt before the maxillary teeth, and girls' teeth usually erupt earlier than boys' teeth.

The permanent teeth develop in a manner similar to that previously described for deciduous teeth (Fig. 19–8). As a permanent tooth grows, the root of the corresponding deciduous tooth is gradually resorbed by osteoclasts. Consequently, when the deciduous tooth is shed, it consists only of the crown and the uppermost portion of the root. The permanent teeth usually begin to erupt during the sixth year and continue appearing until early adulthood.

Enamel Hypoplasia (Fig. 19–9B). Defective enamel formation results in grooves,

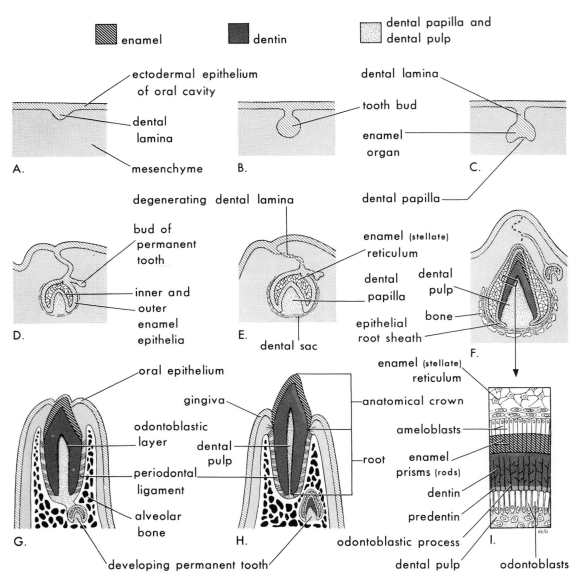

Figure 19–7 Schematic drawings from sagittal sections showing successive stages in the development and eruption of an incisor tooth. *A,* Six weeks, showing the dental lamina. *B,* Seven weeks, showing the bud stage of tooth development. *C,* Eight weeks, showing the cap stage of development of the enamel organ. *D,* 10 weeks, showing the early bell stage of the enamel organ of the deciduous tooth and the bud stage of the developing permanent tooth. *E,* 14 weeks, showing the advanced bell stage of the enamel organ. Note that the connection (dental lamina) of the tooth to the oral epithelium is degenerating. *F,* 28 weeks, showing the enamel and dentin layers. *G,* Six months *postnatal,* showing early tooth eruption. *H,* 18 months *postnatal,* showing a fully erupted deciduous incisor tooth. The permanent incisor tooth now has a well-developed crown. *I,* Section though a developing tooth showing the ameloblasts (enamel producers) and the odontoblasts (dentin producers).

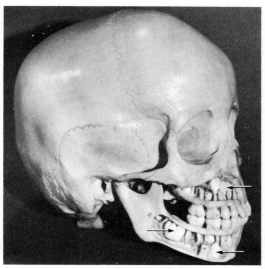

Figure 19–8 Photograph of the skull of a child in the fourth year. The jaws have been dissected to show the relations of the developing permanent teeth (arrows) to the deciduous teeth. (From Moore, K. L.: *The Developing Human: Clinically Oriented Embryology.* 3rd ed. Philadelphia, W. B. Saunders Company, 1982.)

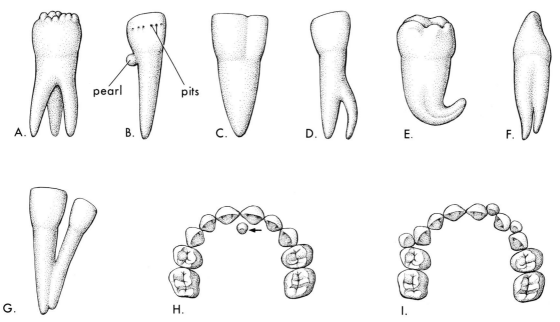

Figure 19–9 Drawings illustrating abnormalities of teeth. *A,* Irregular raspberry-like crown. *B,* Enamel pearl and pits. *C,* Incisor tooth with a double crown. *D,* Abnormal division of root. *E,* Distorted root. *F,* Branched root. *G,* Fused roots. *H,* Hyperdontia, with a supernumerary incisor tooth in the anterior region of the palate (arrow). *I,* Hyperdontia, with 13 deciduous teeth in the upper jaw instead of the normal 10.

pits, or fissures on the enamel surface. These conditions result from a temporary disturbance in enamel formation. Various factors may injure the ameloblasts (e.g., tetracycline therapy and diseases such as measles). *All tetracyclines are extensively incorporated in the enamel and produce ugly brownish yellow discoloration and hypoplasia of the enamel.*

Abnormalities in Shape (Fig. 19–9*A* to *G*). Abnormally shaped teeth are relatively common. Occasionally, spherical masses of enamel, called *enamel pearls*, are attached to the tooth. They are formed by aberrant groups of ameloblasts.

Numerical Abnormalities (Fig. 19–9*H* and *I*). One or more supernumerary teeth may develop, or teeth may not form.

Fused Teeth (Fig. 19–9*C* and *G*). Occasionally, a tooth bud divides or two buds partially fuse to form fused or joined teeth. In some cases the permanent tooth does not form.

SUMMARY

The epidermis and its derivatives (hairs, nails, and glands) are derived from surface ectoderm. Hairs develop from downgrowths of the epidermis into the dermis. The sebaceous glands develop as outgrowths from the side of hair follicles. The sweat and mammary glands develop from epidermal downgrowths. Supernumerary breasts (polymastia) or nipples (polythelia) are relatively common.

The teeth develop from ectoderm and mesoderm. The enamel is produced by cells derived from ectoderm; all other dental tissues develop from mesoderm. The common congenital malformations of teeth are defective formation of enamel and dentin, abnormalities in shape, and variations in number and position.

SUGGESTED SUPPLEMENTARY READING

Haagensen, C. D.: *Diseases of the Breast*, rev. 2nd ed. Philadelphia, W. B. Saunders Company, 1974.
There is a good description of congenital abnormalities of the breasts.
Sperber, G. H.: Development of the dentition; *in* Sperber, G. H.: *Craniofacial Embryology*, 2nd ed. Bristol, John Wright & Sons Ltd. (distributed by Year Book Medical Publishers, Inc., Chicago), 1976, Chapter 18.
This chapter gives details of tooth development.

INDEX

Note: Page numbers in *italics* refer to illustrations; those followed by (t) refer to tables.